30894 C

MATERIALS SCIENCE AND
MANUFACTURING PROCESSES

By the same author:

AN INTRODUCTION TO METALLURGICAL ANALYSIS (S.K. JAIN)

Materials Science
and
Manufacturing
Processes

DR. DHARMENDRA KUMAR
Former Principal
Malviya Regional Engineering College
Jaipur (Raj.)

S.K. JAIN
Reader in Metallurgical Engineering
Malviya Regional Engineering College
Jaipur (Raj.)

A.K. BHARGAVA
Sr. Lecturer in Metallurgical Engineering
Malviya Regional Engineering College
Jaipur (Raj.)

SECOND REVISED EDITION

VIKAS PUBLISHING HOUSE PVT LTD

VIKAS PUBLISHING HOUSE PVT LTD
576 Masjid Road, Jangpura, New Delhi-110014

First Published, 1983
Second Revised Edition, 1993

Printed at Hindustan Offset Printers, Delhi-32.

PREFACE

During the last three decades significant developments have occurred in various materials and new insight has been gained in understanding their nature and structure and their correlation with properties. In fact, perfection and exploitation of any scientific discovery becomes possible only after matching developments in materials, without which the scientific discovery remains merely a laboratory curiosity. Deep insight in materials science has also helped in the development of 'tailor made' new materials with a combination of desirable properties which was not considered possible before.

It has therefore become very important for engineers, technologists and scientists of varying disciplines to have a good understanding of materials science and processes for optimum utilization of resources in scientific research, technological and industrial applications.

The present book has been written to explain the basic principles of materials science and manufacturing processes and efforts have been made to present the subject in a lucid manner to enable the students to acquire a good grasp of the fundamentals. Suitable illustrations and questions haveb een incorporated to make the subject clear and interesting. The book should serve as a valuable study material for engineering students as well as those pursuing part time courses for various professional examinations like associateship examination of professional bodies. Care has been taken to discuss the subject so as to cover sylabii of different institutions.

All the important aspects of material science and processes such as atomic structure, mechanical properties and engineering requirements of materials, electron theory of metals, deformation of metals, equilibrium diagrams, different manufacturing processes and materials have been discussed giving suitable examples.

The authors hope that the book would serve a useful purpose in introducing this important core subject to the engineers and scientists and would promote inter-disciplinary information which is so very important for bringing the fruits of scientific inventions within the reach of the common man.

The authors would welcome any comments and constructive suggestions to further improve the usefulness of the book.

AUTHORS

CONTENTS

1

ATOMIC STRUCTURE

1.1. INTRODUCTION

In a solid, atoms are held together by interatomic bonds. The strength of a solid depends upon the kind of interatomic bond and the length of the bond. A solid may be made of the same kind of atoms or of different kind of atoms and the type of bond formed between them depends upon the atomic structure and electronic distribution of atoms. In this chapter, the structure of atoms is discussed in the light of periodic table and subsequently the chemical bonding and crystal structure are discussed.

1.2. STRUCTURE OF THE ATOM

It is well known that an atom consists of a nucleus surrounded by the moving electrons. The nucleus is composed of two kinds of particles, namely the protons and the neutrons. The weight of an electron is about 1/1840 time the weight of a proton or a neutron and therefore almost all the weight of an atom is centred in the nucleus. Protons carry a positive charge, and electrons carry a negative charge whereas neutrons have no charge on them. The charge on a proton or an electron is equal to 1.602×10^{-19} C (1 eV).

In an atom, the electrons are distributed in different energy levels and in their motion they may jump from one energy level to another by absorbing or emitting energy, i.e., the energy of an electron is quantized. This shows that electrons follow the laws of quantum mechanics. In order to understand these laws, it is necessary to know some important aspects of quantum mechanics.

1.2.1. Salient Aspects of Quantum Mechanics

The first aspect states that the position and momentum of an electron can not be specified precisely in accordance with the Heisenberg uncertainty principle. The product of uncertainty in momentum ($\triangle p$) and the uncertainty in position ($\triangle x$) is always greater than or equal to a certain value $h/2\pi$, that is

$$\triangle p \cdot \triangle x \geqslant \frac{h}{2\pi} \qquad \qquad ...(1.1)$$

where h is the Planck's constant and is equal to 6.63×10^{-27} ergs/sec. $\triangle x$ is the most probable region in space where an electron exists.

The state of an electron can be described by a set of four quantum numbers, n, l, m_l and m_s. 'n' is the principal quantum number and represents the major energy level (or shell). 'n' can take integral values, 1, 2, 3 etc. The total number of electrons in a given energy level is given as $2n^2$. The larger the value of 'n' the farther is the energy level from the nucleus.

'l' is the orbital angular momentum quantum number and also called the azimuthal quantum number. It measures the angular momentum of an electron. The quantum number 'l' can take values from 0 to $(n-1)$. The state with $l=0$ does not mean that the electron is at rest, rather, it is the state in which the motion of the electron does not give rise to angular momentum. 'l' indicates a sub-division of the principal quantum number. For the sake of convenience to show the order of filling electrons, the values of l are given specific notations. Thus, for $l=0$, 1, 2 and 3 the notations are s, p, d and f respectively. The designations s, p, d and f are called the sub-shells or orbitals and indicate the special volume around the nucleus in which an electron spends about 90 pct. of its time. Therefore, the orbitals s, p, d, and f differ from each other principally in shapes.

'm_l' is the magnetic quantum number and is a measure of the component of the angular momentum in a specific direction. Therefore, this quantum number is a further sub-division of sub shells and may have integral values from $-l$ to $+l$ including zero [i.e., $-l$, $(-l+1)$, $(-l+2)$, ... -1, 0, 1, ... $l-1$, l . . .].

'm_s' is the spin quantum number and is introduced because an electron behaves in a way as if it were spinning about its own axis besides orbitting about the nucleus. Magnetic properties of a solid are associated with this spin. It has been observed that two opposite spin directions are possible. Thus, the fourth quantum number m_s, may have values $+\frac{1}{2}$ or $-\frac{1}{2}$.

At absolute zero temperature all the electrons have tendency to occupy the lowest energy state (the ground state) in order to minimise the total energy of the atom. But this does not happen according to Pauli's exclusion principle (the second aspect of quantum mechanics) which states that not more than one electron can have the same set of four quantum number (or not more than two electrons with opposite spins can be occupied in an energy state defined by the first three quantum numbers). Electrons begin to fill up energy states starting from the lowest energy without violating the Pauli's principle. The energy of a state depends upon 'n' and 'l'. Within an energy level, the electrons of an 's' orbital have the least energy whereas those in the 'f' orbitals have the most energy. Depending upon the number of electrons in an atom, the sequence in which the electrons fill up the orbitals is given as:

$1s$, $2s$, $2p$, $3s$, $3p$, $4s$, $3d$, $4p$, $5s$, $4d$. $5p$, $6s$, $4f$, $5d$, $6p$ and $7s$.

This sequence of filling electrons is shown in Fig. 1.1 in the form of an energy level diagram. In the above order, the first digit stands

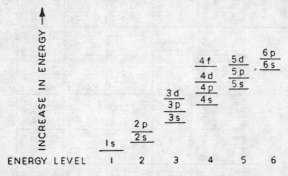

FIG. 1.1. Energy values for orbitals is the first six levels. '*s*' orbital of an energy level requires less energy than the '*d*' orbital of the preceding level.

for the principal quantum number n and the second indicates an orbital. For example, a $2p$ state is defined as $n=2$ and $l=1$.

The third important feature of the quantum mechanics is the quantisation of energy which an electron can possess. That is, an electron can have only certain value of energies and it can not have any energy between these allowed values. If an electron changes its energy, it must make a quantum jump to another allowed energy level or d state. The electron can jump to a higher energy state by absorbing radiant energy or to a lower energy state by emitting radiant energy. The frequency of the energy emitted or absorbed is given by the Einstein's equation:

$$\triangle E = E_2 - E_1 = h\nu \qquad \qquad \ldots (1.2)$$

where h is Planck's constant, E_2 is the energy after the jump and E_1 is the energy before the jump. A negative $\triangle E$ means that energy is emitted. The frequency of the radiant enery in terms of the velocity of light (c) is expressed as—

$$\nu = \frac{C}{\lambda} \qquad \qquad \ldots (1.3)$$

where λ is the wave length of the radiant energy.

1 3. THE PERIODIC TABLE

The lightest element is hydrogen in the periodic table of elements as shown in Table 1.1. Hydrogen has one electron in its ground state showing the simplest shape of the orbital '*s*'. It resembles a sphere (a circle in two dimensions) with the nucleus at the centre (Fig 1.2). The dirgram shows dots representing points where the probability of finding the hydrogen electron is high. The volume enclosed by the

PERIODIC TABLE

←————— METALS —————→ ————— NON METALS —————

THE PERIODIC TABLE
1 THE ATOMIC NUMBER IS SHOWN AT THE TOP.
2 THE MIDDLE LINE INDICATES THE ATOMIC MASS IN AMU.
3 THE OUTER ELECTRON CONFIGURATION IS SHOWN AT THE BOTTOM

IA	IIA	IIIB	IVB	VB	VIB	VIIB	VIII	VIII	VIII	IB	IIB	IIIA	IVA	VA	VIA	VIIA	O
1 H 1.008 $1s^1$																	2 He 4.00 $1s^2$
3 Li 6.939 $2s^1$	4 Be 9.012 $2s^2$											5 B 10.81 $2s^2 2p^1$	6 C 12.01 $2s^2 2p^2$	7 N 14.01 $2s^2 2p^3$	8 O 16.00 $2s^2 2p^4$	9 F 19.00 $2s^2 2p^5$	10 Ne 20.18 $2s^2 2p^6$
11 Na 22.99 $3s^1$	12 Mg 24.31 $3s^2$											13 Al 26.98 $3s^2 3p^1$	14 Si 28.09 $3s^2 3p^2$	15 P 30.97 $3s^2 3p^3$	16 S 32.06 $3s^2 3p^4$	17 Cl 35.45 $3s^2 3p^5$	18 Ar 39.95 $3s^2 3p^6$
19 K 39.10 $4s^1$	20 Ca 40.08 $4s^2$	21 Sc 44.96 $3d^1 4s^2$	22 Ti 47.90 $3d^2 4s^2$	23 V 50.94 $3d^3 4s^2$	24 Cr 52.00 $3d^5 4s^1$	25 Mn 54.94 $3d^5 4s^2$	26 Fe 55.85 $3d^6 4s^2$	27 Co 58.93 $3d^7 4s^2$	28 Ni 58.71 $3d^8 4s^2$	29 Cu 63.54 $3d^{10} 4s^1$	30 Zn 65.37 $3d^{10} 4s^2$	31 Ga 69.72 $4s^2 4p^1$	32 Ge 72.59 $4s^2 4p^2$	33 As 74.92 $4s^2 4p^3$	34 Se 78.96 $4s^2 4p^4$	35 Br 79.90 $4s^2 4p^5$	36 Kr 83.80 $4s^2 4p^6$
37 Rb 85.47 $5s^1$	38 Sr 87.62 $5s^2$	39 Y 88.91 $4d^1 5s^2$	40 Zr 91.22 $4d^2 5s^2$	41 Nb 92.91 $4d^4 5s^1$	42 Mo 95.94 $4d^5 5s^1$	43 Tc 99 $4d^5 5s^2$	44 Ru 101.1 $4d^7 5s^1$	45 Rh 102.9 $4d^8 5s^1$	46 Pd 106.4 $4d^{10}$	47 Ag 107.9 $4d^{10} 5s^1$	48 Cd 112.4 $4d^{10} 5s^2$	49 In 114.8 $5s^2 5p^1$	50 Sn 118.7 $5s^2 5p^2$	51 Sb 121.7 $5s^2 5p^3$	52 Te 127.6 $5s^2 5p^4$	53 I 126.9 $5s^2 5p^5$	54 Xe 131.3 $5s^2 5p^6$
55 Cs 132.9 $6s^1$	56 Ba 137.3 $6s^2$	57 La 138.9 $5d^1 6s^2$	72 Hf 179.5 $5d^2 6s^2$	73 Ta 180.9 $5d^3 6s^2$	74 W 183.9 $5d^4 6s^2$	75 Re 186.2 $5d^5 6s^2$	76 Os 190.2 $5d^6 6s^2$	77 Ir 192.2 $5d^9$	78 Pt 195.1 $5d^9 6s^1$	79 Au 197.0 $5d^{10} 6s^1$	80 Hg 200.3 $5d^{10} 6s^2$	81 Tl 204.4 $6s^2 6p^1$	82 Pb 207.2 $6s^2 6p^2$	83 Bi 209.0 $6s^2 6p^3$	84 Po 210 $6s^2 6p^4$	85 At 211 $6s^2 6p^5$	86 Rn 222 $6s^2 6p^6$
87 Fr 223 $7s^1$	88 Ra 226 $7s^2$	89 Ac 227 $6d^1 7s^2$															

Lanthanide series:

58 Ce 140.1 $4f^2 6s^2$	59 Pr 140.9 $4f^3 6s^2$	60 Nd 144.3 $4f^4 6s^2$	61 Pm 147 $4f^5 6s^2$	62 Sm 150.3 $4f^6 6s^2$	63 Eu 152.0 $4f^7 6s^2$	64 Gd 157.3 $4f^7 5d^1 6s^2$	65 Tb 158.9 $4f^8 5d^1 6s^2$	66 Dy 162.5 $4f^{10} 6s^2$	67 Ho 164.9 $4f^{11} 6s^2$	68 Er 167.3 $4f^{12} 6s^2$	69 Tm 169.9 $4f^{13} 6s^2$	70 Yb 173.0 $4f^{14} 6s^2$	71 Lu 175.0 $4f^{14} 5d^1 6s^2$

Actinide series:

90 Th 232 $6d^2 7s^2$	91 Pa 231 $5f^2$	92 U 238 $5f^3$	93 Np 237 $5f^5 7s^2$	94 Pu 244 $5f^6 7s^2$	95 Am 243 $5f^7 7s^2$	96 Cm 247 $5f^7$	97 Bk 247 $5f^8$	98 Cf 251 $5f^{10} 7s^2$	99 Es 254 $5f^{11} 7s^2$	100 Fm 257 $5f^{12} 7s^2$	101 Md 256 $5f^{13} 7s^2$	102 No 254 $5f^{14} 7s^2$	103 Lw 257 $5f^{14}$

broken line contains about 90 pct. of the dots and is considered to be that portion of an electron cloud in which the electron probability density of the atom is highest. Thus, the electron probability density cloud of an 's' orbital is spherically symmetric. It may be observed from Fig. 1.2 that the radial density which measures the probability of finding the electron in a thin spherical shell around the nucleus is zero at the nucleus. It increases to a maximum at a certain distance from the nucleus shown by the dotted circle and then slowly decreases to zero outside the circle.

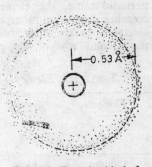

FIG. 1.2. The 's' orbital of an electron.

The electronic configuration of hydrogen atom in its ground state can be represented diagramatically as:

$$1\ s' \boxed{\uparrow} \text{ or } \boxed{\downarrow}$$

Here the electron is represented by an arrow showing the possible direction of spin and is enclosed in a square. The energy of the ground state of hydrogen atom is -13 eV (i.e. -2.18×10^{-18} Joules). The state of zero energy is the one where the electron is at an infinite distance from the nucleus and when it jumps from infinity to the ground state it radiates energy to the surrounding. Hence, a negative sign is attached to the energy of the 1s state. The energy of the orbitals increases with the distance from the nucleus. The energy of the 2s orbital of hydrogen atom (which is normally vacant) is -3.4 eV which is higher than that of the ground state. Therefore 2s is the immediate excited state in the hydrogen atom.

The element next to the hydrogen in the first row of the periodic table is helium. The atomic number of helium is 2 and atomic weight is 4. The two electrons lie in the first principal shell.

When $n = 1$, $l = 0$, $m_l = 0$, $m_s = \pm\frac{1}{2}$, the electronic configuration of He in its ground state is, therefore,

$$1s^2 \boxed{\uparrow \downarrow}$$

Since there are two electrons with anti-parallel spins, the 's' state (or sub-shell) is closed completely. The electron probability density cloud is spherically symmetric. Since there is no valence electron in the He atom to take part in a chemical reaction, He is an inert gas. In the ground state of He, the 2s orbital is vacant.

When $n = 2$ the number and the shape of possible states are given as

$$l=0, m_l=0, \quad m_s=+\tfrac{1}{2}\ 2s$$
$$\left.\begin{array}{l} l=1, m_l=-1, m_s=+\tfrac{1}{2} \\ \quad m_l=0, \quad m_s=+\tfrac{1}{2} \\ \quad m_l=+1, m_s = \pm\tfrac{1}{2} \end{array}\right\} 2p$$

Therefore, the total number of electrons in the second principal shell can be as high as 8. All the atoms with more than four electrons have p orbitals in addition to s orbitals. Since in the periodic table, the elements are arranged in the order of their increasing atomic number, the last element in this row has eight electrons in its outer shell. Accordingly there are eight elements in the second row of the periodic table (the electron filling order is

TABLE 1.2: *Elements in the second row of the periodic table.*

Elements	Symbol	At No.	Electronic Configuration	Electron spin distribution in 'p' orbitals		
				p_x	p_y	p_z
Lithium	Li	3	$1s^2$ $2s^1$	—	—	—
Beryllium	Be	4	$1s^2$ $2s^2$	—	—	—
Boron	B	5	$1s^2$ $2s^2$ $2p^1$	↑	—	—
Carbon	C	6	$1s^2$ $2s^2$ $2p^2$	↑	↑	—
Nitrogen	N	7	$1s^2$ $2s^2$ $2p^3$	↑	↑	↑
Oxygen	O	8	$1s^2$ $2s^2$ $2p^4$	↑ ↓	↑	↑
Fluorine	F	9	$1s^2$ $2s^2$ $2p^5$	↑ ↓	↑ ↓	↑
Neon	Ne	10	$1s^2$ $2s^2$ $2p^6$	↑ ↓	↑ ↓	↑ ↓

shown in Table 1.2). The first element in the second row is the alkali metal lithium with atomic number 3. The electrons are distributed in the orbitals in accordance with the Pauli's principle and the minimum energy criterion. Thus, there are two electrons in the $1s$ state and one in the $2s$ state. It is apparent from the periodic table that all the alkali metals Li, Na, K, Rb, Cs and Fr are characterised for a single outermost s^1 electron outside the full inner shells. Another interesting point to be noted here is that all the alkali metals are characterised for the same behaviour in chemical reaction. They are all very reactive, are monovalent metals and form similar compounds with, for example, Cl or F. Chlorides of all these metals form transparent, insulating crystals. They are all soluble to greater or lesser extent in water and have sufficiently high melting points (of the order of 700°C).

The element next to Li is Be with atomic number 4 and its ground state can be represented as:

$$Be \ 1s^2 \ \boxed{↑ \ ↓}$$

$$2s^2 \ \boxed{↑ \ ↓} \ 2p^° \ \boxed{\ | \ | \ }$$

According to this configuration, the electron probability density cloud is spherically symmetric about the nucleus. After Be, the electrons start on filling 'p' states of the second principal shell. As shown above for $n=2$ that 'p' orbital can hold as many as six electrons in accordance with Pauli's principle. Since, m_l measures the component of l in a particular direction, the p orbital of an electron consists of 3-balloon shaped clouds (p_x, p_y and p_z) at right angles to each other and each consists of two parts (corresponding to $m_s = \pm 1/2$ for each $m_l = +1$, 0, and -1) as shown in Fig. 1.3. Since p_x, p_y and p_z are at right

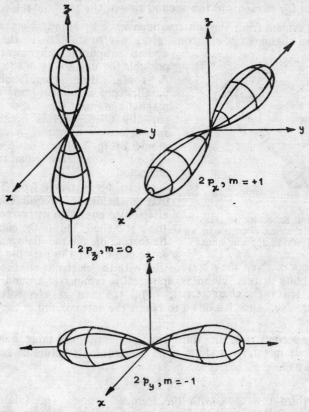

FIG. 1.3. The p orbitals. The p_x, p_y and p_z orbitals are at right angles to each other.

angles to each other, p orbitals are directional and an incomplete p state gives rise to directional distribution of electron density cloud. Each p_x, p_y and p_z has the maximum density along one of the three coordinate directions. This is the reason why the bonds between two p orbitals are directional as they are characterised in covalent bonding discussed in section 1.7.3.

Hunds deduced from his spectroscopic measurement that states of different m_l are filled first with electrons having the same m_s value i.e. $m_s = +1/2$. Thus, first state to fill is that with $m_l = -l$, $m_s = +1/2$, the second state to fill is that $m_l = -l+1$ with $m_s = +1/2$ and so on.

When the orbital is half filled, then according to Pauli, no more electrons with $m_s = +1/2$ are allowed and therefore the second half shell fills in sequence $m_l = -1$, $m_s = -1/2$ then $m_l = (-l_1 + 1)$, $m_s = -1/2$ and so on. Table 1 2 shows the order of filling electrons in the p orbitals in accordance with Hund's rule keeping in view the Pauli's concept for elements in the second row of the periodic table.

It is evident from the observations made by Hunds that the parallel spin alignment of electrons gives rise to stability to the system

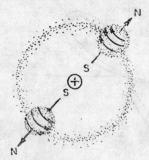

and an antiparallel alignment is responsible for unstability of the system. A configuration corresponding to parallel spin alignment leads to a net magnetic moment if p, d, or f state is partially filled. This is because each spin electron measures a magnetic moment (Fig. 1.4) and has a value of $+\frac{1}{2}$ or $-\frac{1}{2}$ which is equal to 1 Bohr magneton.

FIG. 1.4. Schematic representation of the two electrons in an arbital having opposite spins.

It can be observed from Table 1.2 that the halogen F requires only one electron to complete its *octet* and close the p sub-shell. This is the characteristic feature of all the halogens in the same column of the periodic table. In the atom of Ne, the p state is full with the electrons so the electron probability density cloud is spherically symmetric around the nucleus. This is the characteristic of all the inert gas elements namely, A, Kr, Xe, and Rn down to Ne in the last column of the periodic table.

Like second row, the third row of the periodic table begins with an alkali metal, i.e. sodium. The electronic structure of Na is described as:

$$1s^2\ 2s^2\ 2p^6\ 3s^1$$

The third row ends with the element argon. The total possible number of electrons in the third principal shell is 18 (in accordance with $2n^2$) and their distribution in the sub-shells is represented as:

for $n = 3$, $l = 0$, 1, and 2.

$l = 0$, $m_l = 0$, $m_s = +1/2$ and $-1/2$ $-3s$

$\left. \begin{array}{l} l = 1,\ m_l = -1,\ m_s = \pm 1/2 \\ m_l = 0,\ m_s = \pm 1/2 \\ m_l = +1,\ m_s = \pm 1/2 \end{array} \right\}$ $-3p$

$\left. \begin{array}{l} l = 2,\ m_l = -2,\ m_s = \pm 1/2 \\ m_l = -1,\ m_s = \pm 1/2 \\ m_l = 0,\ m_s = \pm 1/2 \\ m_l = +1,\ m_s = \pm 1/2 \\ m_l = +2,\ m_s = \pm 1/2 \end{array} \right\}$ $-3d$

However, the $3d$ states corresponding to $l = 2$, do not start on filling until fourth row begins. This means that the third row of the periodic table includes only 8 elements with the last element argon. The electronic configuration of argon is:

$$1s^2 \, 2s^2 \, 2p^6 \, 3s^2 \, 3p^6$$

The first element of the 4th row in the periodic table is K with one $4s$ electon in its outer-most orbit. Next to K is Ca. The $3d$ orbital starts on filling with electrons starting from Sc and completes with Cu. The first transition series begins with Sc. Like p orbitals, d orbitals are directional and can hold as many as 10 electrons. The filling of electrons in the $3d$ state is shown in Table 1.3.

The interesting point to be noted in Table 1.3 is that the order of filling electrons in $3d$ orbital is in accordance with the Hunds rule starting from Sc to V and then it breaks down in Cr. Chromium has five $3d$ electrons instead of four according to Hunds rule. This is because of the fact that the configuration with the half filled $3d$ state with parallel spin electrons is more stable than 4 parallel spins in the $3d$ state. One electron is transferred from $4s$ to $3d$ state to complete half of the $3d$ states. The change in enrgy due to exchange interaction is negative and its contribution predominates over the increase in K. E. when an electron transits from $4s$ to $3d$ state. A similar exchange interaction involves in Cu in which the $3d$ state is full and $4s$ state is partially filled. A partially filled $3d$ state gives rise to a net magnetic moment. When the $3d$ states are full, the electron probability density cloud becomes spherically symmetric as in Cu and Zn. Next to Zn, p orbitals start on filling in Ga and subsequent elements in the row. $4p$ state is complete when Kr is reached.

The order of filling electrons is the same in the 5th row of the periodic table and it also consists of elements belonging to transition series. The $4f$ and $5f$ orbitals are filled, in the 6th and 7the rows of the periodic table. The capacity of f orbitals to hold electrons is 14 with 7 energy states in different directions. The elements with partially filled $3d$ states in the 4th row of the periodic table are called transition elements whereas those with partially filled $4f$ orbitals of the 6th row are designated as rare earth elements.

1.4. IONISATION POTENTIAL

The valence electrons in an atom are not as tightly bound to the nucleus as the inner (or core) electrons and therefore they can easily be knocked out of the atom on the application of small external energy. The energy required to remove an outer valence electron out of the atom is known as ionisation potential (I.P.). When the electron is removed out of the atom, correspondingly a positive charge appears at the core or ion. The energy required to remove first electron from the outermost shell of an atom is called its first ionisation potential. The energy required to remove the second valence electron is called the second ionisation potential and so on.

The first ionisation potential of various elements as a function o'

TABLE: 1.3: Elements of the first transition series

Elements	Symbol	At. No.	Outer shell electron configuration	Electron spin distribution in 3d orbitals				
				d_1	d_2	d_3	d_4	d_5
Scondium	Sc	21	$3s^2\,3p^6\,3d^1\,4s^2$	↑				
Titanium	Ti	22	$3s^2\,3p^6\,3d^2\,4s^2$	↑	↑			
Vanadium	V	23	$3s^2\,3p^6\,3d^3\,4s^2$	↑	↑	↑		
Chromium	Cr	24	$3s^2\,3p^6\,3d^5\,4s^1$	↑	↑	↑	↑	↑
Manganese	Mn	25	$3s^2\,3p^6\,3d^5\,4s^2$	↑	↑	↑	↑	↑
Iron	Fe	26	$3s^2\,3p^6\,3d^6\,4s^2$	↑↓	↑	↑	↑	↑
Cobalt	Co	27	$3s^2\,3p^6\,3d^7\,4s^2$	↑↓	↑↓	↑	↑	↑
Nickel	Ni	28	$3s^2\,3p^6\,3d^8\,4s^2$	↑↓	↑↓	↑↓	↑	↑
Copper	Cu	29	$3s^2\,3p^6\,3d^{10}\,4s^1$	↑↓	↑↓	↑↓	↑↓	↑↓
Zinc	Zn	30	$3s^2\,3p^6\,3d^{10}\,4s^2$	↑↓	↑↓	↑↓	↑↓	↑↓

their atomic number are plotted in Fig. 1.5. It can be noted that in general, the first ionisation potential increases for elements as we

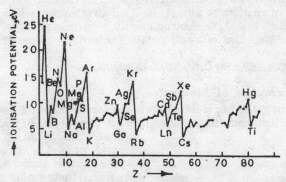

FIG. 1 5. The first ionisation potential of various elements as a function of atomic number.

move from left to right in a row of the periodic table. For example, the I. P. is least for the first element in a row of the periodic table (such as Li in the second row) and is most for the last elements in the same row (i.e. Ne in this case). On the other hand, the first ionisation potential decreases for the elements from top to bottom of a column of the periodic table. For example, Li is the first alkali metal in the first column of the periodic table for which I. P. is most and is least for Cs in the same column. This decrease in I. P. from Li to Cs is due to the increase of atomic number and consequently the lone s electron moves farther from the nucleus.

The second ionisation potential and the subsequent ones increase for multivalence elements because once the first electron is removed from the atom, there is a decrease in mutual repulsion between the orbital electrons. They can approach to one another more closely and therefore, are attached more strongly to the nucleus. Thus the orbitals are compressed.

1.5. ELECTRON AFFINITY

The energy required to attract an isolated electron from infinity to the outer most orbital of a neutral atom is known as electron affinity. The elements such as halogens have only one electron short in their outermost shell to complete their octet and therefore they have highest affinity for an electron. In doing so, the force of attraction of the electrons to the nucleus is reduced. Consequently the resulting orbital is expanded and hence the size of the atom is increased.

1.6. ELECTRONEGATIVITY

Electronegativity is the measure of the tendency of a neutral atom to acquire a negative charge by taking an electron from other atom so as to form stable outer shell. Thus, a bonding results between the atoms. One should not be confused between electron affinity and electronegativity. The former is a measure of tendency of a neutral atom to attract an isolated electron whereas the latter measures the tendency of an atom to attract to itself an electron which is bound to the other atom. Like electron affinity, electronegativity of halogens is most whereas that of alkali metals it is least.

1.7. MOLECULES AND CHEMICAL BONDING

1.7.1. Formation of Molecules

The simplest example to illustrate the formation of molecules is the diatomic hydrogen molecule. Consider two atoms of hydrogen H_a

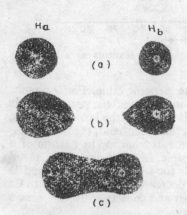

and H_b (Fig. 1.6) in their normal state, i.e. the state with the electron in the $1s$ orbital. When these atoms are widely separated, they behave as free or isolated atoms. When these atoms approach one another they experience a variety of forces as follows:

(i) the electron of each atom begins to be attracted by the nucleus of the other atom;

(ii) the two nuclei repel one another;

(iii) the two electrons repel one another.

FIG. 1.6. Formation of Hydrogen Molecule: (a) Isolated atom, (b) Distorted electron clouds caused by the attractive forces (the two electron spins are antiparallel), and (c) Electrons sharing the same wave function (in equilibrium).

Initially a force of attraction is experienced by the two atoms if their electrons have opposite spins. The force of attraction (Fa) predominates over the force of repulsion (Fr) as the separation 'r' decreases and according to Pauli's principle, the two electrons with opposite spins occupy the same region of space. The forces between the atoms as a function of their separation 'r' are shown in Fig. 1.7.

The atoms are thus pulled together until their electron clouds overlap one another (Fig. 1.6 c). The net force is attractive upto this separation. If the separation between the atoms is further reduced, the force of repulsion overcomes the force of attraction and rises rapidly with the decrease in r. At equilibrium separation r_0, the force of attraction balances exactly with the force of repulsion and the net force is zero. The potential energy (W) of the system corresponding to the minimum separation r_0 is minimum and the magnitude of the minimum energy W_0 is termed as bond energy. In hydrogen molecule, this minimum separation between H_a and H_b is 0.74A°. The bond energy is usually expressed as eV per bond or kJ/mole of the bonds.

Now let us consider the formation of a molecule between heavier atoms such as sodium. In Na atom, the first and the second principal shells are closed and the state of the valence electron is 's'. Therefore the electron density cloud is spherically symmetric round the nucleus. The inner cores of the two atoms are, therefore, represented by spheres in Fig. 1.8. When the two atoms Na_a and Na_b are approached each other, their outer shell will overlap to form a bond due to force of attraction. The force of repulsion will not overcome the force of attraction until their inner core shells will overlap. However, the overlapping of the core shells could not be possible in this case because in each closed shell the electrons are aligned antiparallel, the overlapping is, therefore, not allowed. In general, the overlapping could be possible only if the electron spins were opposed i.e., aligned antiparallel.

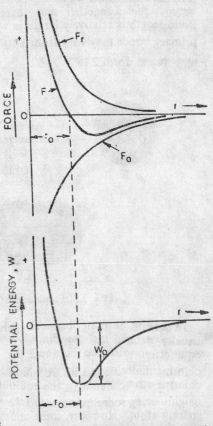

FIG. 1.7. Interatomic forces and potential energy in a system of two atoms, as a function of their distance of separation 'r'.

Thus the equilibrium separation is determined by the radius of the core shell and the molecule resembles a pair of nearly rigid spheres glued together.

1.7.2. Bond Type and Bond Length

Depending upon the strength and bond energy, the chemical bonds may broadly be classified as primary bonds and secondary bonds. The bond energies in primary bonds may vary in the range of 1 to 10 eV The examples of primary bonds are ionic bond, covalent bond and metallic bond. Metallic bonds are relatively weaker than the other two. Secondary bonds such as Vander Waals and hydrogen bonds may have energies ranging from 0.01 to 0 50 eV.

Bond length is defined as the centre to centre distance of the atoms forming a molecule. A strong bond strength means the atoms are strongly pulled together and therefore, the bond length is short. Bond length is relatively larger in weaker bonds. The bond length in primary bonds may vary from 1 to 2 Å and that in secondary bonds may range from 2 to 5 Å.

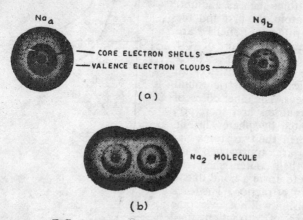

FIG. 1.8. Formation of a sodium molecule.

In case of bonding between similar atoms, the bond length is usually defined as the diameter of the atom. For example, the equilibrium distance between the atomic centres in the diatomic chlorine molecule is 1.81 Å which is nothing but the diameter of chlorine atom. Similarly, the equilibrium separation r_0 between two neighbouring sodiums atoms is 3.72 Å which is also the diameter of the sodium atom. However, some anomalies are found in this definition that the bond length of similar atom is equal to the diameter of the atom concerned. For instance, the diameter of iron is 2.48 Å when it forms a BCC crystal structure whereas the diameter is 2.54 Å when iron forms FCC crystal structure. With more adjacent number of atoms, there is less attraction to any specific neighbouring atom and consequently the interatomic distances are increased.

If a bond is formed between two dissimilar atoms, then the bond length is usually the sum of the radii of the participating atoms.

1.7.3. Primary Bondings

Ionic bonding. Ionic bonding involves exchange of electrons between the neighbouring atoms leaving them oppositely charged ions. The two oppositely charged ions are held together by an electrostatic force of attraction. The type of bond developed in this way is known as ionic bond. A typical example of ionic bond is NaCl molecule. Sodium has one lone electron which it can easily lose and become positively charged ion. On the other hand, chlorine which has very high electronegativity can take this electron given by sodium to complete its octet and become negatively charged ion. A mutual force of attraction arises between the two oppositely charged ions and bond is developed between the neighbouring ions. During the formation of the molecule, some energy is released from the system which corresponds to the decrease in potential energy due to electrostatic force of attraction.

Covalent bonding. The bonding between two hydrogen atoms described in section 1.7.1 is the simplest example of covalent bonding where the valence electrons of the two atoms share in pairs by overlapping of electron clouds of one another. The electronic structure of an atom is found to be relatively stable if the outer shell has eight electrons except the K-shell (the 1st principal shell), which attains relative stability with only two electrons with opposite spins (as in hydrogen molecule). The chlorine atom has 7 electrons in its outermost orbit. The filling of electrons in the $3s$ and $3p$ orbitals is represented as:

$$3s^2 \;\boxed{\uparrow \; \downarrow}\; 3d^5 \;\boxed{\uparrow\downarrow}\boxed{\uparrow\downarrow}\boxed{\uparrow\downarrow}$$

It can be seen from the above that six electrons are paired while the seventh is unpaired identical to the one electron in hydrogen. This 7th electron will always be 'looking for' another unpaired electron or a lone electron so as to close the shell. When another chlorine atom with a lone unpaired electron comes near it, the two electrons get paired off by making their spins antiparallel ($\uparrow \; \downarrow$). This pair remains common to two atoms so that both of the atoms attain an octet structure. The bonding between two chlorine atoms can be represented as follows:

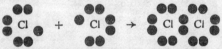

The electron density cloud is concentrated along the line joining the nuclei (Fig. 1.6) and therefore, a directionality in bonds results. In case such as chlorine, partially filled p orbitals take part in the bonding. Since p orbitals are perpendicular to one another (Fig. 1.3), the bonding between p orbitals leads to directionality of bonds.

The stability of interatomic bonds depends upon the extent of overlapping of orbitals. In the same shell, p orbitals tend to overlap more than the s orbitals when the two atoms come close together. Therefore, p orbitals are preferred for most stable interatomic bonds. The resulting bond angles are obviously close to 90° since this is the angle the p orbitals make with one another. In some cases the bonds are partially ionic in character and therefore large deviation in bond angles result. The bond angles in such cases may be of the order of 110° or so. The deviation in bond angles from 90° may be due to hybridisation of the s and p orbitals (or the wave functions).

A typical example of hybrid bonding is carbon-carbon bonds formed in diamond. Besides diamond, hybridisation occurs in organic molecules, such as methane. Each carbon atom has four valence electrons that can take part in covalent bonding. Covalent bonds are formed not only due to overlapping of pure 's' or pure 'p' orbitals but also due to overlapping of 's' and 'p' orbitals, called the hybrid bonding. The electronic configuration of normal carbon atom is $1s^2\ 2s^2\ 2p^2$ with the electron spin paired in the $1s$ and $2s$ orbitals. Only the $2p$ electron spins are unpaired and are free to form bonds. Therefore, one can expect only two carbon bonds. But when the carbon atoms approach each other, the s and p orbitals overlap. As a consequence one 's' electron is excited to p orbital and aligns itself parallel to other two. This is in accordance with the Hunds rule that p orbital is half filled now. The electronic configuration of a carbon atom now can be represented as $1s^2\ 2s^1\ 2p^3$ and the electron spins are distributed as:

$$1s^2\ (\uparrow\ \downarrow)\ 2s\ (\uparrow)\ 2p^3\ (\uparrow\ \uparrow\ \uparrow)$$

This configuration results in four unpaired electron spins and these unpaired electrons interact rather strongly with one another and modify the shapes of s and p orbitals. The electrostatic repulsion is so great that each 'electron's cloud' concentrates itself away from those of the other three (Fig. 1.9) and the four arrange themselves with the largest possible angle 109.5°, between each pair. The favourable bonding directions of these orbitals are disposed towards 4 corners of a regular tetrahedron (Fig. 1.10). Such a rearrangement of orbitals is called hybridisation and the four orbitals are called sp^3 hybrids. The four bonds are of equal strength.

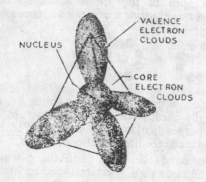

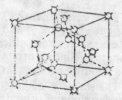

FIG. 1.9. The lobe shaped valence electron clouds in the carbon atom.

FIG. 1.10. The structure of diamond.

Because of the strong repulsion, this rearrangement is difficult to distort and the carbon atoms are joined up with the electron clouds of the other neighbouring atoms pointing towards one another. Thus each carbon atom is surrounded by 8 electrons which is in agreement with the 8-N rule. The structure so formed can be considered as interpenetrating two FCC lattices along the body diagonal by 1/4 cube edge as illustrated in Fig. 1.10. This structure is very strong and rigid.

Covalent bonds similar to diamond are also found in CCl_4, SiF_4, CH_4, etc. The bond in graphite is sp^2 hybrid in which 3 bonds are formed in a plane with interbond angles of 120° and the fourth bond is formed in a direction perpendicular to sp^2 bonds and between p orbital and sp^2 bonds as shown in Fig. 1.11. The perpendicular bond is however a weak bond and hence graphite has very low yield strength in this direction. This is why graphite is flaky in nature.

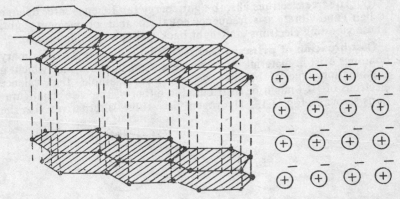

FIG. 1.11. The structure of graphite.

FIG. 1.12. Schematic representation of metallic bond.

Metallic bonding. Almost 70 pct. of the elements in the periodic table are metals. Metals are characterised by their availability of large number of valence electrons which they can lose with ease and thus becoming positively charged particles or ions (Fig. 1.12). The valence electrons in a metal are assumed to be 'free' electrons and they constitute an electron cloud. This electron cloud is not attached firmly to a particular positively charge core but is supposed to move about the crystal lattice freely. Thus the electron cloud is equally associated to all core ions just as in covalent bonding where the electrons are shared between the atoms. The electron cloud is bound with the core ions in a way the oppositely charged ions bond together in ionic bonding. This type of bonding in metals is known as metallic bonding showing a dual character of bonding. In such an arrangement of atoms and electrons, the atoms can interchange their positions without breaking up the bonds. Because of this nature of metallic bond, metals have shown some important mechanical properties such as plasticity, elasticity, etc.

The following properties of metals can be explained on the basis of metallic bonding:

(i) High electrical conductivity of metals is due to the free movement of electrons in a particular direction under an electrified field.

(*ii*) High thermal conductivity of metals largely arises because the electron cloud absorbs the kinetic energy and being more free to move to transfer thermal energy from high temperature level to low temperature level.

(*iii*) The crystalline structure of metals decides the mechanical properties. For instance, metals with face centred cubic structure are usually ductile.

(*iv*) The free electrons absorb light energy (and hence are opaque to light) and vibrate at a frequency equal to that of incident light. These vibrating electrons emit light back giving a metallic lusture.

Combination of primary bonds. Usually three types of primary bondings exist in materials but, there are some materials in which a combination type of bonding occurs. For example, the valence electrons of HCl might be distributed in either of the two configurations shown in F.g. 1.13. Hydrogen has three alternatives for the

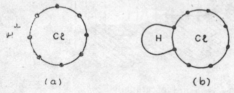

(a)   (b)

FIG. 1.13. Distribution of valence electron of HCl. (*a*) Ionic, and (*b*) Covalent.

distribution of its valence electrons. In the two arrangements it forms an ionic bond while in the third, it forms a covalent bond. Each of the three arrangements are found in a hydrogen molecule.

1.7.4. Secondary Bonding

The inert gases and the other molecular gases such as CH_4, O_2, H_2, CO_2, etc. are condensed to form solids at sufficiently low temperatures. This shows that there must be some kind of bonding between the gaseous atoms and molecules which hold them together in a solid form. Although these gases do not have valence electrons to form a bond with other atoms or molecules, nevertheless they condense to solid phase due to weaker forces in between the molecules. This type of bonding is known as secondary bonding. The secondary bonding is of two types, namely 'Vander Waal's bonding' and 'hydrogen bonding'.

Vander Waal's bonding. Vander Waal's forces may exist between symmetric as well as assymmetric molecules. The forces between assymmetric molecules arise from electrostatic dipoles. Let us consider a typical example of dipole formation. In a molecule of HF, hydrogen is least electronegative and F is most electronegative. When

H and F form a covalent bond (Fig. 1.14) by sharing electrons which align in antiparallel pairs, the fluorine tends to acquire a negative

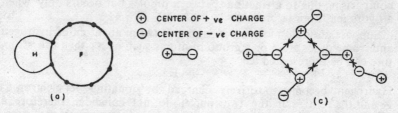

FIG. 1 14 Polarisation: (a) An electrical imbalance or polarisation (occurring in asymmetric molecules), (b) an electrical dipole resulting due to electrical imbalance, and (c) holding together of resulting dipoles by Vander Wall's force.

charge due to its high electronegativity whereas hydrogen which is losing its electron for its high electro positivity becomes positively charged. As a consequence the centres of the two opposite chages do not exactly coincide with one another and therefore a dipole is formed. The resulting dipoles introduce a weak Vander Waals forces of attraction between the molecules as illustrated in Fig. 1.14c.

Symmetric molecules, by contrast, are unable to form dipoles since the shared electrons spend most of their time equally on all sides of the molecule. During their fluctuations, a majority of shared electrons spend more time on one side of a molecule than on the opposite side for a short period of time. Thus, for a moment a negative charge

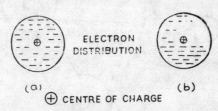

FIG. 1.15. Electric polarisation: (a) uniform electron distribution, and (b) momentary polarised distribution.

arises on one side of the molecule, whereas, a positive charge on the other side (Fig. 1.15). The Vander Waals forces between symmetric molecules are, thus, due to momentary polarisation effect. This conclusion is supported by the fact that substances which have small molecules and which are bonded by Vander Waal's forces are gases at room temperature.

Symmetric molecules such as CO_2, CH_4, etc. have a greater number of electrons in their molecules and therefore there will be a greater probability of imbalance. This leads to greater Vander Waal's forces and higher condensing temperature.

Hydrogen bond. Hydrogen bond is very much alike Vander Waals bond arising due to attraction between dipoles but occurs only when a hydrogen atom is present.

Suppose an ionic molecule is formed between an atom of hydrogen and some other atom or a group of atoms such as X, then the structure can be represented as:

$$X^- ——H^+$$

Hydrogen becomes positively charged by donating its electron to X and the centres of the two nuclei do not coincide, therefore, a dipole results. The positive charge on hydrogen can attract the negative charge on a third ion or a group of atoms (usually a part of another molecule) in a way analogous to ionic bond. Thus, the latter bond is somewhat stronger than otherwise. This dipole-dipole attraction is exactly the same as in Vander Waals bond. The structure after the third ionic group is attached to the positive hydrogen ion can be represented as:

$$X^- ——H^+ ——Y^-$$

A typical example of hydrogen bond (also called hydrogen bridge) is dipole-dipole attraction between water molecules as illustrated in Fig. 1.16. In water molecule, the half filled p orbitals of oxygen are

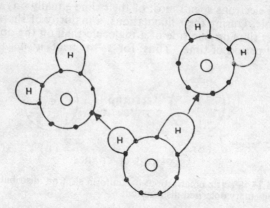

FIG. 1.16. A schematic diagram showing hydrogen bridge (bond).

shared with the two hydrogen atoms. The shared electrons spend more time in between the two atoms so that oxygen atom tends to form a negative pole and the hydrogen atom a positive pole of a dipole.

The hydrogen bridge is not limited to water or ice, but it may also be found in some other molecules such as NH_3.

1.8. CRYSTAL STRUCTURE

In a crystal the atoms or molecules are arranged in some specific order in a three dimensional space. The points where the atoms are situated in the lattice are known as lattice points and the space with these points is known as space lattice. The most important characteristic of a space lattice is that each lattice point has identical surroundings to that of every other point so that one point can not be distinguished from another.

A space lattice differs from a crystal structure in that a space lattice is an array of points in 3-dimensional space whereas a crystal structure is an arrangement of atoms and molecules that usually exist in a crystal. A crystal is generally accompanied with imperfections.

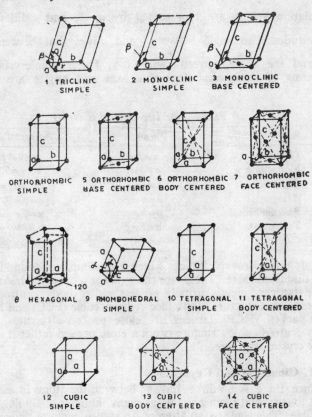

1 TRICLINIC SIMPLE

2 MONOCLINIC SIMPLE

3 MONOCLINIC BASE CENTERED

ORTHORHOMBIC SIMPLE

5 ORTHORHOMBIC BASE CENTERED

6 ORTHORHOMBIC BODY CENTERED

7 ORTHORHOMBIC FACE CENTERED

8 HEXAGONAL

9 RHOMBOHEDRAL SIMPLE

10 TETRAGONAL SIMPLE

11 TETRAGONAL BODY CENTERED

12 CUBIC SIMPLE

13 CUBIC BODY CENTERED

14 CUBIC FACE CENTERED

FIG. 1.17. The fourteen Bravais lattices as shown by their unit cells.

A space lattice is usually represented by a unit cell. A unit cell is the smallest volume of the space lattice in which the atoms are located at some specific lattice sites. When such unit cells are put side by side in three directions and extended to long distances in each directions, they form a space lattice. Thus, a unit cell represents a space lattice or a crystal structure.

A three dimensional lattice is in fact formed by repeated transla-
tion of three non-coplanar vectors, namely $\vec{a}$, $\vec{b}$ and $\vec{c}$. There are fourteen ways in which the atoms can be arranged in a 3-dimensional re-
petitions pattern, so that in each case every lattice point has identical
surroundings. These lattices are usually known as Bravais lattices
after their originator and are shown in Fig. 1.17 by their unit cells.

All the Bravais lattices belong to basically 7 crystal system, viz,
triclinic, mono clinic, orthorhombic, hexagonal, rhombohedral,
tetragonal and cubic. In these systems, the three non-coplanar
translation vectors are represented by $\vec{a}$, $\vec{b}$, and $\vec{c}$ lines as their
magnitudes. The angle between $\vec{b}$ and $\vec{c}$ is α, that between $\vec{c}$ and $\vec{a}$
is β and the angle between $\vec{a}$ and $\vec{b}$ is γ. These seven crystal systems
in terms of their crystallographic axes and angles are shown in
Table 1.4.

TABLE 1.4. *The Crystal Systems*

System	Parameters	Interaxial angles
Triclinic	$a \neq b \neq c$	$\alpha \neq \beta \neq \gamma$
Monoclinic	$a \neq b \neq c$	$\alpha = \gamma = 90° \neq \beta$
Orthorhombic	$a \neq b \neq c$	$\alpha = \beta = \gamma = 90°$
Hexagonal	$a = b \neq c$	$\alpha = \beta = 90°, \gamma = 120°$
Rhombohedral	$a = b = c$	$\alpha = \beta = \gamma \neq 90°$
Tetragonal	$a = b \neq c$	$\alpha = \beta = \gamma = 90°$
Cubic	$a = b = c$	$\alpha = \beta = \gamma = 90°$

Only those Bravais lattices which are commonly found in metals
are discussed here. These are the cubic and hexagonal. Among the
cubic lattices, metals usually possess either body centred or face
centred cubic stucture. Both face centred cubic (FCC) and hexagonal
close packed (HCP) lattices are close packed structures, whereas,
body-centred cubic structure is not a close packed rather it is an open
pack crystal structure.

1.8.1. Close Packed Crystals

Since there is no direct linkage between the atoms in metals, they
tend to surround themselves by as many number of similar atoms as
possible. This leads to an attempt to secure a close pack structure.
The interatomic spacing between the atoms is such that their electron
shells do not interfere with one another but an electron exchange may
occur. The atoms of a crystal are assumed to be spheres.

Let us place a layer of spheres A in which each sphere is in contact with six adjacent spheres in the same plane (Fig. 1.18a). The
second layer of spheres B is now placed over the A layer so that the
spheres of the B layer rest in the pockets (or the so called cavities) of
the first layer and that each sphere of the B layer is in contact with

three spheres below it. This can be done in two ways as shown in Fig. 1.18b and 1.18c. If the planes are extended infinitely, the two arrangements are equivalent.

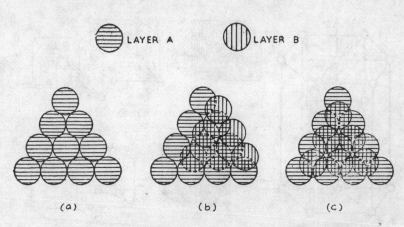

FIG. 1.18. Closed packed crystals: (a) layer A consisting of 10 spheres, (b, c) two methods of placing layer B consisting of 10 spheres [5 interstices in (b) and 3 interstices in (c)].

A third layer of spheres C can be placed over the B layer in two ways, each with equal efficiency of packing but resulting in either a

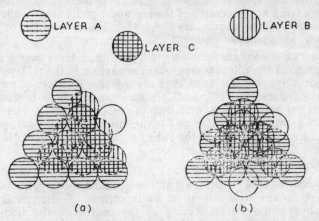

FIG. 1.19. Close packed structures: (a) layer C placed over layer B so that the five interstices remain open (HCP), and (b) layer C placed so that all interstices are closed (F.C.C.).

FCC crystal or HCP crystal. In Fig. 1.19a, the layer C is so stacked that each C sphere comes over the spheres of the A layer and the cavities of the first layer which were not filled by the spheres of the *B* layer, still remain vacant. In this packing, the layers *A* and *C* are identical and the packing can be considered as *AB AB* . . . ., and arrangement that results in HCP crystal structure. A unit cell of HCP crystal is shown in Fig. 1.20*a*. It can

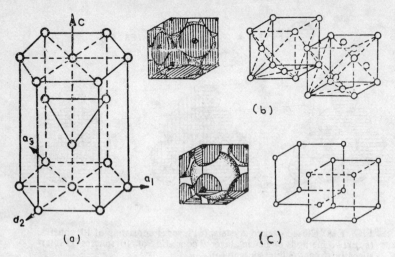

FIG. 1.20. Different unit cells: (*a*) HCP crystal, (*b*) FCC crystal and (*c*) BCC crystal.

be seen that one atom is situated at each 12 corners of the cell. Two atoms are lying at the centres of the top and bottom faces (called the basal planes). Three atoms are lying inside the body of the cell and are facing alternate prismatic planes.

Fig. 1.19 *b* shows another way of putting *C* layer over *B* layer. Each sphere of the *C* layer rests over the cavities in the *A* layer that were not filled by the spheres in the *B* layer. This type of packing can be considered as *ABC, ABC*. . . . an arrangement that results in FCC crystal structure. A unit cell of FCC crystal is shown in Fig. 1.20 *b*, where in addition to 8 corner atoms, 6 atoms are placed at the centres of the faces of the cube.

1.8.2. Open Packed Crystals

Body centred cubic structure is an open packed crystal structure in which there are eight atoms at each corner of the cubic cell (Fig. 1.20 *c*) and one atom is lying at the centre of the body and hence the name is body-centred cubic structure.

1.8.3. Lattice Parameter

The linear dimension which represents the distance between the atoms of the adjacent parallel planes of atoms is known as Lattice Parameter.

1.8.4. Coordination Number

Coordination number of an atom in a crystal structure is defined as the number of nearest neighbour atoms which it can have.

☞ The coordination number for BCC, FCC, and HCP crystals are respectively 8, 12, and 12, and are illustrated in Fig. 1.21. Fig. 1.21(a)

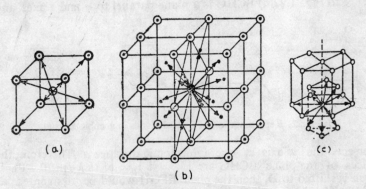

(a)

(b)

(c)

FIG. 1.21. Schematic representation of coordination number in different crystals: (a) BCC crystal, (b) FCC crystal, and (c) HCP crystal.

shows that the corner atoms of the unit cell are touching the body centred atom as indicated by arrows. In the FCC unit cell each atom is in contact with 12 adjacent atoms as shown in Fig 1.21(b) where 8 unit cells are drawn for simplicity. The atom which is at the centre of the body constituting 8-FCC unit cells (all the face centred atoms are not shown here), is in contact with four atoms in three planes that are normal to each other. Thus, the coordination number is 12 as indicated by arrows in three planes. It is obvious from Fig. 1.21(c) that each atom is surrounded by 6 atoms in its own plane, 3 other atoms in the lower plane and 3 other atoms in the plane above, making the coordination number 12.

1.8.5. Crystal Planes and Directions

Crystal planes. From the section 1.8.1, it is apparent that several different atomic planes may pass through atoms at definite lattice points of a crystal. The orientation of planes in a crystal can be defined by certain notations called Miller indices, after the name of the inventor. Since a lattice is formed by three non-coplanar vectors $\vec{a}$, $\vec{b}$ and $\vec{c}$, these in a crystal are defined as crystallographic axes and are designated as $\vec{x}$, $\vec{y}$ and $\vec{z}$ in a cubic crystal. A given plane in a crystal, in general, will be tilted with respect to the crystallographic axes. The miller indices of this plane can be described as the reciprocals of the fractional intercepts made by this plane with the crystallographic axes. For instance, if the Miller indices of a plane are $(h\ k\ l)$, written in parentheses, then the intercepts made by the plane with the axes are $(1/h\ 1/k\ 1/l)$. If the axial lengths are a, b, and c, the actual intercepts made by the plane with the axes are given as $(a/h\ b/k\ c/l)$. There may be many planes parallel to each other, the Miller indices (hkl) usually refer to a plane which is closest to the origin. With reference to Fig. 1.22(a) BCHG is a plane parallel to x and z axes and

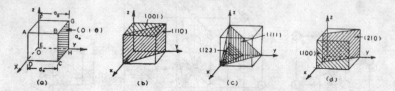

FIG. 1.22. Representation of typical planes in a cubic crystal.

intersects the y axis at one interatomic distance a. Therefore, the indices of the plane BCHG are $1/\infty\ 1/1\ 1/\infty$ or $(h\ k\ l) = (0\ 1\ 0)$. If origin is shifted to D, then the plane EFGH would be designated as $(\bar{1}\ 0\ 0)$. The bar over the integer indicates that the plane intersects one of the axes in a negative direction. Figs. 1.22(b), 1.22(c) and 1.22(d) represent various planes in a cubic lattice.

In a HCP crystal, there are four indices of the type $(h\ k\ i\ l)$ to specify a plane. These indices are based on the four axes, the three axes a_1, a_2, a_3 are coplannar and the angle between one another is $120°$. This plane is usually termed as basal plane. The vertical c axis is normal to the basal plane. These axes and some typical planes are illustrated in Fig. 1.23.

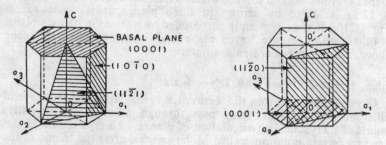

FIG. 1.23. Representation of typical planes in HCP crystal.

A set of planes of a given form such as $(1\ 0\ 0)$, $(0\ 1\ 0)$, $(0\ 0\ 1)$, $(\bar{1}\ 0\ 0)$, $(0\ \bar{1}\ 0)$ and $(0\ 0\ \bar{1})$ in a cubic lattice are represented as a family of planes since, these are crystallographically equivalent. The indices for a family of planes are enclosed in braces i.e. $\{1\ 0\ 0\}$ Similarly the octahedral planes $(1\ 1\ 1)$, $(\bar{1}\ 1\ 1)$, $(1\ \bar{1}\ 1)$ and $(1\ 1\ \bar{1})$ are represented by a family of planes as $\{1\ 1\ 1\}$. The closest pack planes in FCC and HCP crystals are $(1\ 1\ 1)$ and $(0\ 0\ 0\ 1)$ respectively.

Crystal directions. The direction of a given line in a unit cell of a crystal lattice can be determined by first drawing a line parallel to the given line and passing through the origin of the unit cell. Now assign indices of any point on the line drawn. Suppose u, v, w are the coordinates of a point on the line through origin, where these numbers may not necessarily be integral. The points $2u, 2v, 2w$ and $3u, 3v, 3w$ must also lie on the same line. These indices are enclosed in square brackets as $[u\ v\ w]$ showing the direction of a given line, drawn parallel to to the given line. These are also the indices of the direction of the given line.

For example, HC is a given direction in a unit cell of a cubic crystal. (Fig. 1.24a). Then EB is the line parallel to HC and passing through the origin E. EB lying in X-Y plane and can be indexed by moving a unit distance from E to A along x-axis and then moving through a unit distance along a direction parallel to y axis i.e. from A to B. Then EB is the vector sum of EA and AB and represents the direction of the given line. Fig. 1.24 represents various different directions in a cubic and hexagonal unit cells.

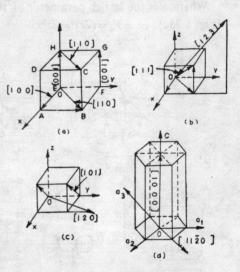

A family of crystallographically equivalent directions are designated by enclosing the indices in diamond brackets as $<u\ v\ w>$. In a cubic lattice, a direction is always perpendicular to the plane having the same indices. The closest

FIG. 1.24. Representation of typical directions in a cubic and hexagonal unit cells.

pack directions in BCC, FCC, and HCP crystals are [1 1 1], [1 1 0] and [1 1 $\bar{2}$ 0] respectively.

1.8.6. Atomic Packing Factor

Atomic packing factor of a crystal, or a plane in the crystal or a direction in a crystal shows how closely the atoms are packed in the crystal, the plane and along the direction respectively. Atomic packing factor (APF) for a crystal, plane and direction is defined as the ratios:

$$\frac{V_a}{V_c}\ ,\ \frac{A_a}{A_p}\ ,\ \frac{L_a}{L_s}\ \text{respectively.}$$

Where V, A, and L represent volume of the crystal, area of the plane and length or direction respectively. The subscript a, c, p and s are designations for atom, crystal, plane and side of a crystal.

APF of a simple cubic cell $= \dfrac{V_a}{V_c}$

There is one atom per unit cell in a simple cubic lattice (since each corner atom is shared by 8 unit cells in a crystal). Therefore $V_a = \dfrac{4}{3}\pi r^3$ where r is the radius of the atom if an atom is assumed to be a sphere.

$V_c =$ Volume of the cell and is given as a^3

Where a is the lattice parameter of the unit cell and is equal to $2r$ (Fig. 1.25a) i.e.α $V_c = (2r)^3 = 8r^3$

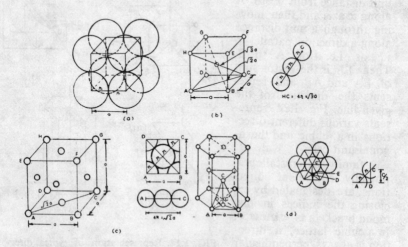

FIG. 1.25. (a, b and c) showing relation between 'a' and 'c' respectively in simple cubic, BCC and FCC unit cells and (d) shows determination of area of the basal plane and the height of the unit cell.

and APF of simple cubic cell $= \dfrac{4/3\pi r^3}{8r^2}$

$$= 0.52.$$

This shows that the volume occupied by atoms in a simple cubic cell is 52 pct. of the cell volume.

APF of body centred cubic lattice. The volume of the cell is given as a^3. From the geometry shown in Fig. 1.25(b).

$$4r = 3a$$

or $$a = \frac{4}{3} r \text{ and } V_c = \left(\frac{4}{3} r \right)^3$$

The effective number of atoms in a BCC unit cell $= 1/8 \times 8 + 1 = 2$

Therefore, $$V_a = \left(\frac{4}{3} \pi r^3 \right) \times 2$$

and $$\frac{V_a}{V_c} = \frac{(4/3 \pi r^3) \times 2}{\left(\frac{4}{3} r \right)^3} \simeq 0.68 = APF$$

Thus the volume of the cell occupied by atoms is 68 pct.

APF of a face centred cubic cell. The volume of the cell $V_c = a^3$. From the geometry shown in Fig. 1.25c.

$$a = \frac{4r}{\sqrt{2}}$$

Thus $$V_c = \left(\frac{4r}{\sqrt{2}} \right)^3$$

The effective number of corner atoms in FCC unit cell $1/8 \times 8 = 1$.

Since each face centred atom in a cubic crystal is shared by two unit cells, and there are six face centred atoms in the FCC unit cell, therefore, the effective number of face centred atoms $= 1/2 \times 6 = 3$. Therefore, the total effective no. of atoms in FCC unit cell is 4.

Thus $$V_a = 4 \times 4/3 \pi r^3$$

$$APF = \frac{V_a}{V_c} = \frac{4 \times 4/3 \pi r^3}{(4r/\sqrt{2})^3} \simeq 0.74$$

APF of a hexagonal close packed cell. The volume of the unit cell is given as the product of area of the base and the height (*c*) of the cell.

With reference to Fig. 1.25d, the basal plane can be divided into six equilateral triangles. Each edge of such triangles is '*a*' which is equal to 2*r*. So the area of the equilateral triangle is given as:

$$ABC^1 = 1/2 . 2r . 2r \sin 60°$$
$$= 2r^2 . \sqrt{3}/2 = \sqrt{3}r^2$$

Therefore, the total area of the basal plane $= 6 \sqrt{3} \ r^2$

As shown in Fig. 1.25(*d*), CD is the height of an atom from the basal plane and is equal to 1/2 the total height of the unit cell. From the geometry pictured separately (Fig. 1.25 *d*)

$$C/2 = \sqrt{AC^2 - AD^2}$$

or $$c/2 = \sqrt{4r^2 - 4/3r^2} \quad \text{(Since } AD = 2/3 \ AE\text{)}$$

or $$c/2 = \sqrt{8/3} \ r^2$$

or $\qquad c/2 = 2\sqrt{2/3}\, r$

or $\qquad c = 4\sqrt{2/3}\, r$

Thus the volume of the cell $= 4\sqrt{2/3} \cdot 6\sqrt{\cdot 3}\, r^3$

or $\qquad V_c = 24\sqrt{2} r^3$

The effective number of atoms per unit cell in HCP structure is
$$= (1/6 \times 6 \times 2) + (1/2 \times 2) + 3$$
$$= 2 + 1 + 3 = 6$$
$$V_a = 6 . 4/3 \pi r^3$$

then $\qquad \text{APF} = \dfrac{V_a}{V_c} = \dfrac{6.4/3\ \pi\ r^3}{24\sqrt{2}\ r^3} = 0.74$

Therefore, the volume of the unit cell occupied by atoms in the HCP crystal structure is 74 pct. and is equal to that of FCC crystal structure.

Thus the efficiency of packing atoms in a FCC structure is the same as that of a HCP structure, though the arrangement of atoms is different in the crystals.

In a HCP crystal structure there is an important ratio, i.e c/a ratio.

The ideal c/a ratio is expressed as

$$c/a = \frac{24\sqrt{2}\, r}{\sqrt{3} \times 2r} = 1.633$$

In metals possession HCP structure, c/a ratio is not equal to 1.633 but is some what greater in some metals and is somewhat lesser than the idal value in others. As a consequence, the lattice is distorted somewhat.

Just like the Atomic packing factor of a crystal, the APF of a plane or a direction in the crystal can be determined. The APF is a measure of atomic packing density of a crystal, plane or direction.

1.9. CRYSTAL DEFECTS

So far we have discussed an ideal crystal. An ideal crystal is a perfect crystal in which each atom has identical surroundings. A real crystal, however, always consists of a large number of imperfections in the lattice. Since a crystal is a three dimensional pattern, the defects in a crystal may also be classified on geometrical basis. The important and most commonly occurring imperfection in a crystal are zero dimensional (or point), one dimensional (i.e. line) and two dimensional (i.e. surface).

1.9.1. Point Imperfections

A point imperfection, as the name implies, is an imperfection of zero dimension and is highly localised interruption in the regularity of a lattice. A point defect may arise due to missing of an atom from its normal site or due to the presence of an impurity atom in the lattice. There are four kinds of point defects which are commonly exist in crystals. These are, vacancy defect, substitutional impurity atom defect, interstitial impurity atom defect, Frankel defect, and Schottky defect.

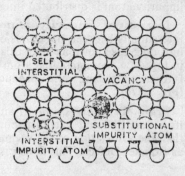

Vacancy defect. If an atom is missing from its normal site in the matrix, the defect so created is known as a vacancy defect and is illustrated in Fig. 1.26. At equilibrium, the fraction of lattice sites that are vacant at a given temperature is given approximately by the relation:

FIG. **1.26**. Schematic representation of some possible point defects in two dimensional crystal.

$$\frac{n}{N} = \exp. ^{-\bar{E}_{s}/kT} \ (\text{or} \ e^{-E_{s}/k_{T}}) \qquad \qquad \ldots (1.4)$$

where n is the number of vacant sites in N sites, $-E_s$ is the energy required to move an atom from the interior of the crystal to its surface, k is Boltzman's constant and T is the temperature in °K. In a perfect crystal all the atoms are in their minimum enrgy state due to

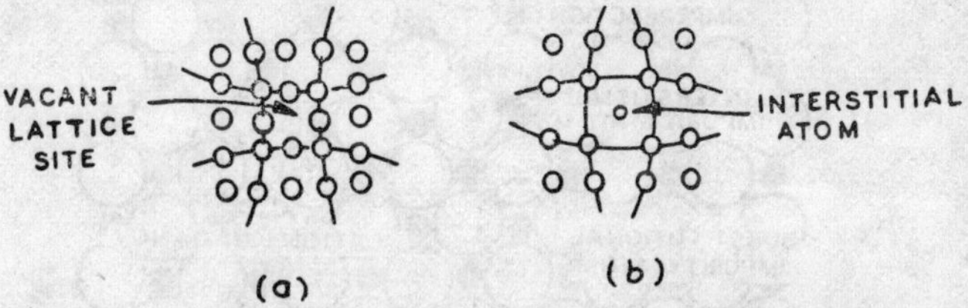

VACANT LATTICE SITE

INTERSTITIAL ATOM

(a)   **(b)**

FIG. **1.27**. Schematic representation of the types of elastic stress field introduced in a crystal lattice due to (a) vacancy defect and (b) impurity atom such as substitutional or interstitial defect.

force of attraction among them. If an atom leaves its normal site whereby, creating a vacancy, then the atoms surrounding the vacancy tend to be closure together (i.e. to be pulled towards the vacant site) due to force of attraction, as illustrated in Fig. 1.27a, and thereby, bring about distortion in the lattice planes.

Substitutional impurity atom. When an impurity (or a foreign) atom takes a normal site in the lattice in place of an atom of the matrix, the resulting defect is called a substitutional impurity atom defect (Fig 1.26). If the size of the substitutional impurity atom is less than the size of an atom of the normal latice, then the type of lattice distortion brought about is analogous to that arises in the presence of a vacancy in matrix (Fig. 1.27a). On the contrary, if the size of the impurity atom is somewhat larger than the atoms of the matrix, the type of lattice distortion is analogous to that when an impurity atom is distributed interstitially in the lattice (Fig. 1.27b).

Interstitial impurity atom. If a foreign atom is distributed interstitially between the atoms of a matrix, then the type of defect introduced is known as interstitial impurity atom defect, as illustrated in Fig. 1.26. An interstitial atom tends to push the surrounding atoms farther apart and also produces distortion of the lattice planes (Fig. 1.27b).

Frankel imperfection. If an atom creates a vacancy by leaving its normal site and gets distributed itself interstitially in the matrix, then the association of the vacancy and the interstitial atom is known as Frankel Defect. This defect is illustrated in Fig. 1.28.

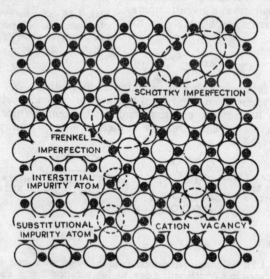

FIG. 1.28. Schematic representation of number of possible point defects in an ionic solid in two dimensions (Cations and anions are respectively shown by small and large circles).

Schottky Imperfection. When a cation vacancy is associated with an anion vacancy, the pair is called a Schottky defect (Fig. 1.28).

1.9.2. Line Imperfections

Line imperfections are one dimensional defects and are most important kind of defects as they considerably affect the various physical and mechanical properties of materials. In section 1 9.1 it has been described that a point defect is one in which the defect is surrounded by a distortion. Similarly, the distortion around a line imperfection is centred along a line. Thus, a line defect is a boundary of separating two regions that are perfect themselves but are out of order across the boundary, i.e., there is a wrong bond relationship across the boundary between the two regions. In order to understand a line defect, consider a crystal undergoing shear, as shown in Fig. 1.29. As shear proceeds, the unit cells of the upper part of the crystal are pushed ahead one full step, where they can again register with most of the cells in the lower part of the crystal. As a result, a part of the crystal is slipped with respect to other. The line (D) separating the slipped and unslipped regions is called a dislocation line. Under continuation of shear stress on the crystal,

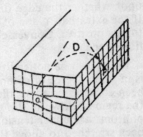

FIG. 1.29. A three dimensional crystal undergoing shear and showing the dislocation line D.

the line, D moves through the crystal until it reaches to the surface and gets disappeared.

Though in general, dislocations are produced in a crystal on the application of shear stress but they are also generated via other modes such as during solidification, application of thermal energy or in the presence of impurities in the system. In an undeformed crystal, the usual density of dislocations is about $10^8/cm^2$ and after severe deformation the value may reach to as high as $10^{12}/cm^2$.

Edge dislocation. It can be seen from Fig. 1.29 that the right side view of the crystal shows the direction of slip normal to the dislocation loop D.

This part of the dislocation loop D is called an edge dislocation, since along this part, the edge of an extra half plane of atoms can

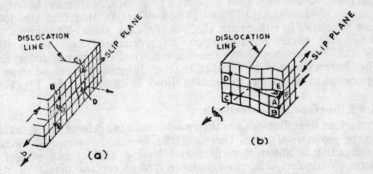

FIG. 1.30. (a) Edge dislocation and (b) screw dislocation showing construction of Burgers circuit.

be seen in the right side view of the crystal shown separately in Fig. 1.30a. Thus, an edge dislocation is one in which there is an extra half plane of atoms above or below the slip plane and that the direction of slip (i.e. slip vector) is normal to the dislocation line. An edge dislocation is represented by a symbol ⊥ or ⊤ depending upon whether the edge dislocation is positive or negative respectively. If the extra half plane of atoms lies above the slip plane, the dislocation is positive. Conversely, if it lies below the slip plane, the dislocation is negative.

It can also be noticed that the plane of atoms above the slip plane is in some degree of compression (Fig. 1.30b). The bond lengths have been compressed to smaller than the equilibrium value. However, the region below the slip plane is somewhat expanded (i.e. the planes of atoms are under tension). The bond lengths in this region have been stretched to above the normal values. This distorted configuration extends all along the edge into the crystal.

Screw dislocation. The front view of the crystal (Fig. 1.30b) shows that the part of the dislocation loop D is parallel to the slip direction. This part of the dislocation loop is called a screw dislocation. In this the atoms are displaced in two separate planes that are perpendicular to each other. Under the influence of shear stress, the direction of slip is normal to the direction of motion of the dislocation line.

Burgers vector. Burgers vector is a measure of magnitude and direction of slip. The magnitude of Burgers vector means the extent to which a metal is deformed. Burgers vector of a screw or an edge dislocation can be determined by constructing a rectangular loop (or a circuit) around the dislocation concerned. In a perfect crystal a rectangular circuit completes itself around a line but in the presence of a dislocation, the circuit around the dislocation line fails to close. Figs. 1.30a and 1.30b illustrate the construction of a Burgers circuit. A Burgers circuit around a dislocation is constructed by starting from the point A. The loop ends at point F (Fig. 1.30). It may be noted that the distances (AB + FE) = CD and BC = DE, therefore the loop is a rectangle. In either case, the loop fails to close. The extent to which the circuit remains open is represented by the symbol '*b*' the Burgers vector (or the slip vector). In the screw dislocation the Burgers vector is parallel to the dislocation line whereas it is normal to the edge dislocation line, as illustrated in Fig. 1.30.

1.9.3. Surface Imperfections

Surface imperfections are the two dimensional defects in a crystal in the geometrical sense. These are the localised regions of disturbances that lie about a surface and having a thickness of a few atomic diameters. The most common type of surface defect in any crystal is its surface itself. Since at the surface the atoms are not surrounded by as many number of atoms as those inside the crystal, the energy inside the crystal is less than that at the surface. For the same crystal structure, the coordination number of an atom inside the crystal is different from that of an atom at the surface, therefore surface of the crystal itself is a defect in its own. The other surface defects found in crystals are stacking faults, grain boundaries, and twinning.

Stacking faults. Stacking faults are the planer imperfections which result when the stacking sequence of atomic planes in a close packed crystal breaks up, i.e., if an atomic plane is missing from the normal sequence, a fault is created. For example, the normal sequence of stacking atomic planes in FCC crystal is

$$\downarrow$$
$$\ldots. \text{ABC ABC ABC} \ldots.$$

If the plane, A of atoms, as indicated above by an arrow is missing, the sequence becomes

$$\ldots.. \text{ABC ABC : BC ABC} \ldots..$$

The stacking in the missing region is ...BC BC ... which is nothing but HCP stacking. This surface imperfection is called a stacking fault. The nearest neighbour bonds of an atom in the faulted region is 12 which is a characteristic of FCC crystals. However, the second nearest bond relationship does not hold good for an atom in the faulted region as it should in a perfect FCC crystal. Hence, a small surface energy is associated with the faulted region, in the range of 0.01—0 05 Joules/M². In the same way, a stacking fault in a HCP crystal may be defined as a thin region of FCC stacking.

Grain boundaries. Grain boundaries are the surfaces which separate two crystals (or grains) orienting in different directions (Fig. 1.31). In the grain boundary region the atoms are not arranged

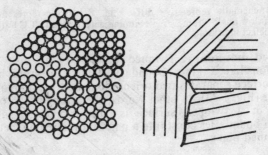

FIG. 1.31. (a) Arrangement of atoms at the grain boundary and (b) Large angle grain boundary.

in proper order and they are always under pull by the two adjacent grains. As a consequence, grain boundary atom cannot join either of the crystals and therefore, takes up a compromising position. Obviously, the grain boundary atoms are not surrounded by as many number of atoms as those inside the crystals. Therefore, the energy of the grain boundaries is more than that of grains. The thickness of grain boundary surface is only a few atomic diameters because the opposing forces experienced by grain boundary atoms is restricted to short distances only.

If the misorientation between the two grains is more than 10—15°, the grain boundary is called a high angle grain boundary.

If the angle between the orientations of the two graines is less than 10°, the boundary is known as a low angle grain boundary. In general a low angle grain boundary may be regarded as an array of dislocations (Fig. 1.32). The two grains across the boundary seems to be tilted with respect to each other and thus the low angle grain boundary is also called a low angle tilt boundary.

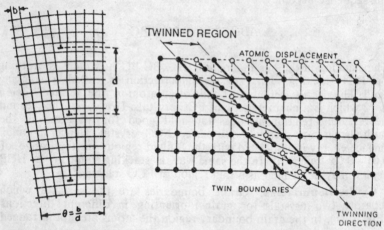

FIG. 1.32. Schematic representation of low angle grain boundary defect in crystal.

FIG. 1.33. Schematic representation of twinning defect in an FCC lattice.

Twinned boundary. Twinned boundaries are also the surface imperfections like a grain boundary. Unlike a grain boundary, a twinned surface separates two orientations that are mirror image of each other (Fig. 1.33). In other words, the arrangement of atoms on one side of a twinned surface is a mirror reflection of the other side. Twin boundaries constitute a pair and the region between them is the twinned plane.

QUESTIONS

1. Describe the important aspects of quantum mechanics.

2. What is Hunds rule? Indicate the electronic configuration of Cr, Mn, Fe, and Cu in their ground state.

3. Enlist the important characteristics of the elements in the first column of the periodic table down to hydrogen.

4. Explain the terms ionisation potential, electron affinity and electronegativity.

5. What are primary and secondary bondings? Explain with schematic diagram the term metallic bonding.

6. Explain why covalent bond is directional whereas the ionic and metallic bonds are non-directional.

7. Both diamond and graphite are states of carbon but markedly differ in physical properties. Explain why?

8. Discuss hydrogen bond and Vander Waal bonding with schematic representation.

9. Define the term unit cell. Sketch unit cells of (i) iron, (ii) cabalt, and (iii) nickel.

10. What do you understand by the term Miller indices? Represent the 1 2 3, 0 0 1, and 1 1 1 planes and directions in a cubic unit cell and 0 $\bar{1}$ 1 0 planes in a hexagonal unit cell.

11. Define the term coordination number. What is the coordination of BCC, FCC and HCP unit cells? Represent schematically the coordination number in a FCC unit cell.

12. Define atomic packing factor for a crystal plane. Determine the atomic packing factor of a plane (1 1 0) in a close packed cubic cell.

13. What is the significance of c/a ratio in HCP crystals?

14. What are point defects? Show them schematically.

15. Differentiate between edge and screw dislocations. Define Burgers vector.

16. What do you mean by stacking fault? What type of stacking fault occurs in FCC crystals?

17. Differentiate between high angle grain boundaries and low angle grain boundaries.

2

MECHANICAL PROPERTIES
AND ENGINEERING REQUIREMENTS
OF MATERIALS

2.1. INTRODUCTION

Mechanical properties of a material may be defined as the ability of it to resist mechanical forces and loads. In other words mechanical properties describe the mechanical behaviour of a material under the application of mecanical forces. Mechanical behaviour is one of the most important criterion while designing, fabricating and selecting a material for a particular application. Before a material is put into service, it should be tested mechanically according to the engineering requirements. For example, a material may be required to work under severe conditions of high or low temperatures, corrosive environment, static or dynamic loading, and other conditions. Therefore, it is desirable to test the material under the required service conditions. The various mechanical tests that are necessary for engineering requirements include tensile, hardness, impact, fatigue, and creep tests. Before discussing all these tests, important definitions related to mechanical testing are given first.

2.1.1. Stress

When an external force is applied to a solid, an internal resisting force which is equal in magnitude and opposite in direction to the applied force is developed. This internal resisting force arises because the atoms in a metal are in their minimum energy state and in order to displace them from their equilibrium position, an external force is required. So, when an external force is applied to a solid, the force of attraction between the atoms tends to oppose it. If the applied external force is enough then the atoms may either be displaced closer together or moved farther apart from the equilibrium position. In each case the internal force tends to restore the atoms to their original positions. This internally developed force is qualitatively expressed as the stress and quantitatively as the force per unit areas

$$\text{i.e. stress} = \frac{\text{force}}{\text{area}}$$

The unit of stress is expressed as N/M^2 (Newton/metre^2).

In general there are three types of stresses, viz., tensile, compressive and shear which are illustrated in Fig. 2.1. When the stresses are compressive, the member carrying the load tends to shorten in the

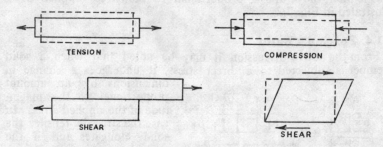

FIG. 2.1. Effect of types of stresses on a solid body.

direction of the applied stress. In case of tensile stresses, the member under stress tends to elongate in the direction of the applied stress. Shear stress causes one portion of the body to move with respect to other so that two surfaces would tend to move over one another. In majority of stressed members all the three kinds of stress are found. In bending, for example, there is a combination of tension. and compression together with some shear. In torsion, as in a shaft transmitting power, the shear stresses are very important but the shear is coupled with some tensile and compressive stresses also.

2.1.2. Strain

The change in length or width brought about under the applied tensile or compressive forces on a body is called the strain of the body. The strain can be evaluated in two ways, i.e. (1) the number of milimetres of deformation per milimetre and (2) the deformation length as a percentage of the original length. Since strain is a ratio of the two lengths, it has no units.

2.1.3. Elastic Strain

When an external load is applied to a solid material, its atoms displace from their equilibrium position and result in straining. As the applied force increases, the displacement of atoms from their equilibrium point increases. When the load is released, if the atoms return back to their original position due to restoring force, then the solid will regain its original dimensions. If, on the other hand, the applied stress is such that after removal of load, the restoring force is no longer be effective, the displaced atoms cannot attain the

FIG. 2 2. Stress-strain curve showing proportionation relationship between stress and strain.

original position. The limit of force under which a material regains its original dimension, is known as elastic limit. The strain produced under elastic load is called elastic strain and is reversible. Under the elastic limit, the strain is proportional to the stress applied as is illustrated in Fig. 2.2.

2.1.4. Poisson's Ratio

From the above discussion it may be noted that when a solid member is subjected to a direct stress, it undergoes a change in dimensions by an amount proportional to the magnitude of the applied stress. In case the stress is tensile, the solid elongates and if the stress is compressive, it contracts. However, besides this direct effect of the applied stress, the body simultaneously undergoes a change in its lateral dimension. Thus, for the solid bar shown in Fig. 2.3, when a tensile force is applied in the direction shown, the bar elongates from L to $L+\epsilon L$, while at the same time, its sides contract from their original dimensions of w and h. If the ratio of the lateral strain to the longitudinal strain is expressed as,

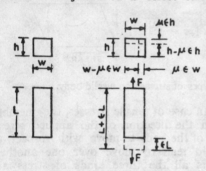

(a) UNSTRESSED (b) STRESSED BAR BAR

FIG. 2 3. Lateral strain due to lateral stress.

$$\mu = \frac{\epsilon_w}{\epsilon_y} \text{ and } \mu = \frac{\epsilon_h}{\epsilon_y} \qquad \ldots(2.1)$$

Then this ratio 'μ' is known as Poisson' ratio. Poisson's ratio for steel is approximately 0.3 and it usually varies from 0.28 to 0.35 for most of the metals and alloys.

The point to be noted here is that if the longitudinal strain causes extension, the lateral strain will be compressive and vice versa, i.e., if the applied stress causes bar to elongate in the direction of the applied force, the bar will contract in the other two directions.

2.1.5. Elasticity

Elasticity of a stressed material is its ability to return to its original dimensions when the stress is removed from it. More is the capability of a material to resist load without being deformed permanently, more is the elasticity.

2.1.6. Modulus of Elasticity

Modulus of elasticity of a material is defined as the ratio of the applied stress to the strain produced within the elastic limit of the material The area under the elastic curve on the stress-strain diagram is a measure of stiffness or the so called rigidity of the material. The unit of modulus of elasticity is the same as that of stress, i.e., N/M². Modulus of elasticity of a material directly depends upon its composition and is indirectly affected by the other properties.

2.1.7. Plastic Strain

Plastic strain is also called set or permanent set. Plastic strain is the permanent strain of a material which persists even after the removal of load from the material. In the plastically strained condition, the atoms of the material concerned are displaced permanently from their equilibrium position (or original position).

2.1.8. Plasticity

This property of a material is its capability to deform non-elastically without rupture. This property enables the material to undergo complicated shapes with the aid of plastic deformation as in forging, rolling, extrusion, drawing, etc.

2.2. TENSILE TEST

2.2.1. Theory

Tensile test is one of the most commonly used mechanical tests for metals. In this test a standard size test specimen is subjected to gradually increasing axial load until fracture occurs. During the test, load and elongations are measured at frequent intervals and these are expressed as average stress and strain. The prefix average is used before the stress and strain because the load may not be uniform over the cross-section and the elongation may not be uniform all along the gauge length (i.e. the length of the specimen actually undergoing deformation) of the specimen. A curve is then plotted between stress and strain and is commonly known

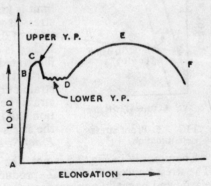

FIG. 2.4. Load elongation curve for mild steel.

as Engineering stress-strain curve. For a specimen of mild steel (M.S.) the relation between load (or stress) and elongation (or strain) is shown in Fig. 2.4.

In the range AB, the strain is reversible and is proportional to the stress. The linear portion AB is therefore called the elastic line. The stress at point B represents the elastic limit or the limit of proportionality. The elastic limit is not a well defined stress. Between B and C, there is relatively rapid extension and at C the load drops suddenly and the strain rises at a constant stress for some value. The point C is called the upper yield point and D is the lower yield point. The deformation then continues with increasing load until at E where load reaches at maximum. After maximum load, considerable localised extension occurs at a load lesser than that at E and eventually fracture results at F which is the breaking point or breaking load. EF is called the localised extension.

A sharp yield point in the stress-strain curve as shown in Fig. 2.4 is characteristic of some materials particularly those with a BCC structure and containing small amount of solute element. These materials exhibit two yield points as in the stress-strain curve for M. S. shown in Fig. 2.4. In these materials, it is easy to specify the upper yield point as a measure of the strength of the material concerned. However, most such materials as soft mild steel, and materials with FCC structure do not exhibit a well defined yield point. From the view point of designing of a ductile material, it is necessary to know a definite stress under which a material can be

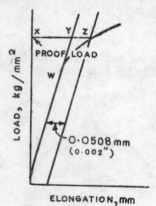

FIG. 2.5. Proof stress determination.

stressed with safety without yielding. Many materials can tolerate small strains beyond the elastic limit without appreciable plastic deformation. These strains are typically 0.1 or 0.2 pct. of the gauge length. The stress required to produce such small strains beyond the elastic limit is known as *Proof Stress*. This is the stress at which a non-proportional elongation of 0.1 pct. of 2 inches, i.e. 0.002 inches is obtained. This is determined, as illustrated in Fig. 2.5, by drawing a line parallel to the leastic line of the stress-strain curve from the point of 0.1 pct. strain (i.e. 0.002 inch along the elongation axis). The point where this line cuts the stress-strain curve gives the value of *Proof Stress*.

The point W in Fig. 2.5 is not the end of all elastic elongation. The stress between W and Z produces a strain which is partially elastic and partially non-proportional (i.e. plastic). At the *Proof Stress* the total strain XZ consists of elastic (or proportional) strain XY and the non-proportional strain YZ.

In general, if the specimen is unloaded from the point Z, the elastic strain XY disappears but the non-proportional strain YZ still persists (except in magnesium alloys where a part of the non-proportional strain also disappears).

The behaviour of the stress-strain curve at the yield point for impure as well as pure metals and alloys is discussed in section 2.2.

Fig. 2.4 shows that during plastic deformation the stress required to elongate the specimen initially rises and then decreases after passing through a maximum. This nature of the curve is because of the two opposing factors. The strain hardening related with the multiplication of dislocations occurs during plastic deformation. The increase in external stress is due to the interaction of the moving dislocations with existing dislocations. On the contrary the specimen elongates, its diameter decreases which leads to decrease in load. Initially, at small value of plastic strains, strain hardening predominates over the decrease in load due to reduced diameter, therefore, the net load increases. However, in the later stages of straining, at larger extensions, decrease in diameter (or thickness) of the specimen is more rapid than the increase in strain hardening and therefore load tends to decrease rapidly after passing through some maximum. At maximum load, the engineering stress is defined as the ratio of the load on to the specimen to the original cross sectional area. This ratio is commonly known as *"ultimate tensile strength"*.

The reason that a peak appears in the load-elongation (or the engineering stress-strain) curve is that at maximum load, a part of the specimen becomes weak due to localised heating, cavities or inclusion present in the test specimen. Consequently under the applied load, the weaker portion of the specimen will tend to elongate to a greater extent than the rest part and hence will decrease the area of cross-section. This results in an increase of stress on the specimen so that further elongation will occur in the nacked region of the specimen. With further elongation beyond the maximum load, elongation mainly occurs in the necked region and therefore, the load decreases rapidly with further elongation until fracture occurs. Though the strain hardening still continues upto fracture with the elongation after necking, the engineering stress-strain curves for ductile materials do not exhibit this phenomenon. This is because of the fact that engineering stress is determined by dividing the load at any instant by the original cross-sectional area, that is, P/A_0. Therefore, stress decreases after the formation of the neck in the specimen at maximum load. On the contrary the actual stress-strain curve shows a continuous strain hardening even after the maximum load has reached. The reason is that the actual stress at any instant is determined by dividing the load by the true area of cross-section at that instant of load measurement. The true stress (σ_t)

$$= \frac{\text{load}}{\text{true area of cross-section}}$$

or $\sigma_t = \dfrac{P_i}{A_i}$ ... (2.2)

where P_i is the load at any instant and A_i is the area of cross-section of the specimen at that instant.

Similarly, true strain is calculated from the instantaneous change in the gauge length of the specimen, i.e.

True strain $(\epsilon_t) = \int_{L_0}^{L_f} \frac{dL}{L}$ ... (2.3)

or $\epsilon_t = ln \left(\dfrac{L_f}{L_0} \right)$ ... (2.4)

Where L_f and L_0 are the final and original length of the specimen, respectively.

Since engineering strain ϵ_e is given as:

$$\epsilon_e = \frac{L_f - L_0}{L_0} = \frac{L_f}{L_0} - 1 \qquad \text{... (2.5)}$$

or $\epsilon_e + 1 = \dfrac{L_f}{L_0}$ ... (2.6)

Therefore, $\epsilon_t = ln \ (\epsilon_e + 1)$ ... (2.7)

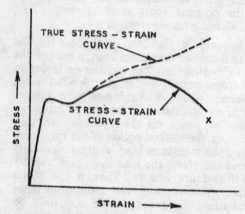

FIG. 2.6. Comparison of the nature of engineering stress-strain and true stress-strain curves.

Also, since the volume of the specimen after plastic deformation remains almost constant, therefore,

$$L_f A_f = L_0 A_0 \qquad \text{...(2.8)}$$
or $L_f/L_0 = A_0/A_f$ ...(2.9)

Where A_0 and A_f are the initial and final area of cross-sections of the test specimen, respectively. From equations (2.4) and (2.9).

$$\epsilon_t = ln \ (A_0/A_f) \quad \text{... (2.10)}$$

Thus a true stress-strain curve can be plotted from the tensile data as shown

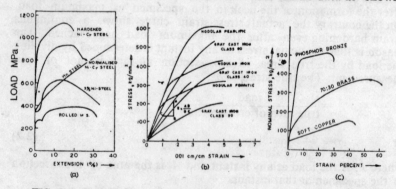

FIG. 2.7. Typical stress-strain curves for (a) some grades of steel, (b) cast irons and (c) copper and its alloys.

in Fig. 2.5. True stress-strain curve and the normal (or engineering)
stress-strain curve are superimposed in Fig. 2.6. It is apparent from
the true curve in Fig. 2.6 that the metal gets stronger upto the point
of rupture.

The engineering stress-strain curves for some grades of steels, cast
irons and copper and its alloys are shown in Fig. 2.7.

2.2.2. Tensile Testing Machine

The most commonly used tensile testing machine in laboratories is
Hounsfield Tensometer. It consists of seven load sprung beams that
can takes loads of 2T, 1T, 500 kg, 250 kg, 125 kg, 62½ kg and 21.25
kg. These loads are interchangeable and enable the tests to be carried
out on a large range of materials. Fig. 2.8 illustrates the various

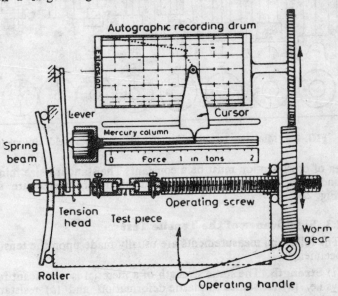

FIG. 2.8. Schematic representation of some salient features of the Houns-
fields tensometer.

important features of the machine. The load is applied at one end
which is measured at the other end, after the pull has been transmitted through the test piece. When the test piece is pulled on the
application of load, it deflects the load beam. The deflection of load
beam is then transmitted through a vertical lever to the mercury
piston. As a result, the mercury rises into the glass tube (i.e. the mercury column) which actuates the *cursor*. The cursor is attached with
a needle which is made to puncture the graph paper at frequent intervals, thus recording the force vertically. The movement of the worm-
gear (which is responsible for the elongation of the test piece) is

transmitted through a series of gears to the recording drum. The rotation of the drum enables elongation to be recorded on the graph paper wrapped on the drum.

For the testing work, standard size test piece is to be used so that for a given per cent elongation the ratio of the gauge length to the

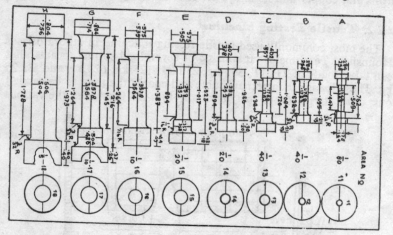

FIG. 2.9. Miniature test piece for use with the Hounsfield tensometer.

area of cross-section must be a constant. The standard size miniature round test specimens required for Hounsfield Tensometer are shown in Fig. 2.9.

2.2.3. Significance of the Tensile Test

The following measurements are usually made upon the tensile test sepecimen:

(i) **Strength**. The static strength of a meterial is significant in two ways i.e. (a) resistance to plastic deformation and (b) resistance to fracture.

The property of a material which determines its strength against being permanently deformed is known as yield point or yield strength. Yield strength is of great significance in that it tends to prevent bending, denting or twisting of a material premanent, in service. On the contrary, the yield point of a material must be exceeded during its fabrication processes involving plastic deformation such as rolling, forging, extrusion or drawing. Thus, yield point is the main criterion while designing a ductile material since it gives the level of stress which should be exceeded during metal working processes but not when the material is in service.

The *ultimate tensile strength* of a material is defined as the property which enables it to exert against being failure in service.

Once the service load reaches the maximum value that may cause localised stress concentration, the material will break. Thus, ultimate tensile point is the maximum level of stress that should neither exceed during metal working process nor in service of a material.

Since, brittle materials exhibit little or no plastic deformation, ultimate tensile point is the basic criterion for their design.

(*ii*) **Ductility.** Ductility of a material is the property by virtue of which it can be formed into different shapes through rolling, forging drawing, bending, stretching, hammering or any other process that involves plastic deformation. Thus, a material that can only be worked out by one of the above processes should possess enough ductility and is almost an essential property. From the tensile data, the extent of ductility of a material can be evaluated by two methods. One of the methods measures ductility in terms of percentage elongation and the other expresses ductility as the percentage reduction in its area of cross-section. Percentage elongation measures the lengthwise stretching of the tensile test specimen upto the fracture and is given as:

$$\text{Elongation} = \frac{\text{Change in gauge length}}{\text{Original gauge length}} \times 100$$

or $\text{Elongation} = \dfrac{L_f - L_o}{L_o} \times 100$ ...(2.11)

Percentage reduction in cross sectional area is a measure of the cross-section when the tensile specimen is stretched and is expressed as:

$$\text{Reduction in area} = \frac{\text{Change in cross-sectional area}}{\text{Original area of cross-section}} \times 100$$

or $\text{Reduction in area} = \dfrac{A_o - A_f}{A_o} \times 100$ ...(2.12)

(*iii*) **Elasticity.** Elasticity of a material enables it to return to the original dimensions after the removal of stress. This property of the material is utilised while designing objects where controlled elastic deformation is needed, for example, springs, beam of a balance, etc. The elasticity of a material is usually expressed in terms of *Modulus of elasticity* which is the slope of stress-strain curve under elastic limit. The area enclosed by the elastic line with the strain axis is a measure of *modulus of resilience*. The greater the modulus of resilience of a material, the stiffer or more rigid it is. As illustrated in

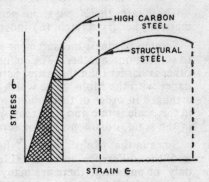

FIG. 2.10. Comparison of stress-strain curves for high and low toughness materials.

Fig 2.10 by the area (cross hatched regions) under the elastic limit, the high carbon spring steel is stiffer than the medium carbon structural steel.

(*iv*) **Toughness**. Toughness of a material is its ability to absorb energy without failure under static load (or stress). Many components such as freight car couplings, gears, chains, cams, crank shafts, crane hooks, etc. are required to withstand occasional stresses above the yield point, therefore, they should be made of a tough material. From the tensile data, toughness can be measured as the total area under the stress-strain curve. Toughness is a function of both strength and ductility. A material with high tensile strength but showing less plastic region in the stress-strain curve is not a tough material. Similarly, a material showing large area under the plastic region on the stres-strain curve but low yield and tensile point is merely a soft or ductile material rather than a tough material. For example, Fig. 2.10 illustrates stress-strain curves for a tough and rigid material (low toughness material). The high carbon spring steel has a higher yield point and tensile strength than the structural steel containing medium carbon. However, the structural steel is more ductile than the high carbon spring steel and has a greater total elongation. The total area under the stress-strain curve is greater for structural steel than that for the high carbon steel. Hence, structural steel is tougher than high carbon spring steel.

2.3. HARDNESS TESTING

Hardness testing is another important mechanical testing after tensile testing and is used in all disciplines of engineering. In general hardness of a material is defined as the resistance offered by it against indentation. For metals, the hardness is a measure of resistance to plastic deformation. Hardness of a material can be varied by applying various different treatments to it. These processes may include heat treatment, metal working, or a combination of the two.

There are three ways, in general, to measure the hardness of a material, i.e. (*i*) scratch, (*ii*) indentation and (*iii*) rebound.

Scratch hardness measurement is based on the ability of minerals to scratch one another. The mineral which makes a scratch on the other is harder than the latter. Scratch hardness is measured in accordance with the Mohs' scale which consists of ten standard minerals arranged in order of their ability to be scratched. The softest mineral in this scale is talc and its *scratch hardness* is one. The hardest mineral in the scale is diamond having scratch hardness of 10.

Since in the Mohs' scale of hardness there are only ten minerals and the difference in hardness between two consecutive minerals is only of one unit, there are many materials which may have varying hardness lying between two consecutive scratch hardnesses according to Mohs' scale. Therefore, Mohs' scale of hardness measurement is primarily restricted to minerological field. In case of metals and alloys, where we need comparative hardness values, Mohs' scale of hardness measurement is not very suitable.

Indentation hardness measurement consists of forcing (or impressing) a penetrator of known geometry into the work piece resting on a rigid platform. The hardness is a measure of area of impression or the depth of penetration made by the penetrator. This method of hardness measurement is most widely used in engineering fields. There are three most common types of indentation hardness testers in use. These are Rockwell, Brinell and Vickers.

In the rebound or the dynamic hardness measurement, the indentor is usually dropped from certain height on to the specimen under test. The hardness is expressed as the energy of impact or the height of rebound of the indentor from the specimen. More is the height of rebound harder is the material. The Shore sceleroscope is the most common example of a dynamic hardness tester.

2.3.1. Rockwell Hardness Tester

Principle of working. In the Rockwell hardness test a penetrator is forced into the work piece under certain static load and the hardness is expressed as the depth of penetration. More is the penetration softer the material is. In this testing no calculation is required, the hardness value being indicated directly on a dial at the front of the tester.

Instead of using the total depth of the indentation, the hardness number is based on the increase in depth obtained when a second load is applied after applying initially a small load called 'minor' load. The second load is called the 'major' load. A minor load of 10 kg is always used to eliminate errors due to surface roughness and elasticity of the specimen under test. The major load used may be 50, 90 or 140 kg depending upon the geometry of the indentor and hardness of the material being tested.

In the Rockwell hardness test, two indentors are in use. The first being a hardened steel ball of 1/16 inch diameter and the other is a spheroconical diamond pyramid indentor, with its apex angle 120°. This indentor is commercially named as a *Brale indentor*. Since a ball indentor is a sphere, its sensitivity to penetrate a material is less than that of a Brale because for the same load, force per unit area exerted on the specimen under test is more for a Brale indentor. Therefore, Brale indentor is usually employed to measure hardness of relatively harder matrials.

The dial of the Rockwill hardness tester is calibrated with two scales, one with black numeral and the other with red numeral. Each scale is indicated by a symbol which denotes the size of the major penetrating load and the accompanying penetrator as shown in table 2.1. The dial on the Rockwell hardness tester is shown in Fig. 2.11.

Dial reading. Reading on the dial is very important factor to be excercised while performing the Rockwell hardness test. The

TABLE 2.1 *Combinations of Load, Indentor and Scale of Rockwell Hardness Test*

Scale Symbol	Indentor used	Major load, kg	Dial used, Numeral	Applications
A	Brale	50	Black	Cemented carbides, ceramics, cermets and thin steel.
B	Ball, 1/16″ dia	90	Red	Unhardened steel, alloys of copper and aluminium.
C	Brale	140	Black	Hard steel, bard cast irons, Ti- alloys and deeply case hardened steel.
D	Brale	90	Black	Medium case hardened steel and razor blade.

accuracy of the test very much depends upon the reading made on

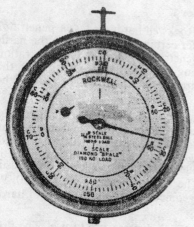

the dial. On the dial shown in Fig. 2.11, there are two pointers, one being the larger and the other smaller. The larger pointer moves when the major load is applied. The extent to which it revolves depends upon three factors, viz., the force applied, the sharpness of the indentor and the resistance to penetration offerred by the material under test. This extent may be more or less than one revolution of the dial. Therefore, it is not sufficient to read the final hardness value by merely observing the final position of the pointer when the test is completed. It is necessary to observe the entire movement of the pointer starting from the instant the major load is applied

FIG. 2.11. Dial on Rockwell machine.

until the pointer comes to the rest when the major load is removed.

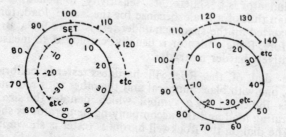

FIG. 2.12. Extensions of dial scales.

The dial scale should not only be considered as ranging from 0-100 but one should take into account that numbers below zero (i.e. the negative number) and that over 100 are overlapping with the portion 0-100, as illustrated in Fig. 2.12. Fig. 2.12 (a) represents the black numbered scale and Fig. 2.12 (b) the red numbered scale. The black scale is numbered from 0-100 with 100 corresponding to the 'Set' postion. The red scale is numbered from 0-130 with 130 as the 'Set' position. There is overlap of 30 Rockwell units on the circular red scale on the dial. Thus, two scales are numerically out of phase with each other by 30 Rockwell units.

Considering Fig. 2.12 when a major load is applied, the pointer moves from 'Set' position of 100 to 90, 80, etc. in the counter clock-wise direction down-scale. If it continues down beyond zero, its position will then be negative. The number 90 is then read as (—10), 80 as (—20) and so on. Subsequently when the major load is removed, the pointer will revert to certain extent to achieve its final position.

Similarly, on the red scale, when the major load is applied, the large pointer starts revolving from its 'Set' position (Fig. 2.12 b) of 130 to 120, 110, etc. downscale. If it so moves as to cross over zero, i t will be in the negative range with 90 being actually (−10), 80, being (—20), and so on. On releasing the major load, the pointer will move back and may or may not cross zero again. If it does, the value of the hardness will be positive. If it does not cross the zero, the hardness will be read as negative.

A negative hardness value is never accepted because it is an outcome due to over penetration of the indentor beyond its calibrated surface zone into the material being tested.

Principle of operation. For illustrating the principle of operation of Rockwell hardness test consider the penetrator as 1/16 inch ball and the scale B on the dial. The load being 100 kg (i.e. Minor+ Major).

Fig. 2.13 shows various positions of indentor with respect to the work piece and corresponding positions of the large pointer on the dial gauge when the minor and major loads are applied.

Fig. 2.13a shows that the work piece being examined is placed on the anvil of the tester and the minor load is yet not applied. The anvil is then slowly raised so as to bring the specimen in contact with the indentor and the capstan is rotated until the small pointer on the dial comes at the dot (red point). This dot is an index mark showing that the minor load is fully applied. Consequently the indentor has been forced into the work piece to a depth of A-B. During minor load application, the large pointer moves clockwise and comes to almost vertical position as shown in Fig. 2.13b. The scale is then rotated until set coincides with the pointer.

Now the major load of 90 kg is applied slowly on to the work piece (Fig. 2.13c) by pushing back the handle mounted on the side of the machine. The total load becomes 100 kg. As a result of application of major load, the ball indentor penetrates the work piece to a depth $B-C$ as indicated in Fig. 2.13c. During this period, pointer

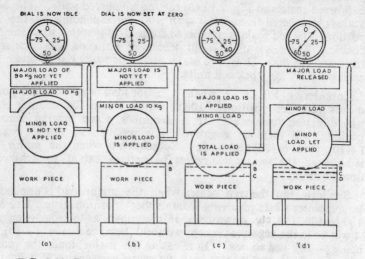

FIG. 2.13. Schematic representation of the principle of operation of Rockewell hardness test.

rotates in the anti-clockwise direction and comes at some point (say 40 as shown) on the dial.

After about 30 seconds, the major load is released and the penetrator moves to some depth upwards corresponding to elastic recovery $(C-D)$ shown in Fig. 2.13d. Simultaneously the elastic recovery is indicated by the pointer on the dial as it moves from number 40 to 60. The final position of the large pointer is at 60 indicating the hardness value on the B scale of the Rockwell tester. This value is represented as R_B 60. This value of hardness is corresponding to the plastic deformation of the work piece or the actual depth of penetration $B-D$.

Finally the minor load is removed by lowering the anvil through capstan wheel.

The machine. Rockwell hardness tester is a fully enclosed machine with cast iron body and the weights applied cannot be seen from outside. The mechanism inside the machine is thus protected against dirt and dust. The basic system consists of weights and levers. The load is applied under hydraulic dash pot, which is adjustable by tune control or manually.

Procedure (*i*) The specimen to be tested is placed on the anvil of the elevating screw and the hand wheel is turned to bring the specimen in contact with the indentor. (*ii*) Raising of the screw is continued until the small pointer indicates that the minor load has been fully applied. (*iii*) Knob of the gauge is turned to set the dia to zero. (iv) The handle is pushed back to apply major load, the pointer (large) moving anti-clockwise. (v) When the large pointer comes to rest, the handle is pulled forward to remove the major load. (vi) The Rockwell hardness number is read from the appropriate scale.

Salient features of Rockwell hardness test. (i) It is the quickest method of indentation hardness measurement as it gives direct reading on the dial gauge. Therefore, it is used for routine work in industries.

(ii) Application of minor load eliminates errors arising due to surface roughness and elasticity of the material. Thus, the test piece does not require polishing to the surface and thereby saving time.

(iii) This test gives reproducible results.

Precautions of the test. (i) The indentor and anvil should be clean and well seated.

(ii) The surface to be tested should be free from any dirt particles, oxides, or debris.

(iii) Special fixtures as anvils are to be used for testing curved or cylindrical surfaces.

(iv) The thickness of the work being tested should be at least ten times the depth of indendation so as to prevent bulging on the reverse side of the work piece.

(v) The surface of test piece should be flat and normal to the indentor.

(vi) The distance between two impressions should be 3-5 times the diameter of the indentation.

2.3.2. Brinell Hardness Testing

Brinell hardness tester makes use of a spherical steel ball indentor. The indentor is forced into the specimen under test and the diameter of impression is measured.

This method of measuring hardness differs from the Rockwell in several ways such as size of indentor and loads, the absence of minor load, the manner of reporting the hardness and like that.

Working principle. Brinell hardness is determined by dividing the load applied by the area of spherical impression and is called the Brinell Hardness Number (BHN).

Usually a load of 3,000 kg with a ball indentor of 10 mm is used to determine BHN of a hard material such as steel. For soft steels the load is reduced to 500 kg. To measure the hardness of very hard materials (BHN may be of the order of 600 or more), a hardened steel ball of 5 or 10 mm diameter is not suitable since it itself will undergo the deformation under static load. In such cases, a special indentor of tungsten carbide ball is used to enforce into the material being tested.

In the Brinell hardness test, the specimen being tested should be highly polished and should be free from any surface irregularity, dirt particles, scale or foreign matter.

The greatest error in Brinell hardness measurements is encountered in the measurement of diameter of impression. The measured diameter may be greater or less than the actual diameter of the impression. This may be due to localised deformation of the metal at the indentation. The localised deformation may result in two types of irregularities in the indentation, i.e., "ridging" and "sinking in". In case of 'ridging' or 'piling up', a lip of metal forms at the rim of the impression and the diameter of this impression is more than the actual diameter (i.e. the diameter of the impression when the indentor is in contact with the test piece). This is illustrated in Fig. 2.14a. On the other hand, if there is depression of metal at the

FIG. 2.14. Cross-section through Brinell indentations illustrating (a) ridging and (b) sinking in.

rim of the impression, the irregularity is known as 'sinking in'. In this case the diameter of the impression to be read out is less than the actual diameter obtainable in the absence of 'sinking in' (Fig. 2.14b). The former behaviour has been found commonly in cold worked metals whereas the latter anomaly usually occurs in annealed metals.

Brinell hardness number of many materials is related with their tensile strength. This relation for some materials is given below:

U.T.S. = (BHN) × (0.21) for heat treated alloy steels.

U.T.S. = (BHN) × (0.22) for heat treated medium carbon steels.

U.T.S. = (BHN) × (0.23) for low carbon steels heat treated.

U.T.S. $= \dfrac{\text{(BHN)}}{4} - 1$ for duralumin (an alloy of aluminium).

Principle of operation. The principle of Brinell hardness tester is based upon the fact that when balls of different diameters are forced into a specimen, similar geometrical impressions having proportional diameters are produced giving the same value of hardness provided the load applied is proportional to the square of the ball diameters.

Brinell hardness is expressed as load P per unit area A of spherical impression

i.e. $$\text{BHN} = \frac{P}{A} = \frac{kg}{mm^2}$$ ...(2.13)

In order to determine area of the spherical impression consider the geometry of the impression shown in Fig. 2.15. From the geometry

$$h = \frac{D}{2} - \sqrt{\left(\frac{D}{2}\right)^2 - \left(\frac{d}{2}\right)^2}$$

or

$$h = \frac{D}{2} - \sqrt{\frac{D^2}{4} - \frac{d^2}{4}}$$

$$...(2.14)$$

Area of the spherical ball $= \pi D^2$

Therefore, the area of the spherical impression

$$A = \frac{h}{D} \cdot \pi D^2 = h\pi D \quad ...(2.15)$$

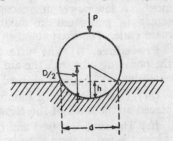

FIG. 2.15. Determination of. area of impression of Brinell indentation.

or

$$A = \frac{\pi D}{2} \cdot [D - \sqrt{D^2 - d^2}] \text{ mm}^2 \qquad ...(2.16)$$

From equations (2.13), (2.14) and (2.16)

$$\text{BHN} = \frac{2P}{\pi D(D - \sqrt{D^2 - d^2})}$$

or

$$\text{BHN} = \frac{2P}{\pi D^2(1 - \sqrt{1 - d/D^2})}$$

or

$$\text{BHN} = \frac{P}{D^2} \cdot \frac{2}{\pi} \cdot \frac{1}{(1 - \sqrt{1 - d^2/D^2})} \text{ kg/mm}^2 \quad ...(2.17)$$

The ratio (d/D) must be constant for similar geometrical impressions. It is apparent from the relation (2.17) that P is proportional to D^2, i.e., P/D^2 is a constant factor and is usually called the 'load factor'.

i.e.

$$\frac{P}{D_1^2} = \frac{P}{D_2^2} = \frac{P}{D_3^2} = \text{costant.}$$

P/D^2 is different for different materials as shown in Table 2.2.

TABLE 2.2. *The relation between the standard load, ball diameter and P/D².*

Ball diameter mm	Load, kg			
	$P/D^2 = 30$	10	5	1
1	30	10	5	1
2	120	40	20	4
5	750	250	125	25
10	3,000	1,000	500	100
Materials	Steel	Brass	Al	Pb, Sn etc.

Brinell hardness testing machine. The machine consists of a system of loads applied hydraulically by means of a pushing arrangement. A low power microscope is attached with the machine. The screen in graduated in millimetres and vernier scale slides over the main scale. The least count of the main scale is 0.1 mm.

Procedure. (*i*) The surface of the given specimen is polished on the polishing unit with the aid of alumina paste.

(*ii*) The specimen is cleaned and dried.

(*iii*) The specimen is mounted in the testing table and the table is placed on the anvil of the elevating screw.

(*iv*) The anvil is raised and the spot is focussed in the microscope where the indentation is to be made.

(*v*) The predetermined load is applied by pushing the knob provided on the side of the machine.

(*vi*) After 15-30 seconds, the load is released by means of a handle in front of the machine.

(*vii*) Diameter of the specimen is read on the eyepiece scale in the normal directions and the average is taken.

(*viii*) The hardness number is read in the table provided along with the machine. The table consists of hardness values corresponding to different diameter of impression for a combination of load and diameter of indentor. Otherwise BHN can also be calculated with the help of the relation 2.17.

Applications of Brinell hardness tester. (*i*) It is used for quality control tests where finished articles are to be tested without any destruction.

(*ii*) Since BHN is a function of carbon control in iron and steel, this tester provides rapid estimation of carbon content in them.

(*iii*) Brinell hardness test is used to examine the effect of heat treatment and cold working in the research laboratories.

(*iv*) It helps in examining the nature of the material in the broken parts where tensile test is not possible.

2.3.3. Vickers Hardness Testing

Vickers hardness tester utilises a square based diamond pyramid indentor under a load of 30 kg. The angle between the opposite faces of the diamond pyramid indentor is 136°. The selection of this angle is made with a view to approximate the most desirable ratio of indentation diameter to ball diameter in the Brinell hardness test. Consequently, both Brinell as well as Vickers hardness test can be performed in the same machine by just changing the indentor and the applied load.

In the Vickers hardness test, the length of the diagonal of the square impression is measured. The hardness is computed as load divided by the surface area of the impression. Like Brinell hardness test, in this test also the diagonal length of the impression is read out with the aid of a lower power microscope attached with the machine.

Principle of operation. This method of measuring hardness is based on the measurement of length of the diagonal of the impression. The hardness is expressed as:

$$\text{Vickers hardness (VHN)} = \frac{\text{Load}}{\text{Lateral area of pyramidal impression}}$$

$$= \frac{P}{A} \text{ kg/mm}^2 \qquad \dots(2.18)$$

The lateral area A of the pyramidal impression is the sum of the areas of the four triangular faces. This can be determined with the help of Fig. 2.16. as following :

$$A = \tfrac{1}{2} \text{ a.s. } 4 = 2a \, S \qquad \dots(2.19)$$

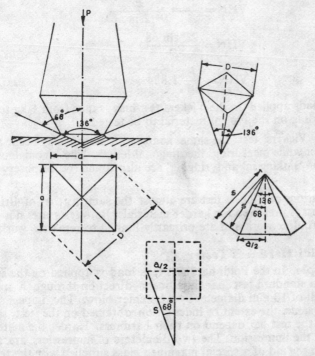

FIG. 2.16. Determination of lateral area of impression of Vickers indentation.

Where 'a' is one of the sides of the square impression or is the base of one of the triangular faces.

The length of the diagonal D is given as:

$$D^2 = 2a^2$$

or
$$a = \frac{D}{\sqrt{2}} \qquad \qquad \ldots(2.20)$$

The height of the triangle is the slante height S (Fig. 2.16) and is given as

$$S = \frac{a/2}{\sin 68} \qquad \qquad \ldots(2.21)$$

Substituting a and S from equations (2.20) and (2.21) in the equation (2.19), we have

$$A = \frac{2D}{\sqrt{2}} \cdot \frac{D/2\sqrt{2}}{\sin 68} = \frac{D^2}{2 \sin 68} \qquad \qquad \ldots(2.22)$$

The Vickers hardness number

$$VHN = \frac{P}{A} = \frac{P}{D^2/2\sin 68}$$

or
$$VHN = \frac{2P \sin 68}{D^-}$$

$$VHN = \frac{P}{D^2} 1.854 \qquad \qquad \ldots(2.23)$$

The loads applied in the Vickers test may range from 1 kg to 120 kg depending on the type of material to be tested.

In the Vickers test the same sources of errors may occur as in Brinell test while measuring the diagonal length. The anomalous behaviour of 'sinking in' and 'ridging' are also found to be observed in this test.

Applications of Vickers test are almost the same as that of Brinell. Vickers test is preferred for harder materials. Both tests are not suitable for routine work and are primarily limited to research work.

2.3.4. Poldi Hardness Tester

Principle. In the Poldi hardness test, load is applied on the specimen and a standard test bar in a linear direction through a special Brinell ball of 10 mm diameter by a hammer blow. The impact load being the same, the extent of indentation obtained on the test specimen and the test bar depend on their hardness. Harder the material, shallow is the impression. The two diameters of impression are measured with the aid of a special magnified glass supplied with the tester. A table of hardness and tensile strength corresponding to both the diameters is also supplemented with the tester. The hardness of the work piece may be read out from this table.

The apparatus simply consists of a spring loaded plunger that makes a firm contact with the standard test bar. The ball indentor of 10 mm diameter is fixed in a hole and remains in contact with the standard test bar. This whole assembly is put on the work piece to be tested and then a blow of hammer is given at the top of the plunger.

Applications of Poldi hardness tester. (*i*) This tester is portable and therefore the hardness of heavy components can be determined by Poldi hardness tester.

(*ii*) It is a quick method of determining BHN of a variety of metals and alloys such as steels, cast irons, and non-ferrous metals and alloys.

(*iii*) This test is suitable for heavy castings and other components such as rolls of rolling mills, sheet metal, etc.

(*iv*) It is used where it is not possible to determine tensile strength of a material, since BHN is related with U.T.S.

2.3.5. Shore Sceleroscope

This tester is the most commonly used among the dynamic hardness testers. This instrument is based on the energy absorbed during the impact of a hard indentor on the test surface. When a soft material is subjected to impact, it absorbs more energy that is used to deform it plastically. On the other hand, a hard material absorbs less energy of impact and causes the indentor to rebound back with a high residual kinetic energy. The height of rebound is a measure of hardness. More is the height of rebound from the surface of the material, harder it is. The indentor is enclosed in a glass tube and is dropped from 25 cm height on the metal surface. The height of rebound is read out on the scale.

This instrument is also portable and is widely employed to test the hardness of heavy components such as rolls.

2.4. IMPACT TESTING

2.4.1. Theory

Impact strength of a material is a measure of toughness when it is subjected to dynamic loading. Toughness of a material under static load can be derived from the load-elongation curve as discussed in sections 2.2. Impact testing (or more frequently the notch bar impact testing) is another method of measuring toughness and it gives results more in conformity with the practical point of view. In the notch bar impact test the basic criterion for toughness is taken as the work necessary to break a test specimen of standard dimension by means of an impact load. Thus, the impact strength of a material is defined as the energy absorbed by the material without failure when it is subjected to impact load.

A material that fails in a ductile manner under static load may behave like a brittle material under dynamic loading. Owing to this anomalous behaviour of some materials, they are to be tested under dynamic load. Appliances such as mining drills, lathe machine tools, etc. frequently experience mechanical shocks during working. They should possess sufficient impact strength, otherwise their failure under service will result in serious accidents. There are three important factors that change the behaviour of a ductile material to brittleness, i.e., (i) a triaxial state of stress, as for instance exists at a notch, (ii) low temperature, and (iii) rapid rate of straining or loading.

It is not necessary that all these factors are present simultaneously but even in the presence of any one of the factors, the material may become brittle. Therefore, when a material is tested for impact strength, it would be better to impose all these three factors simultaneously so that when a tested material will be in service, the probability of serious accidents will be minimised.

The condition of a triaxial state of stress can be provided by making a notch in the specimen being tested. The condition of low temperature can be maintained by an ice box. Rapid rate of loading, of course, is automatically imposed by the swinging pendulum.

A material tested in this manner will give a representative value of impact strength. On the basis of impact value, a suitable material can be selected for a given application.

The most common materials that change their behaviour from ductile to brittle under the conditions stated above are those with BCC structures. Many FCC metals, on the other hand, remain ductile even at very low temperatures. HCP metals in the form of single crystals and under favourable orientation for basal slip, are ductile but may be brittle in polycrystalline form.

There are two methods of measuring impact value of a material depending upon the type of standard specimen. These are Izod Test and Charpy Test. The Izod specimen may be square or round in cross-section and contains a notch of V-shape at the mid-span. The diameter or the thickness of the Izod specimen is 10 mm and length is 56 mm. The depth of the notch is 2 mm with included angle of $45°$. The specimen is clamped vertically at one of the ends as illustrated in Fig. 2.17a with the notch facing the pendulum (or hammer). The hammer strikes the specimen at a distance 22 mm above the notch and to the side of the notch. Since the notch is facing the hammer, the energy required to cause fracture of the specimen is relatively less.

Charpy specimen is square in cross-section and contains a V-shape or key hole shape notch at the centre of the specimen. The Charpy specimen is placed horizontally on the anvil of the tester so that the notch is opposite to the hammer. The hammer strikes at the mid-span of the specimen but opposite to the notch (Fig. 2.17b). In this case, relatively more energy is needed to cause fracture of the specimen.

When the hammer is released from certain predetermined height depending upon the type of test, it possesses the maximum energy when comes to the vertical position. After striking the specimen, some energy still remains in the hammer due to which it swings away further in the same direction.

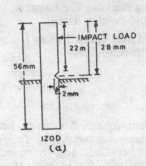

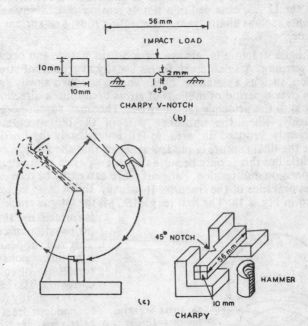

FIG. 2.17. (a) Izod specimen, (b) Charpy specimen, and (c) Schematic diagram of impact testing machine.

2.4.2. Procedure

(i) The hammer of the tester is raised to the height corresponding to the standard test and is fixed in a catch or trigger.

(ii) The specimen is placed (clamped) in the anvil at the bottom of the machine.

(iii) The pointer is set on the dial at the maximum capacity.

(iv) The hammer is released from the catch and the energy used in breaking the specimen is recorded as indicated by the pointer.

Precautions. (*i*) Before releasing the hammer, care is taken about the zero error which should be eliminated.

(*ii*) The operator should keep himself away from the machine during zero the swinging of the pendulum.

2.5. FATIGUE TESTING

2.5.1. Theory

If a ductile wire is bent to and fro many times until fracture occurs,' then it is the simplest example of fatigue failure where a given load or stress is applied and removed repeatedly. The stress required to cause fatigue of a member is considerably lower than the U.T.S. obtained in a simple tension test. Many service components such as shafts, gears, connecting rods, and springs fail due to fatigue.

Fatigue fracture is always of a brittle nature and occurs without any warning. A small crack forms usually at a point of stress concentration, such as a notch or fillet. The crack then slowly spreads out, often over a period of millions of stress cycles, in a direction usually normal to the principle tensile stress. The final rupture occurs rather suddenly, when the unbroken part of the cross-section has been sufficiently reduced in area to fail immediately by brittle fracture. Since the final rupture is sudden, it seems that the fatigue crack itself is brittle but this is only because the crack passes alternately through compression and tension. Fatigue failure can easily be recognised from the appearance of the fracture. It usually shows two zones, as illustrated in Fig. 2.18. The first (e. g. *ABC*) is the fatigue crack itself and is formed by the gradual propagation of crack faces. This zone appears smooth, sometimes polished, and sometimes discoloured by corrosion. The second (e.g. *BCD*) is finally formed due to sudden fracture in a brittle manner. It appears to be rough and granular. The fatigue crack usually shows ring shaped marking which is concentric

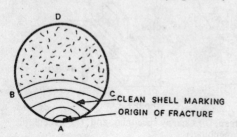

FIG. 2.18. Appearance of a typical fatigue crack.

with the origin of the fracture. These marks are the successive positions of the crack front that results due to variation in the amplitude of stress cycle. Under variable stress amplitudes, the crack may stop spreading when the stress is low (as e.g. when a car moves at a steady speed) and continues to grow when it rises (as when a car moves with increasing acceleration).

Thus, failure under alternating stresses, depends on the range of the stresses as well as upon the maximum stresses. Failure is less likely to occur if the stress varies from zero to some maximum than if it varies from a negative maximum to a positive maximum of the same value, i.e. if the stress cycle is analogous to sinusoidal wave.

Stress raisers such as a fillet, a sharp 'V' thread, a tool mark, a surface imperfection or inclusions within a metal, all promote an early fatigue failure of a material.

There are many ways to perform the fatigue test. One type of fatigue test is the rotating beam test commonly used in laboratory investigations.

2.5.2. Principle of Operation of the Fatigue Test

The set-up for the rotating beam fatigue test is shown in Fig. 2.19a. A test specimen is mounted in the machine. A steady bending

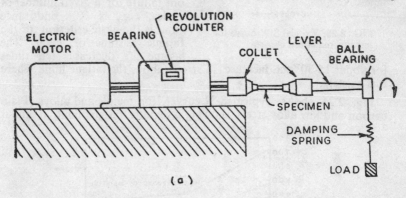

(a)

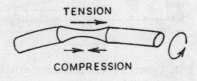

(b)

FIG. 2.19. Experiment set up for fatigue test.

is applied to a rotating shaft through a ball bearing fiitted load hanger. As the shaft rotates, the test piece passes through alternated compressive and tension stresses (Fig. 2.19b) and the number of cycles of stress is equal to the number of revolutions of the machine. The test continues until fracture of the specimen occurs. The number of stress cycles can be read out on the revolution counter attached with the machine shaft. This test is performed for various cyclic stresses. From the data, a curve is then plotted for the stress as a function of logarithm of number of cycles to fracture, as shown in Fig. 2.20. This curve is commonly known as S-N curve. It can be

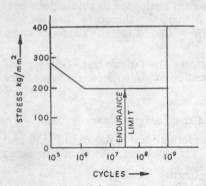

noted from Fig. 2.20, that in the beginning, the stress decreases as the number of cycles increases and after several millions of cycles the stress becomes steady. This steady value of stress is known as the endurance limit of the material concerned for cyclic stress. The endurance limit is, therefore defined as the maximum cyclic stress to which a material can be subjected without failure for a given number of cycles, e.g., $N = 10^7$. Endurance limit is the basic criterion of the fatigue resistance of metals. The fatigue life decreases ten times for about 15-30 pct. increase in stress (above the fatigue limit, where this exists).

FIG. 2.20. Typical S-N curve for ferrous materials.

Fig, 2.21 shows typical S-N curves for metals and alloys. Plain carbon and low alloy steels showing a definite fatigue limit, at about

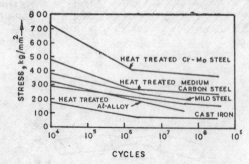

FIG. 2.21. Typical S-N curves under reversal bending.

10^6 cycles and at stresses below this limit their fatigue life becomes virtually infinite. Whereas other metals (non-ferrous metals) and alloys do not exhibit such a limit, at least up to lives of the order of 10^9 cycles.

2.6. CREEP TEST

In a tension test a material deforms plastically under ever increasing stress and after the stress exceeds the tensile strength, fracture occurs. If a material is subjected to a constant stress which is well below the tensile stress and maintained at certain temperature usually a high temperature, then a considerable plastic deformation can be observed. The material will gradually deform plastically under this constant stress and ultimately rupture will occur. This continuous slow deformation of a material under a constant stress is know as *creep*. At temperatures less than 40 pct. of the absolute melting point, the extent of creep is negligible, but at temperatures higher than this, appreciable creep results. Therefore the creep test is commonly referred to as a high temperature test.

2.6.1. Theory

Under constant stress, at certain temperature, if strain of a test specimen is plotted as a function of time until fracture occurs, then

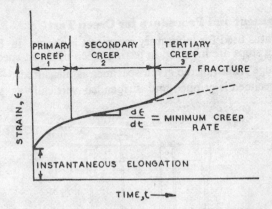

FIG. 2.22. A typical creep curve showing three stages of elongation during creep deformation in metals.

the curve so obtained is called a creep curve. Fig. 2.22 shows a typical creep curve. The curve indicates three different stages of elongation during creep deformation in metals. These are known as (*i*) primary or transient creep, (*ii*) steady state or secondary creep and (*iii*) the tertiary creep.

Primary creep occurs at all temperatures. In this stage of creep, the work hardening of metal is faster than the recovery processes. At low temperatures, the recovery process involves only cross-slip by screw dislocations. Screw dislocations cross glide from one plane to another bypassing some obstacles like forest dislocations. At high temperatures, another recovery process of dislocation climb occurs by diffusion process.

During steady state creep, the recovery process is fast enough to compensate the rate of work hardening and therefore the curve becomes almost constant during this stage. Edge dislocations climb and screw dislocations cross glide to form subgrains within the original grain. The subgrain boundaries consist of network of dislocations. The dislocation density in the subgrain boundaries is more than that within the subgrains.

In a polycrystalline material, in addition to dislocation climb, grain boundary sliding may also occur. As a consequence, steady state creep rate increases with a decrease in grain size.

Tertiary creep may occur due to several factors. Microcracks may develop at the grain boundaries in the sample thus decrease the effective load carrying capacity of the sample. Two types of grain boundary fractures have been observed in creep tested specimens, i.e., the formation of micro voids on the grain boundaries which subsequently grow and coalesce to form a crack and the second results from the formation of cracks at the triple points of the grain boundaries due to their sliding.

2.6.2. Equipment and Procedure for Creep Test

The apparatus used for laboratory creep test is shown in Fig. 2.23. The following steps are involved in testing creep of a test specimen:

(*i*) The gauge length of the given specimen is measured.

(*ii*) The specimen is gripped and suspended vertically as shown in Fig. 2.23.

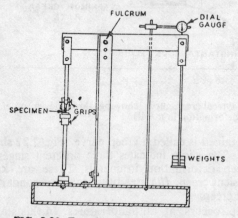

FIG. 2.23. Experimental set up for creep test.

(*iii*) The initial reading of the dial is recorded.

(*iv*) The load is applied by putting weights on the pan.

(*v*) The readings are noted on the dial gauge after every two minutes until fracture occurs.

(*vi*) A curve is plotted between strain and time.

2.6.3. Engineering Requirements for Materials

The various engineering requirements for materials include properties like mechanical, thermal, electrical, magnetic, corrosion resistance, weldability, castability, formability, etc. These requirements for important engineering applications along with the recommended materials are compiled in Table 2.3.

TABLE 2.3 *Properties Requirements of Important Materials Employed in Engineering*

S. No.	Applications	Properties Requirements		Materials Recommended
		Mechanical	Others	
(i)	(ii)	(iii)	(iv)	(v)
1.	Cylinder block and cylinder head for automobile engine	High tensile strength, hardness, wear resistance, damping capacity, and rigidity.	Castability, machinability, anti-scuffing property, and freedom from residual stresses.	(i) Gray cast iron, and (ii) Cast aluminium silicon alloys.
2.	Crank shaft for automobile engine.	Fatigue strength, toughness, and high wear resistance.	Ease of fabrication, and machinability.	(i) Medium carbon heat treated and surface hardened steel, (ii) Nitrided steel, (iii) S.G. cast iron, and (iv) Heat treated steel forgings.
3.	Connecting rod.	Fatigue strength, wear resistance and toughness.	—	(i) Hardened and tempered medium carbon steel, and (ii) Forgings of preformed iron powder sintered block.
4.	Pistons of I.C. engine.	Strength at elevated temperature, strength to weight ratio, and sufficient per cent elongation.	Low thermal expansion, corrosion resistance, castability, and forgeability.	Y-alloy (4 Cu, 1.5 Mg, 2 Ni, 0.6 Si, 0.6 Fe and balance Al).
5.	Transmission gears.	Very high surface hardness and case strength, resistance to impact fatigue, plain impact, and wear.	—	(i) Ni, (ii) Ni-Cr, (iii) Ni-Cr-Mo, and (iv) Cr-Mn steels.
6.	Automobile chassis frames.	High strength to weight ratio, high yield strength, toughness, high modulus of elasticity and moderate per cent elongation.	Excellent weldability, good formability, and high resistance to corrosion.	High strength low alloy (C-Mn, C-Mn-V) steels.

(i)	(ii)	(iii)	(iv)	(v)
7.	Bonnet.	High yield strength, good elongation, high strength to weight ratio, and resistance to mechanical shocks.	Forgeability, weldability, and corrosion resistance.	Duralumin alloys.
8.	Plain bearings.	Good to excellent wear resistance, high hardness, sufficient plasticity under load, capacity to withstand impact action, and good compressive strength.	Low coefficient of friction, sufficiently high melting point, high thermal conductivity, good resistance to corrosion, good castability, and good to fair machinability.	(i) White metal alloys such as Babbit metal, lead base alloys, copper base tin bronzes, phosphorous bronze, and aluminium base bearing alloys for high duty pressure lubricated bearings;
				(ii) Tin bronze and phosphorous bronze for small end bearings;
				(iii) Tin-base, white metal for bearings of turbines, compressors, alternators, etc.;
				(iv) White metal, phosphorous bronze and lead bronze for rolling mill bearings;
				(v) Sintered bronze powder and Cu-Sn-graphite sintered powder for oil impregnated bearings; and
				(vi) Polymeric materials such as nylon for dry bearings.

(i)	(ii)	(iii)	(iv)	(v)
9.	Gas turbine blades.	Very high tensile strength, high ductility, high temperature creep strengh and relatively high fatigue strength.	High resistance to corrosion at high temperature, high thermal conductivity, low thermal expansion and best resistance to thermal fatigue.	Nickel base super alloys.
10.	Gas turibine disc (wheel).	High strength, high creep resistance at the rim, and high fatigue strength.	High resistance to oxidation and corrosion at elevated temperature.	Nickel-base super alloys and iron base super alloys.
11.	Gas turbine nozzle guide vanes.	Relatively low tensile stress, creep strength at very high temperature and thermal fatigue resistance.	High resistance to degradation by oxidation, hot corrosion and hot erosion.	Cobalt base super alloys.
12.	Gas turbine combustion chamber.	Relatively low strength, high creep strength at elevated temperature and resistance to thermal fatigue.	Resistance to corrosion and oxidation, good weldability and formability.	(i) Cobalt base super alloys for hottest portions, and (ii) Nickle base super alloys for relatively cooler regions.
13.	Water turbine rotor.	Creep strength, thermal fatigue, good fracture toughness even at the core, and low impact transition temperature.	Resistance to corrosion.	Cr-Mo-V steel.
14.	Boiler tubing.	Tensile strength.	Corrosion resistance and weldability.	Mild steel.
15.	Generator rotor.	Proof/yield stress, low impact transition temperature.	Good magnetic permeability.	3.5 Ni-Cr-Mo-V steel.
16.	Gas turbine compressor.	High strength to weight ratio, high specific strength at room as well as at elevated temperature, excellent creep and fatigue resistance.		Titanium alloys (Ti-5 Al-2.5 Sn, Ti-6 Al-4V and Ti-4 Al-4 Mo-2 Sn).

(i)	(ii)	(iii)	(iv)	(v)
17.	Space craft ablative shield (as in Apollo).	—	High heat of vaporisation and dissociation, high heat capacity, low thermal conductivity, light weight, and ease of fabrication.	Teflon, glass, nylon fibres, alumina, graphite, fibre reinforced phenolic resins using graphite or elastomeric silicone filler materials.
18.	Condenser.	—	Plain corrosion as well as stress corrosion resistance.	(i) Cu-Ni and (ii) Cu-Al.
19.	Jet engine parts such as cumbustion chamber, turbine blades, and all exhaust pipes of supersonic aircraft.	High strength to weight ratio, high modulus to weight ratio, retention of tensile strength at high temperature and very high creep and fatigue resistance.	Ease of fabrication, and very good resistance to corrosion as well as to oxdation.	Titanium alloys such as Ti-6 Al-4V and Ti-4 Al-2 Sn-4 Mo-1/2 Si.
20.	Springs for automobiles and air crafts.	High elastic limit, high deflection value, maximum possible fatigue strength, and resistance to mechanical shocks.	Reasonable corrosion resistance.	High carbon, Cr-V, Si-Cr, Si-Mn, and Mn-Cr steels.
21.	Springs for watches, electric irons, toasiers, rockets, aircrafts, and nuclear reactors.	High stress, high temperature strength (except for watches), high energy storage capacity (stiffness) and fatigue resistance.	Corrosion resistance and non-magnetic properties.	(i) Ni Co-Cr for non-corrosive environment and (ii) Ni- or Co- base alloys for corrosive environment.
22.	Electrical conductivity springs.	High yield strength, low elastic modulus, and sufficient fatigue strength. Sometimes wear resistance is also required.	Resistance to atmospheric corrosion, machinability, electrical conductivity and non-magnetic characteristic.	(i) Phosphorous bronze, (ii) Beryllium bronze (Cu-Be), and (iii) Nickel silver (German silver).
23.	Tools.	High hardness, toughness, strength at room as well as elevated temperature,	Machinability, resistance to corrosion at room as well as at elevated tempe-	(i) Plain carbon and alloy steels such as high speed steels, and

(i)	(ii)	(iii)	(iv)	(v)
		wear resistance, hardenability, red hardness, non-deformability, and resistance to mechanical shock.	rature, formability, and resistance to thermal shock during heat treatment.	(ii) Cu-Be alloy for non-sparking tools.
24.	Hulls for hydrospace vehicles and motor cases for missiles.	Ultrahigh strength coupled with high toughness.	Resistance to stress corrosion cracking.	Maraging steel.
25.	Yatch and racing crafts in sea water.	High strength to weight ratio.	Resistance to corrosion in sea water.	(i) Titanium alloys. (ii) Aluminium alloys.
26.	Vitreous enameling racks (as in potteries), heat treatment trays, furnace dampers and doors.	Tensile strength.	High heat resistance.	(i) 26 Cr-10 Ni cast steel; (ii) 20-25 Cr-8-12 Ni, 3-4 W steel when resistance to scaling at high temperature is needed.
27.	Annealing and carburising boxes.	—	Maximum heat resistance.	Cast 60 Ni-20 Cr-20 Fe alloy.
28.	Pressure tubes in CANDU type power reactor.	Good ductility relatively low strength, and high creep strength.	Low neutron absorption cross-section.	Zr-Al alloy.
29.	Canning materials in nuclear reactors.	Enough strength and creep resistance to withstand stresses.	Low neutron absorption cross-section, ease of fabrication, high thermal conductivity, and corrosion resistance.	(i) Mg-Al alloys, and (ii) Zr-Al alloys.
30.	Ball and roller bearings requiring corrosion resistance.	High strength, hardness and wear resistance.	Anti-frictional property, resistance to corrosion and other properties required by bearing materials.	(i) Martensitic stainless steel of cutlery grade, (ii) Low carbon-Cr, Ni-Cr, and Ni-Cr-Mo steels.
31.	Oil burner.	High temperature strength is of secondary importance.	Resistance to corrosion, of fabrication and weldability.	Ferritic stainless steels.
32.	Electrical contact materials.	Sufficient mechanical	Sufficient electrical con-	(i) Brass,

(i)	(ii)	(iii)	(iv)	(v)
		strength and wear resistance.	ductivity and joining characterstics.	(ii) Be and p bronze, and (iii) Ni-Silver.
33.	Over head power transmission lines.	Sufficient mechanical strength and ductility should be high enough.	High electrical conductivity, corrosion resistance and capability of joining by welding, brazing or soldering.	(i) Pure copper and steel cored aluminium cables, and (ii) Bimetallic wire consisting of a steel core and a copper jacket is used for telephone and telegraphic line.s
34.	Winding wires and cables.	Mechanical strength is of secondary importance but ductility should be high enough.	High electrical conductivity.	(i) Pure copper and (ii) Aluminium.
35.	Commutator segments.	Relatively higher hardness and strength than that of pure copper.	Sufficiently high electrical conductivity.	Cu-Cd alloy with 0.7 to 1.0 pct. Cd.
36.	Magnetic materials (soft magnets).	—	Low energy loss, low residual induction, low coercivity, high maximum induction, and high initial and maximum permeability, and cold workability.	(i) Commercially pure iron, (ii) Low carbon steel, (iii) Fe-Ni, and (iv) Fe-Al.
37.	Permanent magnets	—	High remanence, high coercive force, high energy product i.e. $(BH)_{max}$.	(i) Martensitic steel. (ii) Alnico, (iii) Vicaloy. (iv) Alcomax, and (v) Columax.
38.	Surgical instruments.	High elastic limit, compressive strength, modulus of elasticity, sufficient ductility, endurance limit, non-susceptibility to stress-corrosion fatigue, compatible coefficient of friction and excellent spring quality.	Resistance to corrosion against physiological fluids, ability to be formed by casting and shaping processes, and chemically inertness.	(i) Austenitic stainless steels (ii) Titanium and its alloys, (iii) Cast cobalt base alloys 30 Cr-5 Mo), (iv) Elgiloy (a complex alloy of cobalt), and (v) Polymers (nylon, teflon, acrylics, etc.).

QUESTIONS

1. Define the terms stress, strain, elastic limit, elasticity and plasticity.

2. What is the difference between the true and the engineering stress-strain curves? Explain the nature of the two curves.

3. Define the terms yield point, tensile strength, toughness, ductility, and rigidity. Explain their importance in the design of a structure.

4. What do you mean by the term proof stress ? What is the necessity of determining proof stress and how is it determined?

5. (a) A steel bar 1.27 cm in diameter, supports a load of 7,000 kg (or force 68,600 N). What is the stress placed on the bar?

(b) If the bar of part (a) has a modulus of elasticity of 209,000 MPa, how much will be the bar be strained with this load?

6. A copper wire has an engineering breaking strength of 32 kg/mm² and a reduction of area of 77 pct. Calculate (i) the true tensile strength and (ii) true strain at the point of fracture.

7. Differentiate between scratch, indentation and rebound hardness measurements.

8. In the Rockwell hardness test, a minor load is always applied before the major load. Why?

9. What are the salient features of Rockwell hardness test ? What precautions are to be taken while determining hardness by this method?

10. Discuss the principle of Brinell hardness test.

11. Explain with the help of diagrams, the terms 'ridging' and 'sinking in'. How do these terms affect the hardness values taken by Brinell or Vickers hardness tester.

12. Write the applications of Brinell hardness test.

13. What is the working principle of Poldi hardness tester? What is the importance of this test over other indentation hardness test?

14. Define impact strength. How is it determined? What is the unit of impact strength ?

15. Discuss the principle of fatigue test.

16. What is creep curve? With the help of a creep curve explain the primary, secondary and tertiary creep.

3

ELECTRON THEORY OF METALS

3.1. CLASSICAL MECHANICS

According to classical mechanics, an atom should not be stable. The orbiting electrons attracted by the positive nucleus should fall into it. As a result, the electrons should lose their energy of motion by emitting electromagnetic radiations. However, experiments have shown that electrons do not fall into nucleus because a force aganist the electrostatic attraction is always associated with the moving electrons. This force is the centrifugal force given as $1/r.mv^2$ where v is the velocity of the electron and m is its mass. Further, the classical theory shows that an electron can move in any of a continuous series of states of motion and in each of these states it has a definite energy, partly the kinetic energy associated with its motion and partly the potential energy. If an electron changes its state of motion, a quantum of electromagnetic radiation is either emitted or absorbed depending upon whether the change of state is from higher to lower or the reverse.

In either case, the difference in energy between the two states, ΔE is related with the frequency, v of the radiations and is given as

$$\Delta E = hv \qquad \qquad \ldots (3.1)$$

where h is the Planck's constant equal to 6.625×10^{-27} ergs seconds. If the states of motion form a continuous series then any value of v is possible. Accordingly, the atomic spectrum should show all values of v. But this is not found to be true in practice. Experiments have shown that the spectrum consists of discrete lines corresponding to specific values of v. Thus, only certain states of motion are allowed and these are termed stationary states as they do not alter with time.

3.2. QUANTUM MECHANICS

De Broglie in 1924 postulated that electrons though possess a mass and a charge, behave as if they had associated with them wavelength

$$\lambda = \frac{h}{mv} \qquad \qquad \ldots (3.2)$$

where h is Planck's constant m is the mass of an electron ($m = 9.115 \times 10^{-28} gm$) and v is the velocity of the wave.

This postulate indicates the dual nature of electromagnetic radiations, i.e., they simultaneously have the properties of particles and of waves. Waves are means of visualising mathematical equations and they do not have actual physical existence.

If, for example, a beam of electrons with a velocity v is allowed to fall on a specimen of metal fillings, it is not scattered in all directions but produces a diffraction pattern. The diffraction pattern shows fine spots in the form of rings (Fig. 3.1) of intense light which is quite analogous to the rings formed by X-rays in the Debye Scherrer method of X-ray diffraction.

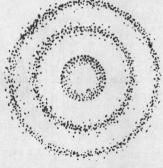

FIG. 3 1. Electron diffraction pattern from a crystal.

By changing the velocity of the electrons, λ is altered. The faster the electrons are travelling, the shorter is the wavelength as is evident from the following equation

$$\frac{1}{\lambda} = \frac{mv}{h} \qquad \qquad \dots(3.3)$$

The wave number or number of waves per centimetre is proportional to the momentum of the electrons in the beam.

Consider a light ray as consisting of a stream of light particles or photons, each of energy $h\nu$. The intensity of the light at any place is proportional to the density of the photons or to the number of photons per unit volume at the place concerned. In order to determine this intensity, one should have to make use of wave equation, with the interpretation that the square of the amplitude at each place is proportional to the density of photons or in other words to the probability of finding a photon at the place concerned.

By the same analogy, one can calculate the density of electrons at a given place using wave equation whose amplitude is to be a measure of the electron density.

Since the "presence" of a light quantum is measured by its intensity, which is proportional to the square of its amplitude, a wave packet like the one shown in Fig. 3.2(a) can be used to represent a quantum that is located to a small region of space. A wave packet consists of waves with slight difference in frequencies which superimpose in a small region Δx whereas the waves interfere at some other place where we cannot find an electron (Fig. 3.2a). The notable point here is that wave packet itself travels through space with a velocity called the group velocity, which is equal to the velocity of the particle as determined by classical mechanics, whereas the individual waves forming the packet have a velocity called the phase velocity. This picture clearly indicates that according to classical mechanics the motion of a particle is exactly spacified whereas quantum mechanics determines the probability of occurrence of any event.

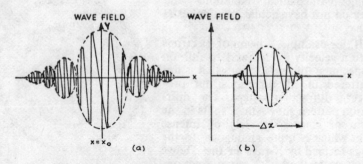

FIG. 3.2. Schematic representation of wave field.

In the wave theory of electrons, a "physical quantity which vibrates" is called ψ and we may call of ψ vibrations. ψ is a complex quantity and when it is said that it vibrates, means a vibration will involves both space and time.

Suppose ψ propagates with a velocity u, then its motion is described as

$$\Delta\psi = \frac{1}{u^2} + \frac{\delta^2\psi}{\delta t^2} \qquad \ldots(3.4)$$

The equation (3.4) is called the wave equation, in which $\Delta\psi$ is the Laplacian operator of the function and is givenas

$$\Delta\psi = \frac{\delta^2 x}{\delta x^2} + \frac{\delta^2\psi}{\delta y^2} + \frac{\delta^2\psi}{\delta x^2} \qquad \ldots(3.5)$$

In the case of harmonic oscillations with a frequency ν, it may be written as follows

$$\psi = \psi_0(xyz)e^{2\pi i\nu t} \qquad \ldots(3.5)$$

Where ψ_0 (xyz) is called the amplitude factor or the space factor and involves only the space coordinates (xyz). The second term is called the time factor.

Differentiating the equation (3.5)

$$\frac{\delta\psi}{\delta t} = 2\pi i\nu\psi_0 e^{2\pi i\nu t} \qquad \ldots(3.6)$$

By differentiating again, following equations are obtained

$$\frac{\delta^2\psi}{\delta t^2} = -4\pi^2\nu^2\psi_0 e^{2\pi i\nu t} \qquad \ldots(3.7)$$

$$\frac{\delta^2\psi}{\delta t^2} = -4n^2\nu^2\psi \qquad \ldots(3.8)$$

On substituting the value of $\dfrac{\delta^2\psi}{\delta t^2}$ in equation (3.4), following relationship is obtained

$$\Delta\psi + 4\pi^2\frac{v^2}{u^2}\ \psi = 0 \qquad \ldots(3.9)$$

Since

$$\lambda = \frac{u}{\nu}$$

$$\Delta\psi + \left(\frac{2\pi}{\lambda}\right)^2\psi = 0$$

or $\qquad \Delta\psi + k^2\psi = 0 \ \left(\text{substituting } k = \dfrac{2\pi}{\lambda}\right)$

or $\qquad \dfrac{\delta^2\psi}{\delta x^2} + \dfrac{\delta^2\psi}{\delta y^2} + \dfrac{\delta^2\psi}{\delta z^2} + k^2\psi = 0 \qquad \ldots(3.10)$

$$k = \frac{2\pi}{\lambda} \text{ is the wave number.}$$

or $\qquad k = \dfrac{2\pi}{h}\ mv \text{ (From Eq. 3.2)}$

or $\qquad k^2 = \dfrac{4\pi^2}{h^2}\ m^2v^2$

or $\qquad k^2 = \dfrac{8\pi^2}{h^2}\ m(\tfrac{1}{2}mv^2) \qquad \ldots(3.11)$

where $\tfrac{1}{2}mv^2$ is the kinetic energy of an electron. On substituting the value of expression k^2 in equation (3.10), the relationship obtained is

$$\frac{\delta^2\psi}{\delta x^2} + \frac{\delta^2\psi}{\delta y^2} + \frac{\delta^2\psi}{\delta z^2} + \frac{8\pi^2}{h^2}\ mE_k\psi = 0 \qquad \ldots(3.12)$$

$$(E_k = \tfrac{1}{2}mv^2)$$

Because the kinetic energy of an electron is the difference of the total energy W and the potential energy V, therefore,

$$\frac{\delta^2\psi}{\delta x^2} + \frac{\delta^2\psi}{\delta y^2} + \frac{\delta^2\psi}{\delta z^2} + \frac{8\pi^2}{h^2}\ m(W-V)\psi = 0 \qquad \ldots(3.13)$$

This equation is the famous equation of *Schrodinger in three dimensional space*.

In the Schrödinger wave equation the quantity ψ^2 is frequently called the probability density, while the function ψ itself is the amplitude of probability.

From the probabilistic interpretation of the wave functions, it follows that the position of a moving electron can not be determined to any degree of accuracy, as in the case of classical mechanics. By calculating the quantity $|\psi|^2$ (i.e, $\psi\psi^*$ where ψ^* is the complex conjugate of ψ) from the wave equation, it is possible to determine only the probability of finding an electron at a given point in space. This peculiarity of quantum mechanics is expressed in the most general form by *Heisenberg's uncertainty principle*. This principle states that if Δx is the uncertainty in position and Δp is the uncertainty in momentum of an electron, then the product $\Delta p.\Delta x$ is greater than or equal to a fixed quantity $h/2\pi$, i.e.,

$$\Delta x.\Delta p \geqslant h/2\pi$$

The Δx (Fig. 3.2) means the length outside which the probability of finding the electron becomes negligible. In other words there is certain probability of finding an electron at one place and another probability at second place and so on. These probabilities tend to vanish as one moves away from the region of greatest probability. Δp measures the most probable velocity of an electron.

Thus Schrödinger's wave quation can be used to describe the motion of electrons in atoms. The Schrödinger equation enables (*i*) to assign energy levels to electrons and (*ii*) to subdivide the energy levels into areas of probable location, i.e., orbitals.

3.3 FREE ELECTRON THEORY FOR STANDING WAVES

The essential difference in the motion of a bound electron (e.g. in the atom) and a free electron consists in the fact that the potential energy of the latter is zero whereas the bound electron is moving in a field of force and posseses a potential energy in addition to kinetic energy.

In the free electron theory, the crystal structure of the metal is ignored and the metal is assumed to consists of an assembly of electrons in an empty box, surrounded by potential walls which prevent the electron from escaping. The following assumptions have been made to develop the free electron model:

(*i*) The valence electrons in a metal are free to move and that their movement is restricted to the boundaries of a metal object. This indicates that the electrons have a lower potential energy inside the metal than outside of it.

(*ii*) The electron moves in a field of constant potential (i e. zero potential) with positive electricity (i.e. +ve charge) distributed isotropically throughout the metal.

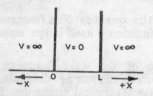

FIG. 3.3. Potential energy defining free electron in box.

Now let us consider the electron in a box and for the sake of simplicity consider the motion of the electron in one dimension only i.e. the box is one dimensional. Suppose the length of the box be L. It is assumed that the potential of the electron inside the box is zero whereas it is infinite outside the box, as illustrated in Fig. 3.3. Since an electron can never possess an infinite energy, it is unable to exist in the region where $V = \infty$

Mathematically

$$V = \infty \text{ for } x < 0 \text{ and } x > L \text{ and}$$

$$V = 0 \text{ for } 0 < x < L \text{ i.e. within the box.}$$

Let us find out the solution to the Schrödinger wave equation for the region outside the box. As we want the electron to be confined within the box, the probability of finding it outside the box must be zero. Thus, the solution of the wave equation must be such that $\psi = 0$ for $x \leqslant 0$ and for $x \geqslant 0$. The wave equation in one dimension is written as

$$\frac{\delta^2 \psi}{\delta x^2} + \frac{8\pi^2 m}{h^2} (W - V)\psi = 0 \qquad \ldots (3.15)$$

It is apparent from the above equation that if V is infinity then,

$$-V\psi = 0$$

Again since V is infinity, so ψ must be zero. Thus, the condition $V = \infty$ outside the box, automatically shows no probability of finding the electron outside the box according to the assumption made.

By rearranging the equation (3.15) following expression may be obtained

$$\frac{1}{\psi} \times \frac{\delta^2 \psi}{\delta x^2} = \text{Constant } (V - W) \qquad \ldots (3.16)$$

Here if $V > W$, the right hand side is positive and therefore, $\frac{\delta \psi}{\delta x^2}$ is positive when ψ is positive and vice varsa. $\delta^2 \psi / \delta x^2$ shows the curvature of the curve plotted between ψ and x while $\delta \psi / \delta x$ is the slope of the curve.

Under such conditions since kinetic energy (K. E.) is less than the potential energy (P. E.), velocity of the electron is therefore low and according to the equation (3.2), λ is very long. Consequently ψ rises infinitely as $x \to \pm \infty$. This condition contradicts the above mentioned assumption that as

$$x \to \pm \infty, \quad \psi = 0.$$

$$\text{At } V = W, \quad \psi = 0 \text{ and } \frac{\delta^2 \psi}{\delta x^2} = 0$$

i.e. a point of inflexion occurs. If $V < W$, then the kinetic energy of the electron is high enough so that $\psi \to 0$ as $x \to \pm \infty$ which coincides with the condition assumed and proved above. Thus $\psi \to 0$ at boundaries of the box. If $V = 0$, the equation (3.15) becomes

$$\frac{\delta^2 \psi}{\delta x^2} + \frac{8\pi^2 m}{h^2} (E_k)\psi = 0 \qquad \ldots (3.17)$$

or $\qquad \dfrac{\delta^2 \psi}{\delta x^2}+\left(\dfrac{2\pi}{\lambda}\right)^2 \psi=0$ $\qquad$ ...(3.18)

or $\qquad \dfrac{\delta^2 \psi}{\delta x^2}+k^2\psi=0$ $\qquad$ ...(3.19)

The generalised solution of this equation (3.19) may be given as follows

$$\psi=A \cos (2\pi x/\lambda)+B \sin (2\pi x/\lambda) \qquad ...(3.20)$$

Where A and B are the constants and can be determined by resuming the boundary conditions, that is

at $\qquad x=0,\ \psi=0$ and $\cos 0=1,\ \sin 0=0$

Then $\qquad A=0$

In order to determine B, let us determine the maximum probability of finding an electron. Since $|\psi|^2$ show, the probability of finding an electron in space and its maximum value is unity. This can be obtained by the total sum of ψ^2 within the space i.e. by integrating ψ^2 according to the relation

$$\int_{0}^{L} \psi^2 dx = 1 \qquad ...(3.21)$$

or $\qquad \displaystyle\int_{0}^{L} B \sin (2\pi x/\lambda)dx=0$ $\qquad$ ...(3.22)

By solving this we get

$$B=\sqrt{2/L} \qquad ...(3.23)$$

Determination of B in equation (3.20) using equation (3.21) is generally termed as normalising the wave function.

Now since $\qquad \psi=0,$ at $x=L$

Then, $\qquad \sin (2\pi L/\lambda)=0$

or $\qquad 2\pi L/\lambda=0+n\pi$

or $\qquad n=2L/\lambda$

or $\qquad \lambda=2L/n$ $\qquad$ ...(3.24)

i.e., the permissible wavelengths are

$$=2L/1,\ 2L/2,\ 2L/3, \ldots \ldots \ldots \ldots 2L/n$$

where n is an integer $(1, 2, 3 \ldots \ldots \ldots$ etc.) and is called the quantum number.

The kinetic energy associated with the electron is given as

$$E= \tfrac{1}{2}mv^2= \dfrac{1}{2m}m^2v^2$$

or $\qquad E=\dfrac{1}{2m}\times\dfrac{h^2n^2}{4L^2}=\dfrac{n^2h^2}{8mL^2}$ $\qquad$ ...(3.25)

Equation (3.25) gives the energy of the electron travelling in one direction and it increases with n^2. Thus, when $n=2$, the electron has four times the K.E. of the electron for which $n=1$ and so on. The electron can take only these energy values i.e. its energy is quantised. It is also clear from equation (3.24) that as n increases, λ decreases which is an agreement with the equation (3.2).

Fig. 3.4(a) illustrates the solution of wave equation $\psi = \sqrt{2/L}$. sin $2\pi x/L$ which is analogous to the waves on a stretched string. When the electron wave reaches the boundary at $x = L$, it is totally reflected back and travels to $x = 0$ where it is again reflected. Thus, the electron wave is stationary x with a probability distribution which is stationary in space. Fig. 3.4(b) illustrates the probability distribution of the electron for a series of value for the interger n.

In a three-dimensional box the electron moves in all directions and thus the quantum number associated with it can be resolved in three directions parallel to the axes, x, y, and z which are normal to each other. For an electron in a cube box, it may be written as

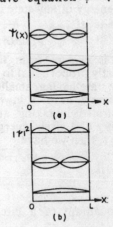

FIG. 3.4. Solution to Schrödinger equation for an electron in a box: (a) the wave function and (b) the probability as a function of position for different quantum number.

$$E = \frac{h^2}{8mL^2} (n_x^2 + n_y^2 + n_z^2) \quad \dots (3.26)$$

where n_x, n_y and n_z are the three quantum numbers (for details of quantum no. see Chapter 1) and each can take an integer 1, 2, 3, ... etc. irrespective of what quantum number the others take. The lowest energy state that an electron can occupy in a 3-dimensional box occurs when n_x, n_y and n_z all have the same value, i.e. when $n_x = n_y = n_z = 1$.

Then, $$E = \frac{h^2}{8mL^2} (1^2 + 1^2 + 1^2) = \frac{3h^2}{8mL^2} \quad \dots (3.27)$$

Following the lowest energy state, there are three states of equal energy obtained by various combinations of the same three integers n_x, n_y and n_z, for example, (112), (121) and (211). Each such combination represents a different wave function but the energy remains the same, i.e.

$$E = \frac{h^2}{8mL^2} (1^2 + 1^2 + 2^2) = \frac{6h^2}{8mL^2} \quad \dots (3.28)$$

Such energy states having the same energy but different quantum numbers are usually called degenerate states.

At absolute zero the electrons have tendency to occupy the lowest energy states in a metal. All the states at this temperature are expected to be filled with a pair of electrons in each state starting from the lowest energy state to some maximum state which is corresponding to the maximum energy.

In order to determine this maximum energy of states, let us first consider an electron in a two dimensional box. In two dimensions, the energy of any state is given as:

$$E = \frac{h^2}{8mL^2} \ (n_x^2 + n_y^2) \qquad \qquad \ldots (3.29)$$

It is evident from this equation (3.29) that the energy of state is directly proportional to the square sum of the two quantum numbers. Any state having smaller value of $n_x^2 + n_y^2$ than the given state will obviously have a lower energy than the given state. This can be illustrated by taking an example. Suppose that E_m is the maximum energy of a given energy state with quantum number $n_x = 15$ and $n_y = 1$, then we have

$$(n_x^2 + n_y^2)_{max.} = r^2 = (15^2 + 1^2)$$

or $$r^2 = 226$$

or $$r = \sqrt{226}$$

A quadrant of a circle has been drawn with a radius $r = \sqrt{226}$,

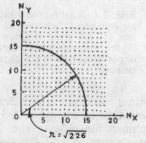

FIG. 3.5. Quantum number space in two dimensions.

which is shown in Fig. 3.5. The area within the arc of the circle represents the total no. of energy states lying in this region. If this area is divided into unit areas each representing an anergy state (as shown by dots in Fig. 3.5) then the energy of any state is clearly less than E_{max}. The area under the arc is given as:

$$Area = \tfrac{1}{4}\pi r^2_{max.} = \frac{\pi}{4}\ (226)$$

$$= 177 \text{ states.}$$

This computed value of quantum state is approximately equal to the number counted from the diagram shown in Fig. 3.5. The accuracy between the two values increases with the increase of E_{max}. Thus, the number of states with an energy equal to or less than E_m is expressed as:

$$\eta = \frac{\pi}{4}\ (n_x^2 + n_y^2)_{max.}$$

or $$\eta = \frac{\pi}{4} \times \frac{8mL^2}{h^2}\ E_{max.}$$

or $$\eta = \frac{2mL^2\pi}{h^2}\ E_m \qquad \qquad \ldots (3.30)$$

Now let us consider a three dimensional picture of an electron in a box. Here, the quantum states with an energy less than or equal to E_m lie inside an octant of a sphere as shown in Fig. 3.6. By an analogy with the two dimensional case, for large values of E_m, the number of quantum states inside the octant is given as the volume of the octant. The radius of the sphere is given as:

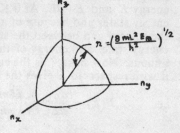

$$r_{max.} = \sqrt{n_x{}^2 + n_y{}^2 + n_z{}^2}$$
$$= \left(\frac{8mL^2}{h^2}\right)^{\frac{1}{2}}$$

Because $\qquad \eta = \frac{1}{8} \times \frac{4\pi}{3} r^3$

FIG. 3.6. Quantum number space in three dimensions.

By substituting the value of r

$$\eta = \frac{1}{8} \times \frac{4\pi}{3} \left\{\frac{8mL^2}{h^2} E_m\right\}^{3/2}$$

or $\qquad \eta = \pi/6 \times \left\{\frac{8mL^2}{h^2} E_m\right\}^{3/2} \qquad \dots (3.31)$

If N be the number of electrons in a metal piece, then at absolute zero, the number of filled energy states is given by $N/2$.

i.e. $\qquad \frac{N}{2} = \frac{\pi}{6} \left\{\frac{8mL^2}{h^2}\right\}^{3/2} E_{max.}{}^{3/2} \qquad \dots (3.32)$

The value of E_m depends on the number of free electrons present and is usually referred to as the *Fermi energy* E_F.

Therefore, $E_F = \left\{\frac{3N}{L^3\pi}\right\}^{2/3} \frac{h^2}{8mL^2}$

or $\qquad E_F = \frac{h^2}{8m} \left\{\frac{3N}{L^3\pi}\right\}^{2/3} \qquad \dots (3.33)$

Where L^3 is the volume of the assumed metal box.

Hence, the maximum energy of eleccron states (i.e. energy states) depends upon N/V, the number of electrons per unit volume in the metal.

Thus according to free electron theory for standing wave (also known as Summerfield theory), all the electrons in a metal fill up the lowest energy states at absolute zero without violating the Pauli's Exclusion principle. The electron state with maximum energy is the Fermi level. The average energy of all the quantum states is found to be $3/5$ E_F. The electrons seated in the vicinity of E_F are at higher energy states and can easily be excited to higher energy states. A higher excitation energy in needed for the deeply seated electrons.

3.4. DENSITY OF STATES

The term density of states $N(E)$ (or the degeneracy) is defined as the number of energy states per unit volume of the crystal at a given energy. The term $N(E)dE$ implies the density of states between the energy E and $E+dE$. At $0°K$, all the electrons occupy the lowest energy states and because of a large number of electrons in a metal, the energy gap between the states is too less to regard a discrete energy state. and energy of the electrons is assumed to be quasi-continuous. Now since η is the energy states upto E_m, the derivative of it with respect to E gives the density of states $N(E)$

i.e. $$N(E) = \frac{d\eta}{dE} = \frac{\pi}{4}\left(\frac{8mL^2}{h^2}\right)^{3/2} E^{\frac{1}{2}} \qquad \ldots (3.34)$$

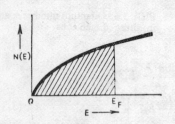

FIG. 3.7 The density of states *vs* energy curve at absolute zero as obtained by free electron theory.

This equation shows that as the energy increases from zero, the $N(E)$ increases parabolically. The $N(E)$ as a function of E is shown in Fig. 3.7. The cross hatched region under the curve represents the total number of energy states with an energy equal to or less than E_F, the Fermi energy and it measures the number of states which are occupied at absolute zero.

3.5. FREE ELECTRON THEORY FOR RUNNING WAVES

In the earlier sections (3.4) the solution to Schrödinger wave equation for standing waves has been discussed, i.e., waves which do not alter their position with time. In terms of electron movement a standing wave does not indicate about the direction of motion of the electron whether it is moving up or down the string or wire. So, in order to consider solution of Schrödinger equation for running waves, time factor has to be included in the wave equation for standing waves. Then the standing wave equation becomes:

$$\psi = \sin 2\pi(x/\lambda - \nu t) \qquad \ldots (3.35)$$

Where ν is the frequency of the wave. Then, as the time t increases, the wave moves towards $+ve$ x direction with a speed $c = \lambda\nu$. A wave moving in opposite direction would be represented by

$$\psi = \sin 2\pi(x/\lambda + \nu t) \qquad \ldots (3.36)$$

However, this wave equation does not satisfy the boundary conditions $\psi = 0$ at $x = 0$ and $x = L$ except at special value of t.

In order to overcome this difficulty, let us consider an electron moving round and round a wire bent in a circular loop. If the circumference of the loop is $2L$ than

$$\lambda = 2L/n$$

where $n = 1, 2, 3, \ldots\ldots$etc. i.e. a whole number of wavelengths must fit round the circle. The energy of such an electron moving round a wire is given as:

$$E = \frac{h^2 k^2}{8m\pi^2} \qquad \dots (3.37)$$

where k is equal to $2\pi/\lambda$ and is known as wave number. Since λ is related with the velocity of the electron according to the equation (3.2), therefore the wave number k is a vector and shows the direction of propagation of the wave packet within the metal or crystal. The magnitude of the wave vector represents the wave length. In three dimensional box or in a crystal, the wave vector k can be resolved in three components parallel to x, y and z axes which are normal to each other.

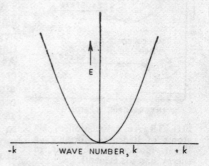

If energy E is plotted as a function of k, the curve so formed is a parabola. For free electrons, where $E = \frac{1}{2}mv^2$, this (E, k) curve is a parabola as shown in Fig. 3.8.

FIG. 3.8. The energy of an electron as a function of its wave number according to free electron theory.

3.6. BAND THEORY

In the free electron model it was assumed that all electrons are truely free to wander in a metal. By contrast band theory assumes that the electrons are bound to their respective nuclei. In an isolated atom the electron can have only certain allowed energy values and that they must occupy the states available in certain allowed energy levels in accordance with the Pauli's principle. However, when an electron is shared between two or more atoms, it is found that many more energy levels are full in the allowed category. The total energy range available in an aggregate of atoms is divided into ranges called the "allowed" and the "forbidden."

Now let us consider what happens when atoms are brought near each other. When the atoms are farther apart, each one has its own set of valence electrons with discrete energy states available to each. As the interatomic distance decreases, atoms start on interchanging their valence electrons with a view to fill up electrons states in accordance with Pauli's exclusion principle and therefore, the original energy leveles composed of orbitals (or quantum states) begin to split up. For instance, when two atoms of hydrogen combine to form a molecule, each atomic states splits up into two $1s$ quantum states for the two electrons. A typical example for a linear molecule of six hydrogen atoms is shown in Fig. 3.9. These two quantum states are capable of holding four electrons with two electrons per energy state. It implies that in general the combination of atoms to form molecules does not alter the total number of quantum states with a particular quantum number, irrespective of how large is the size of molecule.

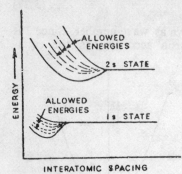

FIG. 3.9. An association of six atoms of hydrogen forming a linear molecule (The split of energy states is evident).

When the atoms come closure together, their outermost energy levels begin to overlap and start on splitting up into allowed energy states. As the interatomic distance is decreased further to an extent that the atoms have interpenetrated each other, then the inner energy level next to the outermost will also begin to overlap and split up. Suppose a molecule is composed of n identical atoms, each having two electrons per $1s$ states then there exists n such states. The energy of these states differ slightly and is computed to be of the order of 10^{-19} electron volt (eV). One electorn volt is equal to the work done in moving an electorn through a potential difference of one volt and is equal to 1.602×10^{-19} Joules. Thus, the energy levels in a crystal split-up into a quasi-continuous distribution of states which is usually called a quasi-continuous energy band or spectrum.

In case of metals, the equilibrium interatomic spacing may be such that besides the outermost energy levels, the inner levels are also overlapped and form several bands corresponding to a kind of quantum states (i.e. s, p, d, and f). A typical example for sodium is illustrated in Fig. 3.10, but in many material they do not overlap. The space between the bands are called forbidden energy gaps, since electrons in the solid do not possess these energy values. The overlapped region showing quasi-continuous band is commonly called the allowed energy or valence band.

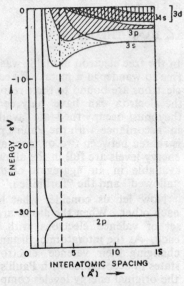

FIG. 3.10. Energy bands in sodium metal showing splitting of the s, p, and d orbitals.

Like free electron model, the electrons in these allowed energy bands start on filling from the lowest energy state and then gradually to some higher energy state at $0°K$. The energy of the highest filled state is called Fermi level or Fermi energy same as in free electron model. The value of E_F depends upon the number of electrons per unit volume of the solid i.e. the density of states. The density of states determines as to how many electrons must go into the bands. At $0°K$, all the states upto E_F are full and those above E_F are empty. At higher temperatures, the electrons just near to E_F can be excited to higher energy states or allowed states in the empty zone but the inner electrons will still remain in the filled zone because the excitation energy is not enough to cause their excitation to empty zone.

The valence electrons at or above E_F are in fact belonging to one of the quantum states (s, p, d, or f) in the crystal. A fermi level electron moving through the lattice is therefore, regarded as free electron. An electron moving with a given velocity is associated with its kinetic energy and the wave number k. Such an electron can freely move in the allowed energy states and its motion is restricted to these bands only because of the existence of the forbidden energy gaps between the allowed energy bands (Fig. 3.10).

3.7. BRILLOUIN ZONE THEORY

Unlike free electron model where it is assumed that all the electrons are free to move in the lattice, zone theory assumes that not all the valence electrons are freely moving and therefore, this theory is also known as nearly free electron theory.

In case of free electron theory we have seen that the wave number k is directly proportional to the momentum, mu. However, when an electron is moving in a periodic field where the atoms or more correctly the positive ions and are arranged in some regular order in the space, the wave number k is still defined by $k = 2\pi/\lambda$, but k is no longer necessarily be proportional to mv.

This complicates the theory. In order to simplify the matter, let us again consider a two dimensional square box rather than a crystal.

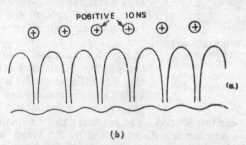

POSITIVE IONS

(a)

(b)

FIG. 3.11. Variation of periodic potential.

If we introduce electrons into the box and correspondingly the positive charges which are assumed to be arranged periodically, then the two dimensional box is equivalent to a two dimensional crystal. Then electrons will find themselves moving in a periodic field, which is the characteristic of the crystal structure concerned. Now let us consider a line passing through the centres of the atoms, the periodic potential varies as shown in Fig. 3.11(a). It is apparent from Fig. 3.11(a) that the potential energy of an electron tends to diminish as it approaches to a nucleus. If we consider any line passing through the nuclei the potential might vary as shown in Fig. 3.11(b).

If an electron is moving through the crystal having sufficient energy, then according to classical model of wave mechanics it can overcome the potential barrier and move freely through the crystal. But if the energy of the electron is not enough to carry it over the peaks, then the electron will be stuck up in the potential hollow, i.e. it behaves as a bound electron. On the other hand, wave mechanics shows that an electron possessing low energy has certain probability of penetrating the potential hill, depending on the width of the potential hill. This is because of the fact that in a periodic field of a crystal, the width of the hill is of the order of 3Å and this is of the same order as λ of the electrons. Thus, quantum mechanics allows a slow electron to penetrate the potential hill and causes free movement of the electrons. This effect is commonly known as *Tunnel effect*, because if the potential hill is very narrow, the electron has a probability, as if it were tunnelling through. Thus, according to quantum mechanics all the electrons have a certain probability of moving freely through the lattice.

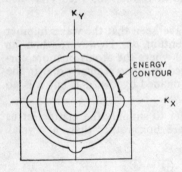

In a crystal, since all the valence electrons are nearly free to move, one can draw a wave number diagram in two dimension as illustrated in Fig. 3.12 for a hypothetical two dimensional crystal.

If the number of electrons are continuously introduced into the empty box, then at absolute zero, the assembly of N electrons will occupy $N/2$ energy states. The occupied states will lie within circles around the origin of the two dimensional wave number diagram (Fig. 3.12.) The diameter of the circles increases continuously as the number of electrons increases in the box. These circles are commonly called *energy contours* and they will no longer be circles after a certain limit

FIG. 3.12. Energy contours showing order of filling electrons in the two dimensional crystal box expressed in the form of wave number diagram.

of electrons were introduced. The reasons can be explained by considering a wave number in a direction OA on the wave number diagram (Fig. 3.13) which corresponds to a definite direction in the real crystal as shown in Fig. 3.14. Suppose $P_1, P_2, P_3, \ldots$ etc. are a set of atomic planes in the path of the wave number in the direction OA

that lies in the crystal. Then, in general, an electron state which is described by this wave number along *OA* which will pass through these planes with only slightly scattering. If the wavelength of the electron is

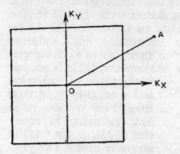

FIG. 3.13. Wave number diagram for a hypothetical two dimensional crystal.

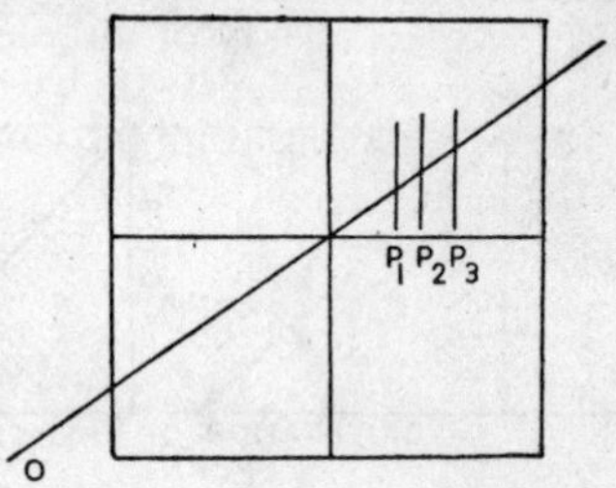

FIG. 3.14. Hypothetical two dimensional real crystal.

$$n\lambda = 2d \sin \theta \qquad \qquad ...(3.38)$$

such that Bragg's law condition is satisfied, then a strong reflection takes place from a set of atomic planes in a crystal. In the above equation, n is an integer, d is the lattice spacing (i.e. interplaner spacing). So Bragg's law shows the conditions under which an electron suffers reflection from a set of atomic planes in a crystal while moving through it. In general, this means that electrons are unable to possess those directions and energies that produce internal reflections. For better understanding the Bragg's law may be considered in more details.

According to De Broglie's relation

$$\lambda = \frac{h}{mv} = \frac{h}{P} \qquad \qquad ...(3.39)$$

Then by substituting the value of λ in equation (3.38).

$$\frac{nh}{P} = 2d \sin \theta$$

or
$$P = \frac{nh}{2d \sin \theta} \qquad \qquad ...(3.40)$$

This relation clearly shows that if an electron possesses a certain combination of direction of motion and magnitude of the momentum of the electron, then it suffers a Bragg reflection:

Since
$$k = 2\pi p/h,$$

$$k = \frac{n\pi}{d \sin \theta}$$

or
$$k \sin \theta = \frac{n\pi}{d} \qquad \qquad ...(3.41)$$

Here k is a vector, the direction of which is the same in which the electron is moving and its magnitude is proportional to the momentum of the electron. $k \sin \theta$ is obviously the vertical component of k and is normal to the reflecting planes, as illustrated in Fig. 3.15 for $n = 1$, i.e. for the Ist reflection. For different directions of k, if its vertical component is normal to the plane of reflection and is equal to $n\pi/d$, then Bragg's law will be satisfied. Referring to equation (3.41), $k \sin \theta$ varies inversely with d, i.e., electrons are first reflected from planes with largest possible d values (the planes of lowest indices). In case of cubic lattices, the Bragg condition is first satisfied for planes of the kind {100}. Next to these, are the planes {110} for which second order reflection may result, provided the direction and wavelength of an electron are in favour to fulfil the Bragg's law conditions.

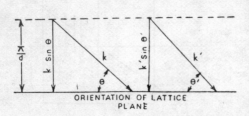

FIG. 3.15. The first Bragg reflection occurs when $k \sin \theta = \lambda/d = $ constant.

In a two dimensional crystal there are two planes of the kind {100} namely (100) vertical and (010) horizontal planes. The first order reflection occurs for these two planes by all the k vectors to the lines $A\,B\,C\,D$ shown in Fig. 3.16. Now imagine an arbitrary wave vector k' that runs from origin to the line AB in the two dimensional k space as shown in Fig. 3.16. It may be noted that AB represents the plane (010) and the vertically resolved component of the vector k' (it makes an angle with the horizontal plane (010) is normal to this plane and equals π/d. In other words, k' satisfies the Bragg's law condition for the plane (010) and this is true for all wave vectors that run from origin to the line AB and CD. In the same way k'' wave vector represents Bragg reflection from the planes (100) in either of the directions i.e. from the lines BC and AD. On the other hand k''' wave vector which does not extend to the boundary $ABCD$ does not show a Bragg reflection to occur and the electrons represented by

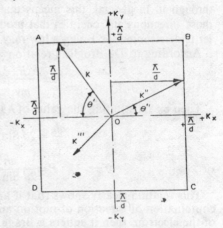

FIG. 3.16. The first Brillouin zone of a two dimensional simple cubic lattice.

this wave vector are freely mobile within the region *ABCD* without scattering. The area enclosed by the boundary *ABCD* is known as a *Brillouin zone*. Since, at the boundary, $n=1$, the zone is called first Brillouin zone. If reflection occurs from the planes {110} for which $n=2$, the zone formed between k_1 and k_2 for $n=1$ and $n=2$ is known as second Brillouin zone shown by the boundary *EFGH* in Fig. 3.17. The second zone itself is shown by the cross-hatched triangles. The sum of the areas of the four triangles is the same as that of the first Brillouin zone. Thus, for each direction of k there will be a series of critical points in the wave number diagram at which wavelength satisfies the Bragg's law condition for one of the sets of atomic planes in the lattice.

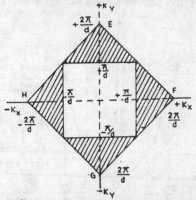

FIG. 3.17. The first and the second Brillouin zones of a simple cubic lattice (The second zone is cross-hatched).

It can also be shown that at each of these critical points there is sudden rise in energy i.e. electrons do not find themselves in that region of energy states which is commonly known as forbidden energy gap.

To illustrate this, let us consider electrons travelling in only one direction, say parallel to X-axis and therefore normal to (100) planes in a cubic crystal. The energy of such electrons in terms of k_x can be expressed as

$$E = \frac{h^2 k_x^2}{8\pi^2 m} \qquad \qquad ...(3.42)$$

This equation shows a parabolic relationship between the energy and the wave number k as shown in Fig. 3.8 and is based on the Sumerfield assumption that potential inside a metal is constant. But in a real crystal the potential is not constant but varies according to crystal structure. Nevertheless, a good approximation of the wave number—energy relationship over most of the energy range is found according to zone theory. However, in zone theory we have seen that for critical values of k corresponding to the integers n, for which electrons suffer Bragg reflection, disruptions are obtained in the energy vs. k diagram.

For electrons in a crystal, these values of k are analogous to the forbidden energies in the band structures as disscussed in the band theory. Hence, one would not find electrons with these energies. Instead of running waves, Bragg reflection then results in two sets of standing waves for the Bragg values of k with each different energy.

The difference between these energies is corresponding to forbidden energy gap as shown in Fig. 3.18. It can be seen from this Fig. that

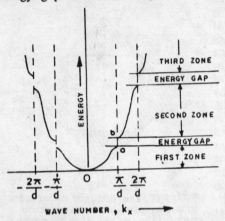

FIG. 3.18. The energy of an electron as a function of wave number according to zone theory.

as k approaches a critical value multiple of π/d, the (E, K) curve perturbs from its simple parabolic nature and energy increases relatively slowly with k in either directions. The curve runs parallel to k axis. At point a i.e. at the critical value k, there is a sharp rise in energy upto b, and a to b is the energy gap where the waves are standing. This means that the position of electrons does not vary with time or the momentum of electrons is zero as if they are bound electrons.

Free electrons considered here, are the valence electrons of the individual atoms whose original energy states (i.e. s, p, d, f) have broadened into a quasi-continuous spectrum. The core electrons are of course unaffected unless the atoms have interpenetrated each other to a considerable extent. These valence electrons are free to travel through the crystal. According to free electron model, all the valence electrons are freely moving through the crystal but as shown earlier, this motion is affected by the periodic field in a crystal which agrees with the zone model concepts. The strong diffraction effects are therefore, due to this periodic potential. Since in metals there are few valence electrons per individual atom, the size of the potential well (i.e. potential width) as shown in Fig. 3.11. is small and electrons with even small K.E. can penetrate this width and move freely. This width of the potential hollow or well is a measure of the width of the energy gap in the (E, K) curve, as illustrated in Figs. 3.19(a) and 3.19(b) for singly and multi-ionised atoms. In case of multi-ionised atoms (as in non-metals) the width of the potential well is large due to high positive charge on the ions. The width of the energy gap in the (E, K) curve for solids formed by multi-ionised atoms is therefore large. The corresponding energy gaps in the band structure of such solids are relatively wide (Fig. 3.19).

It may be observed from Fig. 3.19, that variation of k from zero to a shows the extention of first Brillouin zone boundary in the direction of k. As the direction of k changes, the position of the first energy gap changes in the (E, K) curve. The position of the energy gap is lowest when the k is minimum and the vector touches the centre of the first Brillouin zone and the gap is at highest at the corners of the Brillouin zone. The shape of the first and second

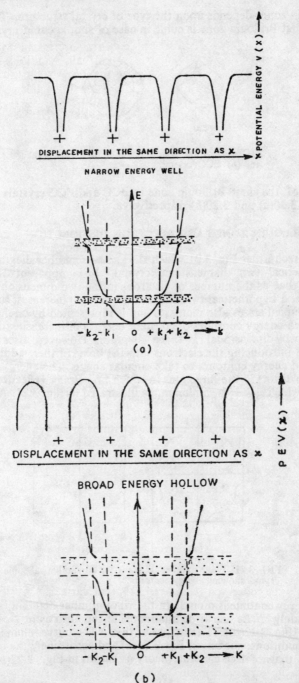

FIG. 3.19. (a) Effect of singly ion charged on the energy gap width.
(b) Effect of multi-ionic charge on the energy gap.

Brillouin zones depends upon the type of crystal structure. The shape of the first Brillouin zone is cubic in case of simple cubic crystal. The

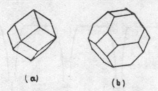

FIG. 3.20. First Brillouin zone in (a) FCC crystal and (b) BCC crystal.

shape of the first Brillouin zone in BCC and FCC crystals is shown in Fig. 3.20(a) and 3.20(b) respectively.

3.8. BRILLOUIN ZONES AND ELECTRON DISTRIBUTION

Let us reconsider Fig. 3.21 which shows wave number diagram for a hypothetical two diamensional crystal. It is apparent from this figure that as the number of electrons in the two dimensional square box (i.e. a hypothetical two dimensional crystal) increases, the energy of occupied states also increases and is represented by circles (or the so colled energy contours of constant energy) of increasing diameters in a two dimensional k space diagram. However, after a certain limit of introducing the electrons into the box, further addition will not lead energy contours to take circular shape. The energy contours tend to distort in the directions in which first Bragg reflection results i.e. in which $|k|$ is minimum, as illustrated in Fig. 3.21. As long as

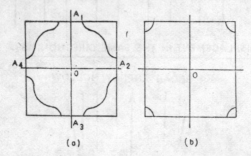

FIG. 3.21. Wave number diagram for a hypothetical cubic crystal showing energy contours.

the energy contour is a circle in the wave number diagram, the corresponding $N(E)$ curve is a parabola in the form as in free electron model [Fig. 3.22(a)]. The nature of the $N(E)$ curve changes under the conditions shown in Fig. 3.21(a) and accordingly the curve rises above that of free electron theory as shown in Fig. 3.22(b). In the

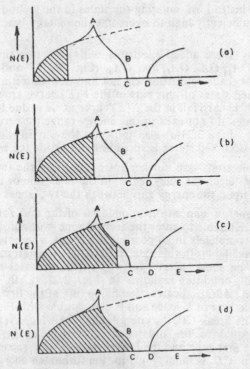

FIG. 3.22. Density of states curves according to zone theory.

three dimensional crystal, the circle is replaced by a sphere and this becomes gradually distorted as the allowed states approach the zone boundary and again the $N(E)$ curve rises above that of the free electron theory. In other words, the constant energy surfaces touch the zone boundary at right angles, as illustrated in Fig. 3.23 for copper (FCC). When this happens, the $N(E)$ curve shows a peak corresponding to just contact of the energy surfaces with the zone boundary. This is due to a sudden change in the shape of the sphere to some complicated form. If the electrons are further added to the two dimensional crystal box, then they will continuously fill up the

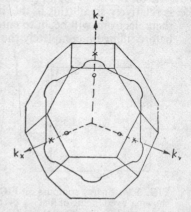

FIG. 3.23. The first Brillouin zone of copper showing constant energy surfaces in a three dimensional lattice.

first zone instead of entering the states in the second zone until the energy is sufficiently high to overcome the energy gap at the zone boundary.

Obviously these added electrons will not enter the states in the directions OA_1, OA_2, OA_3, and OA_4, (Fig. 3.21a) and so the $N(E)$ curve falls because electrons will not find new states in all directions. The occupied states of this part of the $N(E)$ curve are shown in Fig. 3.22(c). This sharp fall in the $N(E)$ curve at A is due to the fact that electron states do not exist in this energy range for certain directions in k space. Fig. 3.21(a) also indicates the way in which the energy contour of occupied states is spreading out inside the zone.

If the electrons are further introduced into the two dimensional lattice box, electrons may enter in the first zone or in second zone depending upon the energy gap between the two zones.

If the energy gap at the boundaries of the first zone is large, the electrons are unable to enter the second zone without filling up the first zone completely in all possible directions whereover the electron states are available. In this case $N(E)$ curve must fall to zero, because there will be some energies for which electron states are impossible. The resulting condition is shown in Fig. 3.22(d). In this diagram, the portion ABC indicates the filling up of the first zone states in certain directions of k space and is comparable with Figs. 3.21(a) and 3.21(b). The break CD, the energy range for which $N(E)$ is zero has a length equal to the difference between the energy of the highest state of the first zone and the lowest state of the second zone. This energy gap CD is analogous to the forbidden energy gap in band theory or in (E, K) curve according to zone theory.

If on the other hand, the energy gap at the surface of the first zone is relatively small (this is the characteristic of majority of metals), then electrons will begin to enter the lowest states in the second zone before filling up completely the highest states of the first zone. Thus,

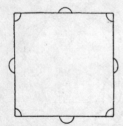

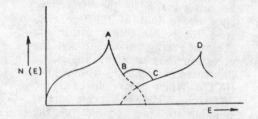

FIG. 3.24. Energy contours showing overlapping of first and second Brillouin zones.

FIG. 3.25. Density of states curve showing overlapping of first and second Brillouin zones [In the overlapped region, the $N(E)$ rises suddenly].

with the increasing number of electrons, the electrons will begin to enter the states of the second zone (Fig. 3.24) in certain directions and the total $N(E)$ curve is the sum of that for the first zone and that for the second zone. In other words we can say that the first and second zones (analogous to energy bands in the band theory) overlap and the opening up of the states in the second zone then produces a sudden rise in the $N(E)$ curve as illustrated in Fig. 3.25.

Then on introducing more and more electrons, the first zone becomes completely filled and the total $N(E)$ curve is that of the second zone alone. With the third and subsequent zones the same process of filling up of electrons (if available) is repeated.

3.9. THE EFFECT OF TEMPERATURE ON THE DISTRIBUTION OF ELECTRONS IN THE ENERGY STATES

Fig. 3.7 which represents the distribution of electrons in various energy states at $0°K$, may be examined for the distribution of electrons when the temperature is increased above $0°K$. In a solid, atoms vibrate about their mean equilibrium position even at absolute zero temperature and as the temperature increases above $0°k$, the amplitude of vibration of atoms also increases. The energy associated with these enhanced vibrations is taken by the electrons near to E_F and they may acquire thermal energy of the order of kT (where k is Boltzmann's constant, T is absolute temperature) and jump to higher energy state above E_F provided that state is not occupied. At room temperature, kT is of the order of 4×10^{-14} ergs which is very less compared to E_F ($E_F \simeq 9 \times 10^{-12}$ ergs for a typical metal, silver) and therefore, only few electrons that are near to E_F can take the states above E_F. The Distribution of electrons at any temperature T, may be assumed according to Fermi-Dirac statistical distribution as illustrated in Fig. 3.26. It can be seen from this figure that some electrons below E_F have transferred to unoccupied states above E_F. This statistical distribution occurs over the range kT above and below E_F. The E_F at any temperature can be defined as the energy of the state that has a 50 pct. probability of being occupied by an electron i.e. the Fermi energy corresponds to the energy where the actual $N(E)$ (line ab) has a value equal to half of the maximum as represented by the line ac in Fig. 3.26.

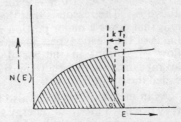

FIG. 3.26. Thermal energy at any temperature only slightly changes the distribution of the electrons in the energy states.

3.10. EXPLANATION OF SOME PHYSICAL PROPERTIES ON THE BASIS OF FREE ELECTRON BAND AND ZONE THEORIES

3.10.1. Electrical Conductivity

(i) **Free electron model of conductivity**. According to quantum free electron model, at any ordinary temperature electrons occupy certain allowed energy states following the Fermi-Dirac distribution. The position and momentum of each valence electron can be ascribed by a set of quantum numbers and hence a specific K.E. When no electric field is applied to a solid, electrons are assumed to move in all possible directions so that on an average an exactly equal number of electrons are moving in opposite directions as illustrated by their density distribution curve in Fig. 3.27(a) along positive x and negative x-directions. Since the electrons are moving with equal velocity v_x but in opposite directions, therefore, net flow of current through the solid is zero. On the application of an electric field, if electrons distribution is accelerated in a particular direction (Fig. 3.27b) so that a net current flows, then the solid is characterised as a metal. From Fig. 3.27(b) it may be noted that only those electrons moving with energies close to E_0 are actually capable of being accelerated in the positive x-direction.

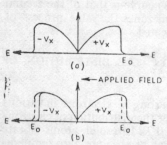

FIG. 3.27. (a) Equilibrium electron distribution curve when no field is applied. (b) A shift in the equilibrium occupied states shown in (a) by an external field.

The excess of electrons having velocity components in the $+x$ direction is then responsible for the electric current produced in the metal. Under electrified field, not all the electrons with energy close to E_0 can travel from $-x$ direction to $+x$ direction in the states above E_0. The reason is that they suffer collisions with the positive ions that cover a major portion in the solid. The collision or scattering is of the elastic type. Thus, electrons encounter a resistance to flow of current in the metal which is inversely proportional to the average distance that they can travel between consecutive collisions, called the mean free path.

As in metals, in insultors also the electrons are free to move but they occupy a group of energy state, the electronic motion of which does not produce a resultant flow in any direction because the applied electric field does not allow electrons to transfer from this group to the new states. In case of metals, on the other hand, the occupied states are accompanied by the other allowed states into which the electrons can be excited even under a low strength field.

According to free electron theory, as the number of valence elelctrons per atom in metals increases, the electrical conductivity should increase since electrons are the charge carrier. Accordingly, metals like Au, Ag, and Cu should have lower conductivity than metals like Al. However, the observed electrical conductivity of Cu and Ag is more than that of Al. This can best be explained from zone theory.

(ii) **Band theory of conductivity.** According to band theory if N number of atoms associate to form a crystal, then each valence state splits up into N states. Thus, an s state with a capacity of holding two electrons with opposite spins, form s band with a holding capacity of $2N$ electrons. A p state of an isolated atom becomes a p band in the crystal with a room of $6N$ electrons and similarly for d and f states. The lowest energy band which is partially filled with electrons is called the conduction band. Electrons in the conduction band of a conductor are generally free to move if they are close to E_F. The band containing the valence electrons is called the valence band. In case of conductors, the valence band is also called the conduction band, since it remains usually partially filled. For example, in Cu, the 4s band is partially filled and the Fermi level lies within the band. This band can be regarded both as valence and as conduction band. In some metals, the valence band is completely full but overlaps with the higher empty (or conduction) band. In these metals, electrons near E_F are still free to move and can be excited to conduction band to conduct electricity. On the other hand, in case of insulators the valence band is completely full and is separated considerably with the conduction band so that electrons can not jump from valence to conduction band under the application of ordinary electric field.

(iii) **Zone theory of conductivity.** Unlike quantum free electron theory, zone theory states that as the number of valence electrons per atom is increased in some metals, does not mean that electrical conductivity increases accordingly. According to zone model, electrical conductivity of a metal depends upon the partially filled Brillouin zone, overlapping of one full zone with the empty zone and the energy gap between the full and empty zones.

In general, metals have overlapping zones and the number of valence electrons per atom must be such that the zone concerned with conductivity (i.e. the conduction zone/band) has plenty of unoccupied allowed states. Fig. 3.28(a), for example, shows the general position in a monovalent metal. Since, there is one valence electron per atom, the first zone is only half filled at $0°K$ and there are plenty of empty states above E_F into which electrons can pass under the influence of an electric field. Fig. 3.28(b) shows density of states curve for a divalent metal in accordance with zone theory. In a divalent metal, there are

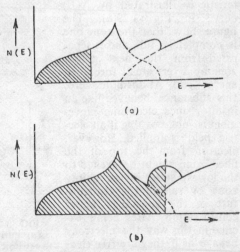

FIG. 3.28. Distribution of electrons in (a) monovalent metals and (b) divalent metals.

two electrons per atom and therefore the first zone is full. Since first zone overlaps with the second, few electrons of the first zone fill up some of the lowest states in the second zone. Thus, some of the upper most states of the first zone and many of the states of the second zone are empty into which electrons can go under the influence of an electric field. With trivalent metal having three valency electrons per atom, all the states of the first zone would be occupied and would account for two electrons per atom. The exact position of the overlap would then determine whether the remaining electrons were all in the second zone or whether some were in the second and some in the third zone.

In general, the conditions favourable for a good conductor are summarised as below:

(a) Conductivity depends upon the width of the conduction band.

(b) Partially filled s band, as for example in Ag and Cu, because s electrons are highly mobile and the band is wide.

(c) Next to s is the p band which has enough width for the mobility of electrons. A partially filled p band is also, therefore favourable to conductivity. A typical example of such metal in which p band is partially filled and s is fully filled at $0^{c}K$, is aluminium. The electronic configuration is given as $1s^{2}2s^{2}2p^{6}3s^{2}3p^{1}$.

(d) If there is overlapping of bands (or Brillouin zones) in metals, they can also conduct electricity, for example, magnesium and zinc.

3.10.2. Semicondutors

Zone and band theories can best explain semiconduction in some materials. Let us consider a substance whose zone characteristic is illustrated by $N(E)$ curve in Fig. 3.29(a). The figure shows that the zone one is completely full and is separated from the next empty zone by a very small forbidden energy gap. At absolute zero, this substance behaves like an insultor since electronic movement is not possible if an electric field is applied. However, electrons from the top of the filled zone might be excited to the lowest states in the empty zone by raising the temperature of the substance under consideration After being excited in this way the electrons behave as if they are free elec-

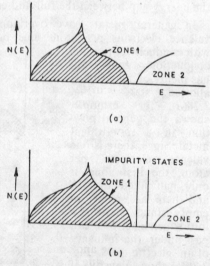

FIG 3 29. Zone characteristic of (a) intrinsic semiconductor and (b) extrinsic semiconductor.

trons with all states of the second zone at their disposal. The notable point here is that it is the thermal excitation and not the action of the electrical field which causes the electronic movement to higher unoccupied states as in metals. The substances in which the 1st filled zone is sparated from the second empty (conduction) zone by a small energy gap and electrical conduction is possible by thermal activation, are known as semiconductors. Pure graphite, for example, is a semiconductor of this kind. A substance like pure graphite, silicon or germanium may be called an intrinsic semiconductor, but there is now an increasing evidence that most semiconductors, owe their properties due to the presence of impurities in them. In such substances, the filled zone is separated by a small energy gap from the next that in turn gets bridged by the energy states of the impurity atoms introduced, as illustrated in Fig. 3.29(b). When the temperature of these substances is raised, one or both of the two processes may occur.

On the one hand, electrons can be thermally excited from the impurity states to the second zone where they are free to act as conduction electrons. These excited electrons will be in the states at the bottom of the second zone and therefore posses most of the features of the ordinary free electrons. The substances in which this process operates are silicon or germanium introduced with impurities like P, As, Sb or Bi that have five valence electrons. When such impurities are introduced in the lattice of Si or Ge, then each impurity atom will contribute one more electron than is needed to form the four covalent bonds per atom in the solid. This extra electron occupies the state well above the valence band but underneath the conduction band. The position of such state at 0°K is shown in Fig. 3.30(a) where it is indicated by donor state. At room temperature, the excitation energy is quite enough to excite the extra electrons from the donor states to conduction band. In the conduction band these excited electrons

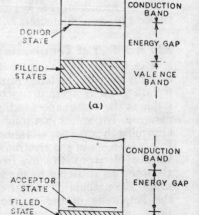

FIG. 3.30. Energy band for (a) n-type semiconductor, and (b) p-type semiconductor.

are free to move and conduct electricity. A semiconductor in which current flow is due to the movement of electrons from donor states to conduction band is known as n-type semiconductor.

On the other hand, electrons may be excited from states at the top of the filled zone into the impurity states. This will leave a few unoccupied states (i e. holes) at the top of the valence zone and as a consequence when an electric field is applied, electronic redistribution leads to electrical conductance in the substance. This type of process occurs in semiconductors, Si or Ge when they are associated with impurities such as Al, B, Ga, In etc. These impurity atoms have three valence electrons per atom in contrast to four in Si or Ge in order to form covalent bonds. As a result, one covalent bond of the solid must have only a single valence electron. Thus, according to zone concept, there remains one state unoccupied lying just above the filled or valence band. The position of this energy state that is usually called the acceptor state with respect to the valence band is represented in Fig. 3.30(b) at absolute zero. At room temperature electronic redistribution takes place according to Fermi-Dirac statistics and few electrons from the top of the valence band are excited to accepter states of the impurity atoms. When this happens, a hole is left behind in the valence band. As the electrons move from valence to conduction band, holes (or the +ve ions) move in the reverse direction and conduct electric current. A semiconductor in which electrical conductivity arises due to the movement of holes in the valence band is called a p-type semiconductor.

The semiconductors associated with impurities are called the extrinsic type semiconductors.

3.10.3. Effect of Temperature on the Conductivity of Metals

It is interesting to note that whereas in intrinsic type semiconductors, an increase in temperature improves conduction, in case of metals, as the temperature increases, the conductivity decreases. This is due to the disturbances in the lattice that occur by raising the temperature. The atoms in a solid vibrates about their mean positions by absorbing heat. The vibrating field of the lattice interacts with the free movement of the electrons in metals and thus preventing the valence electrons to move freely and hence to conduct current. The electrons get scattered by the vibrating field of the atoms into a new state. The probability of scattering is proportional to the square of the amplitude of the atomic vibrations and hence directly proportional to the absolute temperature. Thus, as the temperature of a metal increases above 0°K, the electron scattering also increases that raises the electrical resistivity.

Lattice disturbances may also result in the presence of impurity atoms or defects like dislocations, grain boundaries, etc.

3.10.4. Thermal Conductivity of Metals

In a solid, atoms vibrate about their equilibrium position at ordinary temperature. The amplitude of vibrations decreases to minimum at absolute zero of temperature where the atoms are usually regarded to be at rest. The internal energy in most of the solids arises due to these vibrating atoms only. When a solid absorbs thermal energy, its atoms displace from their mean position and again come to original position on release of thermal energy. Thus, the vibration of atoms brings about elastic distortion in the lattice and therefore, the waves associated with the vibrations are the elastic waves of varying frequencies. At certain places the elastic waves superimpose whereas at other places they interfere. The waves superimpose to form a wave packet or the so called a quantum that moves through the solid. A quantum of energy is known as a phonon. The energy associated with a quantum is given as:

$$E = h\nu \qquad\qquad \ldots (3.43)$$

Where ν is the frequency of vibrations and h is the Planck's constant. The increasing number of vibrations of atoms with temperature are represented by increasing number of phonons passing through the crystal. The thermal conductivity of a solid is proportional to its specific heat and to the mean free path of the particles (i.e. phonons and electron wave packets). The mean free path of phonon is of the order of 10 to 100 A° showing that they undergo more number of collisions. On the other hand, the mean free path of valence electrons is very large and therefore, they undergo less number of collisions. Since in metals, the free electrons are sufficiently mobile (as discussed under secion 3.10.1), they conduct heat together with phonons. Hence, metals have shown high thermal conductivity due to the movement of electrons as well as phonons, whereas in insulators (i.e. ionic and covalent solids) phonons are the only particles to conduct heat as the valence electrons are not as mobile in them as in metals. Phonons, though move at a speed of the order of that of sound, but they collide much more with each other due to poor mean free path. Therefore, ionic and covalent solids are poor conductors of heat. For metals at room temperature, good thermal conductivity is always accompanied by good electrical conductivity because the main mode of heat transfer is by electronic motion. Wiedemann-Franz, theoretically predicted that the ratio of thermal to electrical conductivity in metals is equal to a constant times the absolute temperature and that this proportionality constant is the same for all pure metals. In case of alloys, electrons remain scattered due to the presence of impurity elements and therefore, thermal conductivity is reduced.

3.10.5. Ferromagnetism

In chapter 1, it has been discussed that a spin quantum electron $m_s = +\frac{1}{2}$ or $-\frac{1}{2}$ is associated with a magnetic moment. As a consequence the spin electron behaves as a permanent magnet. The value of the magnetic moment due to spin $=\frac{1}{2}$ is equal to one Bohr magneton. According to Pauli's principle, electrons, having their spins pointing in the same direction are not possible at the same place due to electrostatic repulsion between them. The two electrons can be at the same place if they are spinning in opposite directions. In order to reduce the electron-electron repulsive energy, the electrons tend to align themselves parallel in the p, d and f states and when the shell is half filled, the second half starts on filling with the antiparallel arrangement. This is an accordance with the Hund's rule stated in chapter 1. However, parallel spins correspond to the existence of a resultant magnetisation in the absence of an external field. At the same time, it should be remembered that if all the spins are parallel, the electrons must have a higher mean kinetic energy than if they are paired off into antiparallel pairs. This is because in the latter case there are two electrons for each kinetic energy. On the other hand, if exchange interaction between electrons is involved, then a negative change in energy results. A metal will be a ferromagnetic if the exchange energy is more than the kinetic energy accompanied with the parallel spin alignment. This condition is possible if the energy bands are narrow where the kinetic energy change involved in the exchange interaction is not appreciable.

In a crystal, the atoms are so close together that their outer orbitals and in many cases the inner ones overlap and split up into energy, bands. The broadening of bands depend upon the interatomic distances. Usually the outer states broaden much more but the inner states broaden do not appreciably and are therefore narrow. In the narrow bands parallel alignment of spins is favourable. Thus, the ferromagnetic materials are those with partially filled inner shells The metals showing this characteristic, belong to transition series of the fourth row of the periodic table, namely, iron, nickel and cobalt. One metal gadolinium also belongs to transition group of rare earth metals. Iron, cobalt and nickel have their $3d$ orbitals partially filled, whereas it is the $4f$ state in the gadolinium which is partially filled. Zener suggested that spin exchange interaction occurs in ferromagnetic materials due to overlapping of d (or f in Gd) and s bands.

On the atomic scale, the ferromagnetism can better be explained with the help of an electronic structure of the atoms of Fe, Co and Ni. Each atom of iron, cobalt and nickel consists of two $4s$ electrons and a partially filled $3d$ shell. In their ground states, the filling of electrons in $3d$ and $4s$ states of these metals are represented diagramatically as follows:

$$\text{Fe } 3d^6 \quad \boxed{\uparrow \downarrow \mid \uparrow \mid \uparrow \mid \uparrow \mid \uparrow} \quad 4s^2 \boxed{\uparrow \downarrow}$$

$$\text{Co } 3d^7 \quad \boxed{\uparrow \downarrow \mid \uparrow \mid \downarrow \mid \uparrow \mid \uparrow \mid \uparrow} \quad 4s^2 \boxed{\uparrow \downarrow}$$

$$\text{Ni } 3d^8 \quad \boxed{\uparrow \downarrow \mid \uparrow \mid \downarrow \mid \uparrow \mid \downarrow \mid \uparrow \mid \uparrow} \quad 4s^2 \boxed{\uparrow \downarrow}$$

According to the above electronic structure, the atomic moments of these metals should respectively be 4, 3, and 2 Bohr magnetons. However, in the solid form, the observed values of Bohr magnetons for these metals are different from those on the atomic scale. The observed Bohr magnetons are 2.2, 1.7 and 0.61 respectively for Fe, Co and Ni. This deviation in Bohr magnetons in the crystals can be understood by considering zone or band theory. Let us consider the density of states curve for nickel metal. Fig. 3.31 shows the overlapping of 's' and 'd' zones in the nickel metal. Nickel is strongly paramagnetic metal and becomes ferromagnetic below a certain critical temperature. The saturation magnetic moment 0.6 Bohr magneton in the ferromagnetic state arises because of the spill over of a fraction of electrons from the +spin zone to the —spin zone creating holes in the +spin band. This spill over of electrons gives rise to imbalance of +ve and —ve spins. The term 'fraction of electrons' used here is misnomer. In fact, the electrons are hopping in the two halves of the over-lapped orbitals and most of the time they spend in the negative half

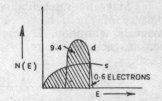

FIG. 3 31. Density of states curve for nickel metal showing overlapping of 3d and 4s zones.

of the overlapped zone. Thus, a resultant magnetic moment pointing in one direction is obtained which is responsible for ferromagnetism in nickel. The transition from paramagnetic to ferromagnetic state of nickel is illustrated by $N(E)$ curves in Fig. 3.32.

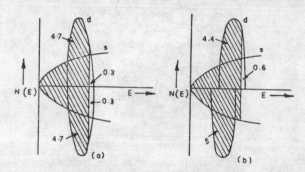

FIG. 3.32. Schematic representation of (a) paramagnetic nickel and (b) ferromagnetic nickel.

The relative occupation of the two zones (i.e. d and s) is determined by the Fermi energy E_F by assuming that on the average, 9.4 electrons of the 10 available 3d states per atom and 0.6 electrons of the 2 available 4s states are occupied [Fig. 3.32(b)]. Of these, 5 must be of the same kind of spin and 4.4 of the other leaving an excess of 0.6 unpaired spins per atom.

Thus in the ferromagnetic materials, the atomic moments are all parallel as shown Fig 3.33(a).

The summarised conditions for ferromagnetism to occur in metals are as follows:

(a) Overlapping of s and d bands (or zones);

(b) Narrow d band;

(c) Partially filled d band;

(d) The mobile s electrons will be scattered back into the unfilled energy states in the d band, therefore, the mobility of s electrons is reduced. Hence the resistance of transition metals is high;

(e) Magnetic susceptibility is directly related with the spin imbalance of the d band. More is the spin imbalance, more is the magnetic saturation. Therefore, the elements like Fe, Co and Ni are ferromagnetic in nature.

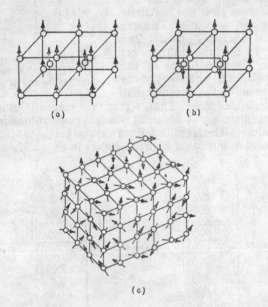

(a)   (b)

(c)

FIG. 3.33. Atomic magnetic moments in a (a) ferromagnetic material, such as iron, (b) antiferromagnetic (i.e. diamagnetic) material such as Cr, and (c) paramagnetic material.

Diamagnetism. Materials in which the magnetic moments are on alternative atom points in opposite directions, are known as diamagnetic materials (Fig. 3.33b). The property is commonly referred to as diamagnetism of the material.

Paramagnetism. In the paramagnetic materials, the directions of atomic moments is random (Fig. 3.33c). If an external field is applied, small degree of alignmets occurs, but this disappears when the field s removed.

QUESTIONS

1. How does quantum mechanics differ from classical mechanics?
2. Derive Schrödinger wave equation.
3. Differentiate between the free electron theory and Brillouin zone theory.
4. What do you mean by "density of states curve"?

5. Explain why :

(a) Elements like Ag, Cu, Au, and Al are very good conductors of electricity and have the same crystal structure (FCC). But their electrical conductivities differ to a considerable extent.

(b) Electrical conductivity of a conductor decreases whereas that of a semi-conductor increases if the temperature is raised.

(c) The calculated value of electrical resistivity of Cu is 16.1×10^7 ohm^{-1} m^{-1} in accordance with the free electron theory whereas the observed value for the same is 5.9×10^7 Ohm^{-1}—m^{-1}.

6. Explain the difference between a conductor and an insulator.

7. Differentiate between extrinsic and intrinsic semiconductors.

8. What are the generalised conditions favourable for a good conductor?

9. What are the conditions for ferromagnetism to occur in metals?

10. Differentiate between ferromagnetism, paramagnetism, and diamagnetism.

4

DEFORMATION OF METALS

4.1. ELASTIC DEFORMATION OF MATERIALS

It has been discussed in Chapter 2, that when a material deforms elastically, the strain is proportional to the stress applied in accordance with Hook's law. The ratio of stress to strain under elastic limit is known as modulus of elasticity (or simply Young's modulus). Young's modulus is a characteristic of a material concerned. Brittle materials, such as cast iron, glass, etc. behave elastically under tensile stress until fracture occurs since they do not show any plasticity like ductile materials. However, elastomeric materials such as rubber have shown a very large elastic strain under tension but Hook's law is not applicable for it.

The magnitude of Young's modulus depends upon the interatomic (or intermolecular) force of attraction and repulsion. Higher the interatomic (or intermolecular) bond strength in a solid, higher is its modulus of elasticity. Materials with three dimensional network of primary bonds exhibit a very large value of modulus of elasticity. For instance, carbon with a three dimensional network of covalent bonds is characterised for high value of Young's modulus, i.e., 1140 GNM^{-2} (1140 × 10³ MPa). In general, modulus of elasticity is an anisotropic property for a crystal. In a crystal, its value varies with crystal direction because the bond length and hence, the bond strength is different in different crystal directions. For example, graphite which has a two dimensional structure, the value of Young's modulus for it is 950 GNM^{-2} (950 × 10³ MPa) in a direction parallel to the sheets whereas the value averaged over all directions is considerably smaller than this. This average value is .8GMN^{-2} (8 × 10³ MPa).

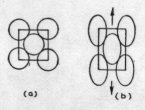

Any elongation or compression of a crystal in one direction due to an axial force results in a corresponding change in dimensions at right angles to the force. For example, Fig. 4.1a shows an unstrained crystal and in Fig. 4.1b a small contraction is indicated at right angles to

FIG. 4.1. (a) Unstrained crystal and (b) strained crystal.

the tensile force. The negative ratio between the lateral strain

ε_w (or ε_h) and the direct tensile strain ε is commonly called Poisson's ratio 'μ' as discussed in the section 2.1.

The elastic deformation of a body does not always result in a lengthwise change of a linear element in a body, but it may also result in a change in the initial angle between any two lines. For example, Fig. 4.2 illustrates a decrease in angle A from 90° by a small amount α when a pure shear stress is applied to the cubic face. The angular change in a right angle is known as *shear strain* 'γ' and is expressed as the displacement 'a' divided by the distance between the planes l. In other words, application of a shear stress results in a displacement of one plane of atoms with respect to the adjacent plane of atoms. The ratio a/l is also a tangent of the shear

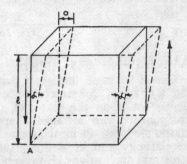

FIG. 4.2. Schematic representation of shear strain.

angle α through which the element has been rotated (as can be seen from the geometry of Fig. 4.2). Thus, shear strain 'γ' is expressed mathematically as:

$$\gamma = a/l = \tan \alpha \qquad \ldots (4.1)$$

For a small shear angle α, $\tan \alpha = \alpha$

Therefore, $\qquad \gamma = \alpha \qquad \ldots (4.2)$

Thus, shear strains can also be expressed as the angle of rotation.

The shear modulus G of a material is, defined as the ratio of shear stress τ to the shear strain γ,

i.e. $\qquad G = \dfrac{\tau}{\gamma} \qquad \ldots (4.3)$

The term shear modulus is also called the modulus of rigidity and is different from modulus of elasticity (E). The two are related according to the following relation:

$$G = \dfrac{E}{2(1+\mu)} \qquad \ldots (4.4)$$

Since, Poisson's ratio, in general, varies between 0.25 and 0.5, the value of G is approximately 35 pct. of E.

i.e. $\qquad G = 0.35\, E \qquad \ldots (4.5)$

A third elastic modulus, the bulk modulus K, is also observed in materials and is defined as the reciprocal of the compressibility, β of the material.

i.e. $\qquad K = \dfrac{1}{\beta} \qquad \ldots (4.6)$

or $$K = \frac{\sigma_h}{\Delta V/V} = \frac{V\sigma_h}{\Delta V} \qquad \ldots (4.7)$$

where σh is the hydrostatic pressure and $\Delta V/V$ is the volume compression.

The bulk modulus in terms of elastic modulus is expressed as:

$$K = \frac{E}{3(1+2\mu)} \qquad \ldots (4.8)$$

4.1.1. Significance of Modulus

One of the most important parameter to be considered for designing a material for structural component is the stiffness. Stiffness is dependent upon the shape of the structural component. For the components with identical shapes, stiffness is proportional to the elastic modulus. Elements, such as diamond has very high modulus of elasticity and at a first glance it seems to be most suitable for structural applications. However, owing to the non-availability, high cost and brittleness, it is not suitable for structural parts. A majority of elements with covalent bonding and high elastic modulus are brittle. Brittle materials are unable to withstand mechanical vibrations during service and result in a catastrophic failure. Hence, they are not suitable for structural purposes inspite of their suitability with regard to high modulus.

On the other hand, ductile materials, such as metals, can withstand sudden loading or mechanical shock during service without being failing catastrophically. However, their modulus is not very high but they may have moderately high modulus. Elements belonging to first series of transition elements have modulus of the order of 200 GNM^{-2} whereas some of the elements of second and third series of transition elements have still higher modulus. Since, structural components require a high modulus coupled with lightness, the elements of the second and third series of transition group are not suitable for structural applications owing to their higher densities. The modulus of light elements such as Al, Ti, Zr, etc. can be improved further by incorporating in them the solute with higher modulus such as B, C, etc.

Besides elements, some of the ionic solids such as MgO, Al_2O_3 TiC, SiC, etc. also possess high modulus owing to primary bonding. These materials are hard and brittle and are therefore, suitable for incorporating in ductile metals.

A material of multicomponents, in which at least one of the components supports the load and prevents catastrophic failure while the other components provide stiffness, is known as a composite material. The second phase in a composite material is usually hard, stiff, and brittle and therefore, supported in a parent soft matrix.

Optimum properties of a composite material can be secured by controlling a balanced proportion of the components and the size, shape and distribution of second phase in the parent phase. The second phase is usually present in the form of fibres, though particles embedded in the matrix of soft metal have also been used.

The Young's modulus of a composite in a direction parallel to the fibres is expressed as a linear function of the modulus of fibres and that of matrix.

i.e. $$Y_c = Y_f V_f + V_m Y_m \qquad \ldots (4.9)$$

where Y_c, Y_m, and Y_f are the Young's moduli of composite, metal matrix, and the fibres respectively. V_f and V_m are the volume fractions of the fibres and matrix respectively. For example, the Young's modulus of a composite of $Al - B$, in which B is 40 pct. in the matrix of Al.

$$Y_{Al-B} = Y_B V_B + V_{Al} Y_{Al}$$
$$Y_{Al-B} = Y_B (0.40) + (0.60) Y_{Al}$$
$$Y_{Al} = 71 \text{ GNM}^{-2}$$
$$Y_B = 440 \text{ GNM}^{-2}$$

then
$$Y_{Al-B} = 0.40 \times 440 + 0.60 \times 71$$
$$= 176 + 42.6$$
$$Y_{Al-B} = 218.6 \simeq 219 \text{ GNM}^{-2}$$

Hence, with 40 volume per cent of B in the Al matrix, the Young's modulus of Al is increased from 71 GNM^{-2} to 219 GNM^{-2} for the composite.

The Young's modulus of steel is 210 GNM^{-2} and steel is about three times heavier than $Al - B$ composite containing 40 volume pct. of Boron. There is a limiting value of volume fraction of fibres to be incorporated in a parent metal beyond which it is not possible to keep fibres separate from each other. Another typical example of a composite is silica glass fibres embedded in an epoxy resin matrix.

Like ductile metals, polymers are also highly plastic but owing to their very poor modulus, are not suitable for structural components. In polymers, the chains are bonded together by Vander Waal's forces or hydrogen bonding.

4.2. PLASTIC DEFORMATION OF METALS

4.2.1. Deformation of a Single Crystal

Plastic deformation of a single crystal may occur by two modes, i.e., slip or twinning. The most common deformation occurs by slip. Whether the crystal is subjected to tensile or compressive stress, both slip and twinning occur by pure shearing stresses.

Slip is a process of displacement of one part of a crystal with respect to another. Slip occurs most readily along certain crystallographic planes and in certain crystallographic directions. These specific crystallographic planes are called the slip or glide planes and the specific directions are the slip directions.

Generally the slip planes are the planes of greatest atomic packing and are the most widely spaced planes in the crystal. Similarly, slip direction is the direction in which the atoms are most closely packed and is within the slip plane. With this statement, one might expect the close packed rows of atoms could slide past each other with ease without coming apart, since the atoms are not bonded directly together but are merely held together by free electron gas (i.e. due to metallic bonding). If close packed rows will not offer resistance to sliding with respect to one another, then the material would have no rigidity at all. However, a solid has got some rigidity and its modulus of rigidity is a measure of the amount of shearing force required to gain a given amount of deformation. This can be explained with the help of Fig. 4.3, which shows two situations of sliding planes of

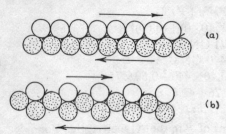

atoms. In case (a) the atoms in each row are closely packed horizontally whereas in case (b) the atoms in each row are rarely (less closely) packed. On comparison between the two, it is clear that for a given amount of deformation (lateral displacement of the top row) less shear force is required in (a) than in (b). This is because in case (b) the cavities between the atoms of the rows

FIG. 4.3. Deformation of a single crystal: (a) Atoms in each row are closely packed and (b) Atoms in each row are rarely packed.

are more deeper than in (a). Therefore, more climb and hence more distortion of the atom's electron cloud in practice is needed for atoms of one row in the cavities of the row below it. In other words, the modulus of rigidity is lower for shear along close-packed planes.

The slip plane together with slip direction constitutes a slip system. In metals with HCP crystal structure, there is only one plane of highest atomic density, i.e., the basal plane (0001). The diagonal axes $<11\bar{2}0>$ are the three closest pack directions. The slip systems for metals Zn, Cd, Co and Mg are (0001) $<11\bar{2}0>$. Since the number of operative slip systems is less for HCP crystals, they exhibit relatively less ductility. The ductility of polycrystalline HCP metals is negligible unless other less common slip systems operate or twinning occurs Due to limited number of slip systems, the ductility in HCP single crystals is highly dependent on orientation.

In FCC crystal structure, the {111} octahedral planes and the $<110>$ directions constitute close packed (or slip) systems. There are four slip planes of the kind {111} each containing three slip directions $<110>$. Thus, there are 12 possible slip systems in FCC crystals as in Cu, Au, Ag, Ni, etc. and, therefore, these are highly ductile metals.

Unlike FCC and HCP crystals, BCC crystal is not a close pack structure and therefore, there is no one plane of predominate atomic packing, as (111) in FCC structure or (0001) in HCP structure. However, the direction <111> in BCC structure is just as close pack as <110> in FCC or <11$\bar{2}$0> in HCP crystals. The possible slip planes in BCC crystals are of the kind {110}, {123} and {211}, among these the most common being the {110}. There are 12 slip systems of the kind {110} <111>, 12 of the kind {211} <111>, and 24 of the kind {123} <111>. Thus there are in total 48 possible slip systems but due to lack of close pack plane, BCC metals do not exhibit as much ductility as those with FCC crystals.

4.2.2. Critical Resolved Shear Stress

Since most of the metals are appreciably weaker under shear stress compared to tension or compression and also that tensile and compressive stresses can be resolved into shear components, deformation occurs due to shear. The shear stress required to initiate slip depends upon the orientation of the applied stress with respect to the slip plane and slip direction. Suppose a tensile force F is applied to a single crystal of cross-sectional area A as illustrated in Fig. 4.4. The axial stress (σ) is given as

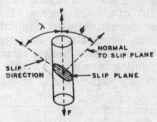

FIG. 4.4. Determination of critical resolved shear stress.

$$\sigma = \frac{F}{A} \qquad \qquad \dots (4.10)$$

Let ϕ be the angle between the tensile axis and the slip plane normal, whereas λ is the angle between the slip direction and the tensile axis. Then the component of the tensile force resolved along the slip direction is $F \cos \lambda$. This shear force is acting on the slip plane, the area (A_s) of which is given as:

$$A_s \cos \phi = A$$

or $$A_s = A/\cos \phi \qquad \qquad \dots (4.11)$$

The sheer stress acting on the slip plane and resolved in the slip direction is expressed as

$$\tau = \frac{F \cos \lambda}{A/\cos \phi} \qquad \qquad \dots (4.12)$$

or $$\tau = \frac{F}{A} \cos \lambda \cos \phi$$

or $$\tau = \sigma \cos \lambda \cos \phi \qquad \qquad \dots (4.13)$$

The equation 4.13 is also known as Schmid's law. The stress required to initiate plastic deformation in a pure and perfect single crystal is known as the *Critical Resolved Shear Stress* (CRSS). Obviously, a shear stress does not exist if either the angle λ or the angle ϕ be 90°, i.e., either the slip plane or the slip direction is perpendicular or parallel to the tensile axis. The critical resolved sheat stress will be maximum when $\lambda = \phi = 45°$.

i.e.
$$\tau_{max} = \frac{\sigma}{2} \qquad \qquad ...(4.14)$$

Slip occurs only when the applied stress exceeds CRSS. The CRSS increases with decrease of λ or ϕ. More is the CRSS for a material, stronger it is.

4.2.3. The Shear Strength of Ideal and Real Crystals

In a perfect crystal all the atoms in their equilibrium positions possess the minimum energy. Internal energy of the crystal r.ses if these atoms are even slightly displaced from their mean position with the aid of external energy. The external energy may be thermal energy or mechanical work. Initially the shear stress is zero and it is also zero when atoms in a row are displaced from their original equilibrium position to next minimum energy position. In between these limiting positions both shear stress as well as potential energy of the system vary. Fig. 4.5 illustrates the stress-potential energy diagrams

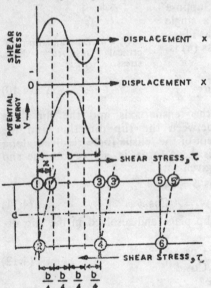

as a function of displacement of atoms from original equilibrium (corresponding to minimum energy) position. When a shear stress (τ) is applied on a plane within a crystal, it causes a displacement 'x' of atoms about their original mean positions (Fig. 4.5). If the displacement is small, the strain produced is elastic because on the release of stress, the atoms restore the energy by returning to their original positions. Initially as the displacement increases, the potential energy rises and the shear stress increases rapidly. When the atoms are displaced quarterway the interatomic spacing b, the shear stress is at maximum and it decreases to zero when the atoms are displaced to

FIG. 4.5. Variation of shear stress and potential energy as a function of displacement.

midway (i.e. $b/2$) between the atoms below. For example, atom 1 is now displaced midway between atoms 2 and 4. At this point the potential energy is maximum and the atom 1 is in metastable equilibrium state with respect to the two atoms. At this point, atom 1 has equal tendency to take itself either over atom 4 or over its original neighbour atom 2. Therefore, the shear stress required to cause displacement in either direction is zero. If under the influence of the shear stress, the atom 1 moves towards the next equilibrium position, i.e., over the atom 4, the slope of the potential energy curve becomes negative. The stress is also negative during this period because a stress in opposite direction is needed to prevent the top plane from sliding into next equilibrium position after the atoms have crossed the midway positions. Thus, it is clear that shearing stress is a periodic function of the displacement. Therefore, the shear stress can be written as

$$\tau = \tau_m \sin \frac{2\pi x}{b} \qquad \qquad \ldots (4.15)$$

Where τ_m is the maximum shear stress corresponding to amplitude of the sine wave and 'b' is the period. For small values of displacement, Hooks law is valid, and hence

$$\tau = G\gamma = G\frac{x}{a} \qquad \qquad \ldots (4.16)$$

Where a is the interplanner spacing.

For small values of $\left(\dfrac{x}{b}\right)$, equation (4.15) can be written as

$$\tau = \tau_m \frac{2\pi x}{b} \qquad \qquad \ldots (4.17)$$

From equations (4.16 and 4.17),

$$\tau_m = \frac{G}{2\pi} \cdot \frac{b}{a} \qquad \qquad \ldots (4.18)$$

For many metals, $\qquad b = a$

Then, $\qquad\qquad \tau_m = \dfrac{G}{2\pi} \simeq \dfrac{G}{6} \qquad \qquad \ldots (4.19)$

τ_m is the maximum shear stress required for plastic deformation to occur. This is the theoretical shear strength of a perfect crystal. Since the shear modulus for majority of ductile metals is in the range of 10^4 to 10^5 MPa, the theoretical shear strength of a perfect (or ideal) crystal should be in the range of 2000—20,000 MPa. However, the observed values of CRSS to initiale plastic deformation of metals is considerably less than these values. In other words real crystals deform at a much lower values of shear stress than the theoretical values calculated for an ideal crystal.

This discrepency between the theoretical and observed values of shear stress is found to be due to the presence of dislocations in real crystals. Dislocations arise due to displacement of bonds of the atoms in a part of the plane of a crystal and are considered to be the weak centres in the crystal.

In the perfect crystal all the atoms above and below the slip plane are in minimum energy state and when the atoms are displaced under shear forces, the same force acts on all the atoms opposing the movement. In the perfect lattice shear occurs by simultaneous displacement of atoms. In the presence of a dislocation in the crystal, all the atoms well away from the dislocation are still in minimum energy state but in vicinity to the dislocation they are not.

When a shear stress is applied parallel to a slip plane in a real crystal, the dislocations on it will move. Fig. 4.6 shows the movement of an edge dislocation to the right in a single crystal under the influence of the shear stress.

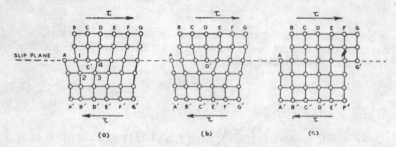

FIG. 4.6. Slip by dislocation movement.

Under shear stress atom 4 is pulled away from its neighbour atom 3, thereby raising the energy in that region. At the same time, however, atom 1 moves closer to its equilibrium distance from its neighbour atom 2 and release the same amount of energy as stored by the atom 1. As a consequence, the dislocation CC moves in the forward direction to the right. The atoms around the dislocation are symmetrically placed on both sides of the extra half plane and provide equal and opposite forces on the atoms at the dislocation, i.e. the row BB assists the motion of dislocation, whereas the row DD opposes the motion with the same force. Therefore, at a first approximation, there is not net force on the dislocation and the stress required to move the dislocation is zero. This condition is analogous to that shown in Fig. 4.5 when the atoms of the top row are midway between the atoms in the bottom row of a perfect crystal and the shear stress is zero at this point.

In practice, certain symmetry condititons give rise to a lattice frictional (resistance) stress to the motion of dislocation through the lattice. This lattice frictional stress is commonly known as Peierls and Nabbro stress after the originators. This frictional stress in much smaller than the theoretical shear stress of a perfect lattice.

The movement of dislocation from one position to the next and subsequent positions involves only a small rearrangement of atomic bonds near the dislocation (Fig. 4.6). This is because the atoms surrounding the dislocation are only at a fraction of interatomic distance from it.

When the dislocation disappears from the crystal, it produces a slip step equal to the magnitude of its Burgers vector.

The mechanism of slip by dislocation is analogous to moving a carpet across a room by working a wrinkle (hump) from one end of the carpet to the other, as illustrated in Fig. 4 7. The carpet instead

FIG. 4.7. Wrinkle analogy to slip.

of moving all along its length as a whole, is caused to move in small humps. As a result, there is no frictional force between the hump or wrinkle and the floor just as the distorted region around a dislocation. Thus much less work is needed to move the carpet from one end to another across the room. For the same reason very small shear stress is needed to move a dislocation through the crystal.

The weakening of an ordinary crystal due to the presence of dislocations can also be realised from the consideration of whiskers, which are the special crystals free from any dislocations. They are in the form of very thin fibres and are capable of withstanding much higher stresses than the ordinary crystals without undergoing plastic deformation.

4.2.4. Dislocation Source

It is shown above that the dislocations in a crystal move under the influence of shear stress and get disappeared after reaching to the surface. In an annealed crystal, the dislocation density is of the order of 10^5 cm^{-2} (10^{10} m^{-2}). It seems that on the application of shear stress, all these dislocations will swept out through the crystal leaving behind a perfect crystal. However, experimental observations show an entirely different picture. The density of dislocation *increases* by the order of 2 to 6 in magnitude depending upon the extent of deformation of the crystal In a heavily deformed crystal, the dislocation density is found to be as high as 10^{16} M^{-2}. This gives an indication that there must be sources of generating new dislocations within the crystal that operate during plastic deformation. One such source is generally called *Frank-read Source*, after the name of originator.

Suppose AB is a segment of a dislocation line lying on a slip plane in a crystal, as illustrated in Fig. 4.8. This segment is associated with a line tension t which keeps the dislocation to its minimum length AB. The points A and B of the segment are immobile under shear stress because they are pinned up by other dislocations of opposite sence lying on other planes in the crystal. These points A and B are, therefore, the nodal points of the dislocation segment. When a shear stress is applied parallel to the slip plane, the segment AB bows out between the anchoring points instead of moving away. As a consequence of bowing out of the segment, its length is increased by increasing energy due to line tension. The increase in energy is compensated by the applied stress. As the shear stress is increased, the

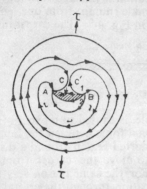

dislocation expands progressively until the radius of curvature becomes one-half the spacing AB. Beyond this point, the radius of curvature increases and the stress required for shear decreases (Fig. 4.8). The vector t points from B to A. If the applied stress increases further, the dislocation bends back around the anchoring points A and B. At this stage, the dislocation becomes screw on the other side of the line AB and at the points C and C' the vector t is in opposite sign. Since, the Burgers vector b is invariant, the two screw dislocations attract each other and get annihilated. Thus, a complete dislocation loop is produced and the remaining parts of the line join together, thereby, reforming the edge dislocation AB of the same sign. The line segment can now repeat this process under the influence of stress and form further loop around itself. The dislocation loop separates the slipped and unslipped region. If the dislocation loops are generated and removed from the crystal surface, an infinite number of loops can be formed. On the other hand if the dislocation loops are piled up at some obstacle such as a grain boundary in a polycrystalline material, then a back stress is developed at the dislocation source. When the back stress is sufficiently high to oppose the applied stress, the source will no longer be in operation.

FIG. 4.8. The successive stages in the operation of a Frank-Read source.

The stress required to operate a Frank-Read source is expressed as:

$$\tau = \frac{Gb}{l} \qquad \ldots (4.20)$$

where l is the length of the segment AB.

4.2.5. Strain Hardening in Single Crystals

It is shown above that when an annealed crystal is deformed, the dislocation density increases because of the presence of numerous sources of generating dislocations that operate under the influence of shear stress. The newly generated dislocations, if swept through the crystal, then the strain produced will be very small. If, on the other hand, these dislocations get piled up at some obstacle, they develop a back stress which opposes the applied stress. So the shear stress required for further straining of the crystal is increased. This increase in stress because of the previous plastic deformation of the crystal is known as *strain hardening*. The back stress developed due to piling up of dislocations at barriers is one of the mechanisms of strain hardening. Strain hardening is one of the most important characteristic of the plastic deformation of metals.

The barriers to the motion of dislocations may be formed by the interaction of gliding dislocations on intersecting slip planes. When two dislocations, for example, are gliding on two slip planes they combine at the line of intersection and form a combined dislocation whose Burgers vector does not lie on either of the two intersecting planes. The dislocations so formed become immobile unless the applied stress is sufficiently high to broken down it and these dislocations are, therefore, called the *Sessile dislocations*. The sessile dislocations produced by the dislocation reaction in FCC metal by slip on intersecting {1 1 1} planes, are known as *Cottrell-Lomer* barriers.

Another mechanism of strain hardening is thought to occur when two dislocations intersect with one another and produce a step or jog. Jogs are formed when dislocations moving in the slip plane cut through other dislocations intersecting the active slip plane. Such dislocations intersecting the active slip plane are commonly called a *dislocation forest*. Hence, the strain hardening is said to occur due to the *intersection* of a forest of dislocations. Fig. 4.9 illustrates the formation of a jog as a result of the intersection of two edge dislocations. Considering Fig. 4.9, an edge dislocation XY with Burgers vector b_1 is gliding on the plane Pxy. During its motion it cuts through another dislocation $X'Y'$ with Burgers vector b_2 intersecting the active slip plane Pxy and lying in the plane $Px'y'$. The intersection produces a jog AA' in the dislocation line $X'Y'$ which is parallel to b_1 but has a Burgers vector b_2 since it has now become a part of dislocation line $X'AA'Y'$. The length of the jog is equal to the magnitude of Burgers vector b_1. It is clear from Fig. 4.9, that the jogs produced in this case are the edge dislocations since their burgers vectors are paral-

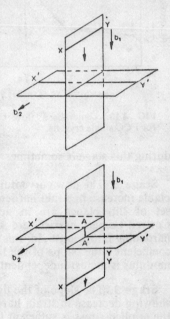

FIG. 4.9. Interaction of two edge dislocations.

lel to that of the original dislocation line containing them. Thus, the jogs can readily move with the rest of the dislocation line. Hence, the jogs resulting from cutting through of edge dislocations do not inhibit their motion. However, extra work must be needed to create a jog in the dislocation line X'Y' (Fig. 4.9) since its length (or the line tension) is increased. Unlike the jogs produced by the intersection of edge dislocations, the jogs formed by the inter·section of screw dislocations impede their motion. This is because of the intersection of screw dislocations resulting in jogs. These jogs are edge dislocations since their Burgers vectors are normal to the original dislocation line. Thus jogs of edge dislocation prevent the motion of screw dislocation. The screw dislociaton or the jog can only move when the jog will climb to other plane.

The generalised features of all the FCC metals can be described with

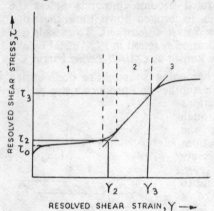

RESOLVED SHEAR STRESS, τ

τ_3
τ_2
τ_0

1   2   3

Y_2 Y_3

RESOLVED SHEAR STRAIN, Y

FIG. 4.10. Generalised flow curve for FCC single crystals.

the help of a resolved shear stress vs. shear strain curve shown in Fig. 4.10. The curve is principally comprised of the following three stages:

Stage 1. During this stage, the crystal undergoes little strain hardening with appreciable strain and therefore, this stage is called the region of *easy glide*. The flow curve is almost flat in this stage. During easy glide, only one slip system is active, therefore, under the influence of shear stress, dislocations generated quickly escape from the crystal surface without encountering barriers. That is why flow during this stage is sometimes referred to as laminar flow.

Stage 2. The flow curve during this stage is linear showing appreciable increase in strain hardening. During this stage, more than one set of slip planes are in action. As a result a greater number of Cottrell-Lomer barrier are formed and hence increase in strain hardening is obvious. In this stage the ratio of strain hardening coefficient (the slope of the linear portion of the curve) to the shear modulus is almost independent of temperature and stress.

Stage 3. The slope of the flow curve decreases rapidly in this stage showing decrease in strain hardening. In this region of the flow curve the applied stress is sufficient to cause cross slip of piled up dislocations at the barriers to glide on low energy planes and eventually escape to the surface of the crystal. This process of cross slip is a recovery process because the strain hardening is reduced. Hence, the stage 3 is commonly called dynamic recovery. The stress at which the third stage begins is highly dependent on temperature. As the temperature of the crystal is raised, recovery process takes place at rapid rate. The only mechanism of strain hardening during the third stage is the intersection of forests of dislocations.

4.2.6. Deformation by Twinning

Twinning is the another mechanism of deformation of metals. Twinning is the process of deformation in which atoms of one part of the crystal are displaced in such a way that the twinned portion is a mirror image of the parent crystal.

Twinning differs from slip in the following ways:

(*i*) Twinned portion of a grain is the mirror image of the original lattice with different orientation (Fig. 1.33), whereas the slipped and unslipped parts of the crystal have the same orientations across the slip-plane.

(*ii*) In the case of slip, the atoms are displaced to a discrete multiple of inter-atomic spacing, whereas twinnig involves atomic movements to much less than an atomic distance.

(*iii*) Twinning usually requires a higher shear stress than slip.

(*iv*) Slip occurs on relatively widely spaced planes, whereas twinning occurs on every atomic plane involved in the deformation.

(*v*) Twinning usually requires higher shear stress than slip.

Twinning usually occurs when deformation by slip is rather difficult. For example, in the case of HCP metals where the number of slip systems is limited, twinning becomes the dominant mode of deformation. Twinning may be caused by impact, by thermal treatment (annealing) and by plastic deformation. In BCC crystals, though the number of slip systems is 48, but the slip planes are not analogous to those in FCC crystals. Therefore, like in HCP crystals, twinning is an important mode of deformation in BCC crystals under favourable conditions of mechanical loading. Under certain conditions, twinning is accompanied with sound (tin cry).

Twinning occurs in a definite direction on a specific crystallographic plane for each crystal structure. Table 4.1 shows the twinning planes and directions far FCC, BCC and HCP crystals.

4.3. PLASTIC DEFORMATION OF POLYCRYSTALLINE MATERIALS

A majority of materials which are being used are the polycrystalline materials. Single crystals owing to their limited size and difficulty in production are used only in electronic and semiconductor devices and in some composites in the form of whiskers. In the polycrystalline materials, because of the presence of grain boundaries, the mechanism of strengthening is quite different from that in single crystals. Grain boundaries is one of the most important factors influencing the mechanical behaviour of polycrystalline metals. The other important factors include the solid solution alloying component, subgrain boundaries, and second phase particles.

4.3.1. Strengthening by Grain Boundaries

Grain boundaries play a vital role in the mechanical behaviour of metals. Depending upon the temperature, strain rate and the purity of the metal, grain boundaries can make the metal stronger or weaker. At low temperature and at relatively higher strain rate (while recovery processes are not significant), grain boundaries increase the rate of strain hardening and hence, increase the strength of the metal. On the other hand, at high temperature and slow strain rate, stress induced migration may cause grain boundary sliding. As a result, the cohesion between the grains is reduced. This leads to localised deformation at the grain boundaries and eventually fracture occurs through these boundaries.

Thus, at low temperature grain boundaries are the strogner portion than the grains whereas at high temperature grain boundaries are the weaker portion than the grains in a polycrystalline metal.

The basic difference in the room temperature deformation of single and polycrystalline metals is that polycrystalline metals show greater rate of strain hardening and therefore in the resolved shear stress-strain curve the first stage of easy glide is absent. The increase in strain hardening in polycrystalline metals results an increase in yield and tensile strengths.

There are basically two factors that affect the strain hardening of polycrystalline metals. The first being the grain boundaries which act as barrier to the motion of dislocations and the second the slip on multiple slip systems in polycrystals.

Since, grain boundaries are the regions of higher energy, dislocations reach the boundaries under the influence of shear stress and reduce their energy. The reduction in energy is due to the two forces. On the one hand, shear stress causes dislocations to be swept to the crystal boundary along the slip plane whereas the grain boundary which in fact itself consists of dislocations repels the

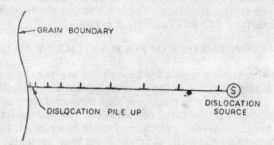

FIG. 4.11. Dislocation pile up at the grain boundary during plastic deformation.

gliding dislocations. When the two forces balance, the gliding dislocations get pinned up with the grain boundaries by reducing the energy in that region. It should be born in mind that dislocations are also the higher energy regions and the energy rise is due to the stress field on distortion created around them. With the increase of shear stress and more number of dislocations move on the slip plane and pile up at the grain boundaries (Fig. 4.11). This dislocation pile up produces a back stress on the dislocation source within the grains. Since the dislocation source operates under the applied stress so indirectly, the back stress opposes the applied stress. Dislocation pile up also exerts shear stress at the head and when this stress becomes high enough, dislocations break down the barrier and move in the neighbouring grain. Once the dislocation pile up breaks down, the strengthening effect is reduced. So the strengthening effect due to dislocation pile up at the grain boundaries is significant in the early stages of deformation, but not at large strains.

Thus, more the number of grains per unit area (as in fine grained metals) more the number of barriers to the motion of dislocations and hence stronger the material is. The increase in strength due to grain boundaries can be expressed as yield strength, tensile strength, fatigue strength, impact strength and hardness depending upon the application of load.

In FCC and BCC metals where slip occurs on the *multiple* slip systems, strain hardening is not appreciable. In case of HCP metals, there is only one equivalent slip plane, and therefore an appreciable rate of strain hardening is observed in them.

For most of the metals the yield strength is related to the grain size according to Hall-Petch relationship:

$$\sigma_o = \sigma_i - k_v D^{-1}/2 \qquad \qquad \ldots (4.21)$$

Where σ_o is the yield strength, σ_i is the lattice frictional stress opposing the motion of dislocations. K_y is the measure of extent to which dislocations are piled up at grain boundaries and D is the diameter of the grain. The above expression (Eq. 4.21) clearly shows a straight line relationship between σ_o and $D^{-1/2}$, i.e. as the grain diameter decreases, the yield strength increases.

4.3.2. Solid-Solution Hardening

Strengthening arises due to the presence of solute atoms distributed substitutionally or interstitially in an alloy and this is known as the solid solution strengthening (hardening). When the solute atoms in the alloy are dispersed substitutionally, the stress field created around them may be shown as in Fig. 1.27. This stress field around solutes interacts with the stress field of a moving dislocation, thereby increasing the resistance to the motion of the dislocation. As a result of this, strengthening occurs irrespective of whether the size of solute atoms is larger or smaller than that of the parent metal. In either case, the dislocations are attracted towards or repelled from the stress field around the solute atoms.

The greater is the size difference between solute and solvent atoms, the more intense is the stress field around the solute atoms and hence more is the force required to move dislocations. Thus, strengthening effect of an alloy increases with the increase in atomic size difference of solute and solvent. Furthermore, strengthening effect enhances with the increase in concentration of solute in the parent metal. The larger the number of solute atoms the more is the corresponding number of barriers in the path of dislocation motion and therefore, greater is the strengthening effect. Thus, the optimum conditions to secure the maximum strengthening effect are the maximum possible size difference and a higher concentration of solute.

If the solute atoms are sufficiently smaller than that of solvent, they disperse interstitially in the matrix. The same factors of atomic size difference and the concentration of solute are applicable for interstitial solute. Usually the interstitial atoms are larger than the interstitial voids in the matrix. These interstitial atoms have preferential sites in the localised higher energy regions such as grain boundaries and distorted region (i.e. expanded region below the slip plane in a positive edge dislocations) around the dislocations. Usually the interstitial atoms are segregated in the distorted region of the dislocation so as to reduce the energy in that part of the crystal. With this effect dislocations become immobile and lead to strengthening effect. A good explanation of the mechanism of strengthening by interstitial solutes is given in section 4.3.3.

Low angle grain boundaries (sub-grains structure) have profound influence on the mechanical properties of polycrystalline metals.

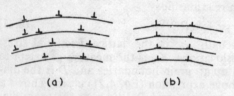

(a)   (b)

FIG. 4.12. Movement of dislocations to produce polygonisation.

When a polycrystal is cold worked, an excess number of dislocations of one sign are introduced. These dislocations are distributed randomly along the glide planes, as shown in Fig. 4.12a. When the metal is recrystallised in the low temperature zone of recrystallization temperature range, these dislocations rearrange themselves into a low energy configuration of low angle grain boundary (Fig. 4.12b) by dislocation climb. It has been observed that the yield strength and tensile strength of a cold worked and annealed polycrystal with a subgrain structure are higher than a metal which has been either only cold worked or only annealed without much change in ductility.

4.3.3. Yield Point Phenomenon

Many metals such as mild steel, polycrystalline molybdenum, titanium and aluminium alloys show a sharp yield point in the stress-strain diagram. In mild steel, for example, carbon is interstitially distributed in the matrix of iron. The carbon atoms segregate around the dislocation core, thereby reducing the overall distortional energy. This configuration is usually known as Cottrell atmosphere which pins up dislocations i.e. due to reduction in energy of dislocations a higher applied stress is needed to move them by breaking the shield of solute atmosphere. The anchorement of dislocations with the Cottrell atmosphere increases the yield point of the polycrystal, as illustrated in Fig. 4.13. In the initial stages of deformation, only few free dislocations are available near the upper yield point in the mild steel. In the later stage of deformation, the applied stress becomes so high that the Cottrell atmosphere breaks up and the pinned up dislocations get free and move at a fast rate. The stress at which unpinning occurs is the upper yield point. As soon as the dislocations are released from the Cottrell atmosphere, the load drops suddenly to the lower yield point. The dislocations then

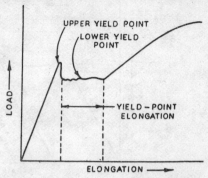

FIG. 4.13. Typical yield point behaviour.

move freely along the slip planes and pile up the grain boundaries. The deformation corresponding to the movement of dislocations along the slip plane from the point of unpinning to the grain boundaries is known as yield point elongation. The yield point elongation occurs at constant load. Thereafter the stress-strain curve shows the usual work hardening effect due to grain boundaries interaction with dislocation pile up.

4.3.4. Strain Age Hardening

Strain age hardening is a type of hardening process which is directly related to the yield point phenomenon. By this hardening mechanism, strength and hardness are improved at the expense of ductility of a metal. Those metals and alloys exhibiting yield point phenomenon are also strain age hardenable. Strain age hardening is not an advantageous strengthening mechanism for all the metals and alloys exhibiting this phenomenon. Due to strain ageing metals become embrittled A typical example is mild steel in which strain age embrittlement is very pronounced due to the presence of carbon and nitrogen solutes.

If a mild steel specimen is strained beyond the yield point and unloaded followed by immediate reloading, the yield point does not occur again, as illustrated in Fig. 4.14. This is because of the fact that upon previous yielding dislocations have been freed from the solute atmosphere of carbon and nitrogen. If the same specimen is reloaded after ageing at room temperature for several days or at temperature about 150°C for several hours, a yield point higher than the unaged cold deformed metal reappears. The reason why the yield point reappears after strain ageing of mild steel is the diffusion of carbon and nitrogen atoms to the dislocations during ageing The dislocation are again anchored by the solute atmosphere and give rise to a second yield point.

Thus, strain ageing results in reappearance of yield point, increase in yield point and yield point elongation, increased rate of work hardening, increased fracture stress, and increased embrittleness.

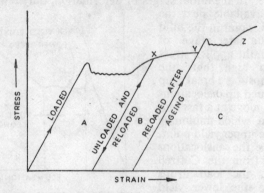

FIG. 4.14. Stress-strain curves for low carbon steel showing effect of strain agening.

Besides mechanical properties, the other properties that are influenced by strain ageing are the electrical and magnetic properties. For example, electrical conductivity of mild steel is found to be increased after strain ageing. In metal the free movement of valence electrons is responsible for electrical conductivity. It has been discussed in the Chapter 3, that the presence of impurity atoms in a pure metal prevents free movement of valence electrons through the process of scattering, thereby, increasing the electrical resistivity of metals. For the same reason, if the carbon and nitrogen atoms are randomly distributed in the matrix of iron, they increase the resistivity by scattering the free electrons. The scattering is not so marked if the solute carbon and nitrogen are segregated to dislocations.

Strain ageing of mild steel can be controlled by the addition of carbide and nitride forming elements such as Al, Ti, V Cb and B.

4.3.5. Work or Strain Hardening

Work hardening mainly occurs due to interaction of dislocations with other dislocations moving on non-parallel planes through the lattice. In case of HCP crystals, the planes of easy slip are the basal planes that are parallel to one another. If the tensile axis is oriented suitably with respect to other non-parallel planes such as prismatic or pyramidal planes, then some strain hardening results due to interaction of dislocations gliding on these non-parallel planes. Hence, HCP polycrystals do not exhibit appreciable strain hardening effect. BCC and FCC polycrystals exhibit appreciable work hardening because they have many active planes that are non-parallel. Dislocations gliding along such planes interact very strongly and thus increase the strain hardening.

The interaction of dislocations gliding on non-parallel planes is illustrated in Fig. 4.15 for a typical FCC crystal. The slip planes in FCC crystal belong to the {1 1 1} family. The direction of slip in this crystal may be one of the <1 1 0> kind. Fig. 4.15 shows that dislocations with Burgers vector $\frac{1}{2}$ [0 $\bar{1}$ 1] moving on ($\bar{1}$ 1 1) plane meet another dislocation with Burgers vector $\frac{1}{2}$[1 0 $\bar{1}$] gliding on (1 $\bar{1}$ 1) plane along the line of intersection of the two planes.

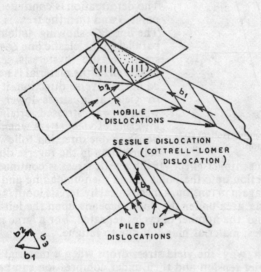

FIG. 4.15. Formation of a sessile dislocation in FCC crystal by a dislocation reaction.

These two dislocations combine and produce a third dislocation by reducing the total energy. The reaction can be represented as:

$$\tfrac{1}{2}[0\ \bar{1}\ 1]+\tfrac{1}{2}[1\ 0\ 1]\rightarrow\tfrac{1}{2}[1\ \bar{1}\ 0] \qquad\qquad \ldots (4.22)$$

The Burgers vector of the resultant dislocation lies on neither of the planes and therefore it becomes immobile and is commonly called *sessile dislocation*. The sessile dislocation now becomes barrier to the subsequent dislocations gliding on respective planes. These dislocations pile up at the baarier and build up a back stress on respective dislocation sources. Consequently the sources will stop generating fresh dislocation and raise the applied stress for further deformation to occur. Under very high shear stress, cross-slip occurs and strain hardening decreases. One of the most important draw-back of strain hardening is that material becomes brittle.

4.3.6. Bauschinger Effect

Under cycling loading, a material fails at a stress considerably lower than that required to cause failure under static loading. Under cyclic stress, the material frequently exhibits compressive and tensile stresses which lower its yield strength. This is due to Bauschinger effect.

When a ductile material is stressed under tensile, stress, plastic defor-

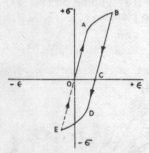

mation starts at a point A as shown on the stress-strain diagram in Fig. 4.16. The deformation is continued upto the point B and then the tress is removed. The line BC showing unloading runs parallel to the elastic line OA since the small elastic hysteresis effects are neglected. If the material is now reloaded in the reverse direction, it is found to yield at a stress lower than that when it was stressed originally. This lowering of yield stress when deforma-

FIG. 4.16. Bauschinger effect and hysteresis loop.

tion is in one direction followed by the deformation in the reverse direction, is called the Bauschinger effect. If the plastic stress is continued in the opposite direction upto the point E and then unloading and reloading the material again in tension, a mechanical hysteresis loop ($OABCDEO$) is formed. The area under the loop depends upon the initial plastic strain AB and the number of cycles repeated. For a large number of repeated cycles, material may fail due to fatigue.

The reason why the yield stress drops when a material is initially deformed under tension and then under compression can be explained with the help of dislocation theory. When the material is deformed from O to B (Fig. 4.16), the strain hardening after plastic deformation initiates at A due to dislocation pile up at barriers which exert a back stress on the source of generating dislocation. When the direction of slip is reversed, the piled up dislocations move in the opposite direction with relative ease. Also, the same dislocation sources which were effective when the material was deformed in tension, may now generate dislocations of opposite kind. With this effect the dislocations of opposite sign will attract and annihilate each other. This explains that why the yield stress in the reverse direction is decreased from that in the original direction.

4 3.7. Strengthening due to Second Phase Particles

In a multiphase alloys, the second phase may be present in the form of particles in the parent matrix. The strengthening produced by a fine dispersion of insoluble second phase particles is known as *dispersion* hardening. If, on the other hand, the second phase particles are precipitates obtained from a super-saturated solid solution upon ageing, the hardening produced is termed as *precipitation* hardening. The two systems differ from each other in the following respects:

(*i*) If the second phase particles are precipitates, they dissolve at high temperature in the parent phase and must exhibit decreasing solubility with decreasing temperature. On the other hand, dispersion particles do not dissolve in the parent phase even at high temperatures.

(*ii*) The precipitate particles are usually coherent or sometimes semi-coherent with the matrix. By contrast dispersion particles are incoherent with the parent phase.

(*iii*) There are limited number of alloys exhibiting precipitation effect and therefore, precipitation hardening is limited to few alloy systems only. On the other hand, a large number of dispersion hardened systems can be produced.

4.3 8. Strengthening Mechanism

The process of interaction of dislocations with the second phase

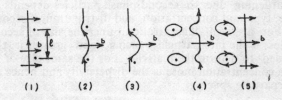

FIG. 4.17. Successive stages in the passage of dislocation past second phase particles—as barriers.

particles (i.e. precipitate or dispersion particles) is illustrated schematically in Fig. 4.17. Stage 1 shows that a straight dislocation line with Burgers vector '*b*' is approaching two particles separated by a distance *l*. The size of the particles is such that the dislocation line cannot cut through the particles. The dislocation line can only by-pass by bending around the particles. Since a dislocation line is associated with a *line tension* which keeps it at its shortest length, the bending or increase in length requires an expenditure of energy. The dislocation line begins to bend between the particles under the applications of shear stress (Stage 2, Fig. 4.17). As the dislocation line bows out between the particles, its radius of curvature decreases. For the minimum values of radius of curvature (called the critical radius of curvature), the required shear stress is maximum. The smallest radius of curvature to which the dislocation line is bent (stage 3) under the influence of shear stress is given as:

$$R = \frac{Gb}{2\tau_m} \qquad \qquad \ldots (4.23)$$

where R is the radius of curvature, G is the shear modulus and τ_m is the maximum shear stress needed to force the dislocation line between the particles. Once the critical radius of curvature is reached, the radius of curvature of the dislocation line increases with the decrease in shear stress (as is apparent from Eq. 4.23). This critical radius of curvature is half of the interparticle spacing l.

The shear stress is then expressed as:

$$\tau_m = \frac{Gb}{2R} = \frac{Gb}{l} \qquad \qquad \ldots (4.24)$$

The dislocation line is then bent round the particles just as the dislocation line bent around the anchored points in the Frank-Read Source. On the opposite side the segments become screw of opposite sign, thereby annihilate each other by attracting and leaving behind dislocation loops around the particles. The rest of the segment reforms to the dislocation with original Burgers vector 'b'. As the subsequent dislocations are approaching the particles, they further form loop around the particles and by-pass. The dislocation loops exert a back stress against the applied stress, thereby raising the shear stress required for further deformation to occur.

The hardening due to second phase particles depends upon the size, shape, type and concentration, and distribution of second phase particles. For a given concentration, finer the size of second phase particles, less is the interparticle spacing l and greater is the shear stress needed to deform the material. For the same size of particles, greater the concentration more is the dispersivity and hence minimum is the interparticle spacing.

Thus, presence of second phase particles in the matrix increases the strain hardening of multiphase alloys.

4.3.8. Mechanism of Creep

The definition of creep and creep curve are already discussed in Section 2.6. There are three mechanisms of creep in metals, viz. dynamic recovery process, diffusional creep, and sliding of neighbouring grains. The third stage or the later stages of plastic deformation are commonly known as dynamic recovery process (section 4.2.5). At low temperatures, recovery processes such as cross slip, play an important role in the creep process. Screw dislocations have their Burgers vector parallel to the dislocation line (or t vector). Therefore, they can cross slip from pile ups to the other plane of lower energy and glide freely on the new plane without encountering an obstacle. Thus, further plastic strain results as a function of time.

Edge dislocations owing to their Burgers vector normal to the dislocation line cannot cross slip like screw dislocations. They can only climb up or down (Fig. 4.18a). This is possible only at high temperatures where diffusion of vacancies is possible. Thus, at high temperature, creep rate increases by climb of edge dislocations up or down. The edge dislocations climb from the pile ups against a barrier and then glide freely on another parallel slip plane of low stress. Conseqently, the creep rate increases as a function of time.

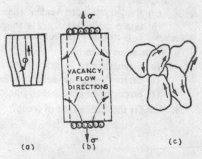

FIG. 4.18. Mechanism of creep (a) dislocation climb, (b) vacancy diffusion and (c) grain boundary sliding.

The diffusional creep mechanism involves the diffusion of vacancies and is different from the climb of edge dislocations. This mechanism is temperature dependent and is significant at high temperatures. Under a combined action of temperature and stress, vacancies diffuse from surfaces normal to the stress axis (Fig. 4.18b) to the surfaces parallel to the stress axis. Since atoms are moving along the direction of stress axis, the specimen elongates along the stress axis and gets compressed across the section. The process occurs as a function of time. Ultimately the specimen will undergo creep.

The third mechanism of creep is the *grain boundary sliding*. It is well known that at elevated temperatures grain boundaries are the weaker region because the atoms in the grain boundary region are highly mobile. As a result of high mobility of grain boundary atoms the cohesion between the grains is reduced considerably. Under the influence of stress, plastic deformation is dominantly concentrated along the grain boundaries. With the effect grains appear as if they are sliding over one another (Fig. 4.18b). Again grain boundary shearing does not become a significant deformation mechanism until the metal is heated to a temperature where recovery can occur.

QUESTIONS

1. Explain the significance of modulus of elasticity.

2. What do you mean by the terms slip plane and slip direction? Explain why the slip most readily occurs on the closest packed planes.

3. What is critical resolved shear stress? Derive an expression for the same.

4. Describe the dislocation source.

5. What do you understand by the following:

   (a) Cottrell Lomer barrier.
   (b) Dislocation forest.
   (c) Dislocation jogs.

6. Distinguish between deformation by slip and that by twinning.

7. Explain:

(a) Real crystals are weaker than perfect crystals.

(b) Grain boundaries are stronger than the grains at low temperature while reverse is true at high temperature.

8. Write short notes on:

(a) Strengthening by grain boundaries.

(b) Strengthening by solid solution.

(c) Strengthening by second phase particles.

9. What is the mechanism of creep?

5

PHASE AND EQUILIBRIUM DIAGRAMS

5.1. INTRODUCTION

A phase can be defined as a physically homogeneous and distinct portion of a material system. A system is a part of the universe selected for consideration. It is isolated from its surroundings in such a way that it remains unaffected by the changes in surroundings. A *homogeneous system* is one in which each point represents the same properties. The matter can exist in one of the three states, viz., solid, liquid and gaseous. A solid element, compound or alloy may consist of one or several phases depending upon the crystal structure. If a liquid is composed of two or more components and the system is homogeneous, then the system is said to consist of a single phase. A system composed of more than one phases such as a liquid and a solid or two solids with different crystal structures, is said to be a heterogeneous system. In a heterogeneous system there is a sharp change in the physical properties at the boundaries of each phase, though the chemical composition may be the same. For example, pure iron in its solid state can exist in four *allotropic* forms, viz., α-iron, β-iron, γ-iron and δ-iron depending upon temperatures. Though the crystal structure of α-iron, β-iron and δ-iron is the same, i.e. BCC but the lattice parameters of the three are different.

A phase diagram is basically a graphical representation of the state of a system which is thermodynamically stable under a given set of conditions of temperature, pressure and concentration. Every material tends to acquire an equilibrium state with its surroundings. A system is said to be in equilibrium state if a finite change in its state does not occur unless the conditions of temperature, pressure or concentration are altered. A graphical representation in which each phase of a system is in equilibrium state is known as an *equilibrium diagram*.

5.2. SOLID SOLUTION

A number of metals form solid solution by dissolving in each other. In a solid solution, atoms of one metal become a part of the space lattice of the other element. A solid solution consists of two parts, the *solute* and the *solvent*. The major constituent of the solution is said to be a solvent with the solute being dissolved in it. When any two metals combine to form an alloy, then the possibility of forma- tion of solid solution as well as the extent of its formation, depends upon several factors given below:

(*i*) **Size factor.** The probability of solid solution forming will be high if the difference in the atomic diameters of the components forming the alloy is less than 14-15 pct. As this difference in atomic diameter increases the probability of forming a solid solution decreas- es and eventually becomes zero. The reason is that a large differ- ence in atomic diameters of solute and solvent introduces an intense elastic strain field around the solute atoms. Consequently the solid solution becomes unstable due to rise in internal energy.

(*ii*) **Crystal structure.** Extensive solid solubility may be expected if the crystal structure of both the solute as well as that of the solvent is the same. For example, in the solid solution alloys such as Cu-Ni, Au-Cu, Cd-Mg, etc. the crystal structures of the constituting elements are the same.

(*iii*) **Valence factor.** The same valence of solute and solvent favour solid solubility. A metal with higher valence is more likely to be soluble in one with lower valence than the reverse. For exam- ple, when zinc (divalent) is dissolved in copper (monovalent), the extent to which a zinc can be dissolved and form a solid solution with copper at room temperature is about 39 pct. On the other hand, if Cu is added to Zn, then a solid solution forms only upto 1 pct. Cu in Zn.

(*iv*) **Electronegativity factor.** A small electronegativity difference between the solute and the solvent favours solid solubility. The more electronegative the solute and the more electropositive the solvent, the greater is the tendency to produce a stable bond between solute and solvent atoms. The effect of electronegativity difference is so strong that even if other conditions (i.e. size factor, crystal structure and valence factor) are favourable, a solid solution may not result if the electronegativity difference of the component elements is large. For instance, Cu and Al have the same crystal structure, and there is not much difference in the atomic diameters ($d_{Cu}=2.56$ Å and $d_{Al}=$ 2.86 Å) of the two. However, owing to the relatively large difference in electronegativities (electronegativity of Cu is 1.9 and that of Al is 1.5), aluminium offers little solubility in copper and the two form a compound rather than a solid solution.

5.2.1. Types of Solid Solution

Solid solutions can broadly be classified into two categories:

(*i*) Primary solid solution, and

(*ii*) Secondary solid solution.

(*i*) **Primary solid solution.** A primary solid solution characterises by its crystal structure being the same as that of the solvent. The structure of the random solid solution differs from that of the solvent with regard to the lattice parameter only. This is because some lattice distortion is brought about due to stress field around the solute atoms which is created by the differeace in atomic diameters of the solute and the solvent.

Primary solid solution can further be subdivided as:

(a) Substitutional solid solution, and

(b) Interstitial solid solution.

Substitutional solid solution. In the substitutional solid solution, the solute atoms take the lattice sites that were occupied by the solvent atoms before the addition of solute. Some examples of substitutional solid solution alloys are Fe-Ni, Cu-Ni, Ag-Au, Pt-Ni, Cu-Au,

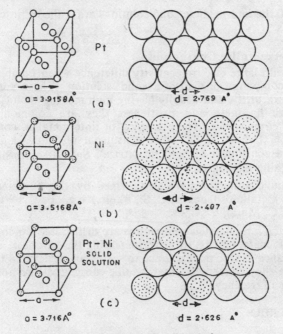

FIG. 5.1. The Pt-Ni solid solution.

etc. A typical example of substitutional solid solution is illustrated in Fig. 5.1. Figs. 5.1a and 5.1b illustrate the arrangement of atoms in the crystal lattice of Pt and Ni respectively showing the lattice parameter 'a' and the atomic diameter 'd'. The crystal structure of the substitutional solid solution of Pt-Ni (50:50) is shown in Fig. 5.1c. Platinum and nickel can form a continuous series of alloys and either of the two can be a solvent.

Interstitial solid solution. In the interstitial solid solution the solute atoms are so small in size that they occupy the interstices in the solvent matrix, e.g., carbon in iron.

The elements other than carbon which can occupy interstitial positions in a metal matrix are H, N, O and B.

(*ii*) **Secondary or intermediate solid solution**. Unlike primary solid solutions, the crystal structure of intermediate or secondary solid solution is different from that of the solvent. Zinc upto about 39 pct. dissolves in copper to form a primary solid solution commonly called α-brass. When more zinc is added to copper, a solid solution with BCC crystal structure forms. This is a secondary or intermediate solid solution and is commonly called β-brass. The composition of β-brass can be 40-55 pct. Zn in copper at about 800°C. If zinc is further added in copper, a second intermediate solid solution, the crystal structure of which is neither that of Cu or Zn is formed.

Many of the intermediate solid solutions are called "intermetallic compounds".

5.2.2. Intermetallic Compounds

Metals with large electronegativity difference when combine, tend to form a compound instead of a solid solution. These compounds are very hard brittle and usually having high melting points. Owing to their high hardness and brittleness they are commonly called *intermetallic compounds*. The examples of intermetallic compounds are, Cu_2Zn_3 (which is the chief constituent of hard white brass), Cu_3Sn (hard constituent of hard tin bronze), SnSb (the constituent of tin-base bearing alloys), etc.

Intermetallic compounds are also formed by the combination of metals and metalloids (such as C, Si, B, etc.) e.g. Fe_3C, WC, Fe_3P, Mn_3C, Mg_3C, Mg_3Si, Cr_4C, etc.

Usually the intermetallic compounds are distributed randomly in a suitable soft metal matrix, thereby, increasing the hardness, strength, wear resistance as well as resistance to softening at elevated temperature, of the alloy concerned. Intermetallic compounds are not restricted by laws of valency.

5.3. PHASE RULE

A system will be composed of matter in the form of one or more phases and may involve metals and non-metals either separately or in any combination. Thus, if the system consists of a solid, a liquid or a gas, then it is a single phase system. If liquid and gas (e.g. water and water vapour) coexist in a system, then the system is referred as a two phase system. If there is a mixture of solid, liquid and gas (for instance, ice, water and water vapour) in a system, then it is said to have three phases. Since, all the gases are miscible in all proportions, there can never be more than one gaseous phase in any system, whereas, a system may contain several solid and/or liquid phases.

An equilibrium phase or state (several phases may be present) is defined as the one which would result if the composition under consideration were held for infinite period of time at the specified pressure and temperature.

Most of the systems consist of simply a chemical element. If a system consists of a single element then it is a single component system. If a system contains two elements, it is denoted to be a *binary* system. Similarly systems with components, 3, 4, and so on are referred to as *ternary, quaternary* respectively, and so forth. In some instances, however, the components of a system may be chemical compounds. For example, a system containing CO_2 and H_2O is referred to a two component or binary system, though it contains three elements.

A system may be defined with the help of three parameters. i.e. (*i*) the concentration of each component in each phase, (*ii*) the temperature of the system, and (*iii*) the pressure. The combination of temperature and pressure is known as thermodynamic environment (i.e. *intensive* properties excluding the effects due to magnetic or electrical fields, etc.) and are usually called external independent variables. The concentration of a component is an extensive property in the thermodynamic sense and is an independent property of the system.

In the equilibrium state an alloy system follows the *Gibbs Phase Rule*. This rule gives a relation among the degree of freedom (F), the number of components (C) and the number of coexisting phases (P) in equilibrium, and is numerically expressed as:

$$F = C + n - P \qquad \qquad \qquad ...(5.1)$$

Where n is the number of independent variables such as temperature and pressure. The degree of freedom is the maximum number of variables that must be fixed in order to define the system completely. These variables are the temperature, pressure and composition which are controllable externally.

Since the study of metals and alloys is usually conducted at atmospheric pressure, the gaseous phase can be ignored and the Eq. (5.1) can be modified as:

$$F = C + 1 - P \qquad \qquad \qquad ...(5.2)$$

Obviously, the degree of freedom can not be less than zero,

i.e. $\qquad \qquad F \geqslant 0$

or $\qquad \qquad C + 1 - P \geqslant 0$

or $\qquad \qquad P \leqslant C + 1 \qquad \qquad \qquad ...(5.3)$

Eq. (5.3) indicates that the number of coexisting phases in a system cannot exceed the number of components plus one.

If any change in any variable (i.e. temperature or composition) causes a phase change, the system is *invariant* and the degree of freedom is zero at invariant point. In a binary diagram, at the invariant point (or invariant equilibrium) the number of coexisting phases can be evaluated as following:

$$0 = 2 + 1 - P$$

or $$P = 3$$

If one of the variables is altered without affecting the number of phases, i.e. if this change does not accompany the disappearance of any phase or the appearance of a new phase in the system, then the system is univariant (or monovariant) and has one degree of freedom. If two variables are altered simultaneously without affecting the phases, the system has two degrees of freedom and so on.

5.4. COOLING CURVES

Cooling curves are time-temperature diagrams obtained by heating a obstance to a temperature below which a phase change has occurred during heating. Consider the case of a single component system involving cooling from the liquid state to room temperature. The component is first heated to molten state and is subsequently cooled at a slow rate. If temperature is recorded at frequent intervals until it drops to room temperature and if a graph is plotted between time and temperature, the nature of the graph so obtained can be represented as shown in Fig 5.2a, from which it may be observed that the curve initially falls continuously as the liquid cools and becomes

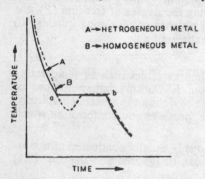

FIG. 5.2. Cooling curve for a pure metal.

constant where freezing occurs. This is in accordance with the phase rule. For a single component system, two phases (i.e. liquid and solid in this case) are in equilibrium at zero degree of freedom. Therefore, temperature remains constant, i.e. the equilibrium is invariant. Any variation in temperature from this equilibrium leads to a phase change, above this temperature only liquid will form while below this temperature only solid is stable. Freezing starts at the point 'a' (Fig. 5.2a) and completes at 'b'. After b, the curve falls again regularly to room temperature. The horizontal span a b indicates the latent heat of solidification and is proportional to the latent heat of solidification as well as the mass of the liquid metal.

Under equilibrium conditions, the temperature at which a given structural change occurs for a given material is characteristic of that material.

However, the nature of the cooling curve is different for a homogeneous component. A homogeneous liquid cannot solidify at its equilibrium freezing temperature because of the difficulty in nucleation of the solid phase. Freezing occurs only at a certain temperature below the equilibrium freezing point. Cooling below the equilibrium freezing temperature is commonly called 'super-cooling'. Once freezing has started, the temperature will again be raised to the equilibrium freezing point and the freezing occurs in the usual way. Fig. 5.2b shows a cooling curve for a homogeneous single component system.

Fig. 5.3 shows a cooling curve for a binary (two components) alloy. The two components are completely miscible in the liquid as well as in the solid state. The alloy of this kind is known as solid solution type alloy. It can be noted in comparison to a pure metal where freezing occurs at constant temperature, freezing in binary alloy occurs over a temperature range. The point 'a' where freezing starts is known as liquidus point and the point 'b' where freezing terminates is known as the solidus point. The temperature corresponding to these points a and b are known as liquidus and solidus temperatures respectively. The liquidus as well as solidus temperature of an alloy depends upon its composition.

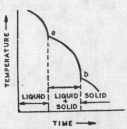

FIG. 5.3. Cooling curve for a binary alloy forming a single solid solution.

However, the nature of the cooling curve changes with the type of alloy. If the components of a binary alloy are completely soluble in the liquid state but are insoluble in the solid state, this type of alloy is known as eutectic alloy. A cooling curve for such an alloy is shown in Fig. 5.4. This curve shows that the portion ab is analogous to that obtained in the cooling curve of the solid solution alloy (Fig. 5.3) while the portion bc is the same as ab in the cooling curve of a pure metal shown in Fig. 5.2. This means that in a eutectic alloy the end of freezing occurs at constant temperature (discussed in the section 5.5).

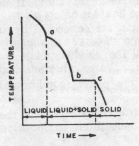

FIG. 5.4. Cooling curve for eutectic type alloy which is not of exact eutectic composition.

5.5. PHASE DIAGRAM

A phase diagram basically represents the state of a given system under equilibrium conditions in which there will be no change with time. A phase diagram is therefore also called an equilibrium diagram and can also be defined as the graphical representation of the phases which exist in equilibrium for any combination of temperature and compositon.

The most important kinds of alloy systems that show the possible conditions of equilibrium between phases in binary alloys are:

(i) Components that are completely soluble in each other in liquid as well as in solid state.

(*ii*) Components that are mutually soluble in liquid state and are completely insoluble in solid state.

(*iii*) The components that are mutually soluble in the liquid phase and are partially soluble in the solid state.

5.5.1. Solid Solution System

The alloy systems in which the constituting metals are soluble in the liquid state as well as in the solid state, are commonly known as

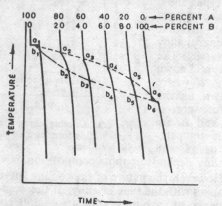

TIME ⟶

FIG. 5.5. Series of cooling curve for different alloys in an isomorphous system.

isomorphous system. A cooling curve of this type of alloy is shown in Fig. 5.3. A series of cooling curves for various alloy compositions with varying concentrations from 100 pct. A and 0 pct. B to 100 pct. B and 0 pct. A is shown in Fig. 5.5. It can be seen from this figure that the addition of B in A decreases the melting point of the resultant alloy. If all the liquidus points $a_1, a_2, ..., a_6$ are connected by a smooth curve and similarly all the solidus points $b_1, b_2, ..., b_6$ are connected

by a smooth curve, the resultant diagram is the phase (equilibrium) diagram for the alloy AB.

The actual phase diagram can be constructed by expressing the results of cooling curve in the form of temperature-composition plot. The appropriate points are taken from the series of cooling curves and are plotted on the temperature-composition diagram as illustrated in Fig. 5.6. In this figure the vertical line to the left of the diagram represents 100 pct. A and the vertical line to the right of the diagram indicates 100 pct. B. Therefore the points a_1 and b_6 must lie respectively on these lines. Since all the intermediate compositions are the percentages of A and B, vertical lines

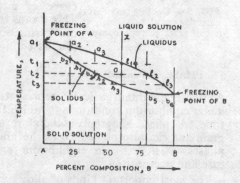

FIG. 5.6. Equilibrium diagram for an isomorphous system.

are drawn corresponding to these compositions (Fig. 5.5) and the points a_2b_2, a_3b_3, etc. are plotted on these respective lines from left to right.

The line joining the points $a_1, a_2, a_3 \ldots, a_5$ is called *liquidus line* while the line connecting the points $b_2, b_3, \ldots, b_6$ is referred to as the *solidus line*. This equilibrium diagram consists of three regions, liquid, liquid plus solid and solid. In the region above the liquidus line, only liquid exists while in the region below solidus only solid persists. The region in between these two lines consists of both solid and liquid, the composition of which depends upon the composition and temperature of the alloy system.

Consider the cooling of an alloy x corresponding to the composition 60 pct. B and 40 pct. A. (Fig. 5.6). The alloy is all liquid above t_1 and begins to solidify at this temperature. Just below t_1, first crystals of solid solution correspond to the composition s_1 form in the liquid. As the temperature decreases from t_1 to t_3, solidification proceeds with the absorption of component B from the liquid. As a result, the solid solution becomes richer in B and the composition of the solid solution changes from s_1 to s_3 with a corresponding change in liquid composition from l_1 to l_3. At t_3 the composition of the solid will be stable at 60 pct. B and 40 pct. A and the alloy will be all solid. Lines l_1s_1 and l_3s_3 are known as tie lines.

At some intermediate temperature t_2 two phases liquid and solid are in equilibrium and their composition at this temperature can be calculated with the help of Lever rule (or also called Lever Arm Principle). According to this rule, the tie line s_2Ol_2 is considered to be a lever with fulcrum at the point O. If the amount of liquid is placed at l_2 and the amount of solid at s_2, at equilibrium the two phases are inversely proportional to the distances from the fulcrum. That is to say, at equilibrium the product of the length s_2O times the weight of the solid solution is equal to the product of the length Ol_2 times the weight of the melt.

Therefore, at temperature t_2

$$\text{liquid} = \frac{s_2O}{s_2l_2} \times 100 \text{ (pct. of liquid)}$$

$$\text{solid} = \frac{l_2O}{s_2l_2} \times 100 \text{ (pct. of solid)}$$

Examples of isomorphous system are Cu-Ni, Au-Ag, Cu-Au, etc.

5.5.2. Eutectic System

Basically no two metals are completely insoluble in each other, however, there are some cases where the solid solubility of one component in other is too small to be of any significance. The phase diagram of such an alloy can be constructed from the series of cooling curves, in a way analogous to that adopted for the solid solution alloy diagram discussed in section 5.5.1. Fig. 5.7a shows the series of cooling curves for various compositions of *AB* alloy. It can be seen that addition of *B* in *A* lowers the freezing point of *A* while the addition of *A* in *B* lowers the freezing point of *B*. Since each metal tends to decrease the freezing point of the other, there must be a compromise temperature where the two freezing points coincide, i.e., where the respective liquidus lines intersect. In Fig. 5.7a these liquidus lines are shown by dotted lines and their point of intersection is at *E*. At the point *E* the composition of the alloy *AB* is 40 *A*: 60*B*. The point *E* is of considerable importance as at this point solidification occurs at constant temperature instead of over a range. This point is commonly known as eutectic point. Among the various alloy compositions, the alloy corresponding to the eutectic point is know as eutectic alloy. The freezing point of the eutectic alloy is the minimum among that of other alloy compositions between 100 *A* to *O B* and 100 *B* to *OA*. The temperature coinciding with the eutectic point it called the eutectic temperature. Further more, each cooling curve for a particular composition of *AB*, shows that the end of solidification occurs at a constant temperature. This constant temperature is the eutectic temperature and is shown by a horizontal line (Fig. 5.7a).

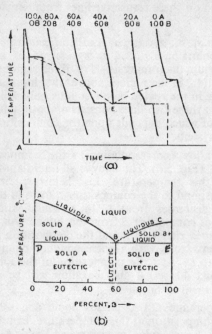

FIG. 5.7. (a) Series of cooling curves for different alloys in an eutectic system, and (b) Equilibrium diagram for a eutectic system.

Taking appropriate points from the series of cooling curves, an equilibrium diagram is constructed as shown in Fig. 5.7b. It is evident from this diagram that at the eutectic point, the liquid phase is in equilibrium with two solids, solid *A* and *B*. Thus, there are three phases in equilibrium at the eutectic point and the degree of freedom at this point is zero. Above the liquidus line *ABC* the alloy is completely liquid. Any alloy with composition to the left of *B* is usually termed as hypoeutectic alloy. Consider the solidification of hypoeutectic alloy. The alloy will begin to solidify only when the liquidus line *AB* will be reached. As the temperature decreases from liquidus, the solid A progressively separates out of the liquid. The liquid, thereby, becomes richer in B. The separation of excess phase A is continued until the eutectic temperature. At the eutectic temperature, the remaining liquid containing both A and B, will decompose into eutectic mixture. It may be noted that between the liquidus and eutectic temperature two phases liquid plus solid A are coexisting while below the eutectic temperature the phases are solid $A+$ solid eutectic mixture.

Now consider the solidification of hypereutectic alloy AB. The alloy is a uniform liquid above the liquidus line BC. Solidification will start at a temperature just below the liquidus. As the temperature decreases below the liquidus line, the solid B is progressively separated out of the liquid. The liquid becoming richer with regard to A. The excess phase continues to form until the eutectic temperature, below which the remaining liquid will decompose to a eutectic mixture. Thus, between the lines BC and BE there are two phases, namely, liquid and solid B. The region below the eutectic line and to the right of B is composed of solid B and eutectic mixture. Examples of eutectic system are Fe-C, Pb-Bi, Cd-Bi, etc.

5.5.3. Combination Type System

The components that are partially soluble in the solid state, form a combination of eutectic and solid solution type of phase diagram. There is limited solubility of one component in another. Fig. 5.8 represents a combination type of equilibrium diagram for the alloy AB. Point D indicates the maximum solid solubility of component B in A (in the α-solid solution) whereas the point E shows the maximum solubility of component A in B (in the β-solid solution). As the temperature decreases below the line DE, the solid solubility of each component in the other decreases. The lines DG and EF are

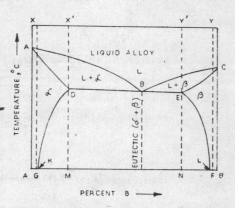

FIG. 5.8. Equilibrium diagram for a combination type of system.

known as *solvus lines*. It can be noted that instead of separating out the pure components A and B, from the melt at the liquidus ABC, crystals of the α-solid solution of component B in A (line AB) and crystals of the β-solid solution of component A in B (line CB) are separated out. At the point B, liquid transforms to a eutectic mixture of α and β crystals.

The line ABC in Fig. 5.8 is the liquidus line and is analogous to the ABC line on the eutectic diagram (Fig. 5.7b). The solidus line

$ADBEC$ contains two parts AD and EC which are analogous to the solidus line shown on the solid solution diagram (Fig. 5.6). Thus, the region to the left of XG line and right of YF line are showing the characteristic of solid solution alloys whereas the region between the lines $X'M$ and $Y'N$ is exactly the same as in Fig. 5.7b. Examples of this system are Pb-Sn, Cu-Be, Al-Cu, Al-Si, Cu-Sn Mg-Al, etc.

5.5.4. Other Binary Systems

In addition to the most common types of binary systems discussed above, there are also other binary systems of interest. These are, the peritectic, eutectoid, peritectoid, monotectic, and syntectic systems.

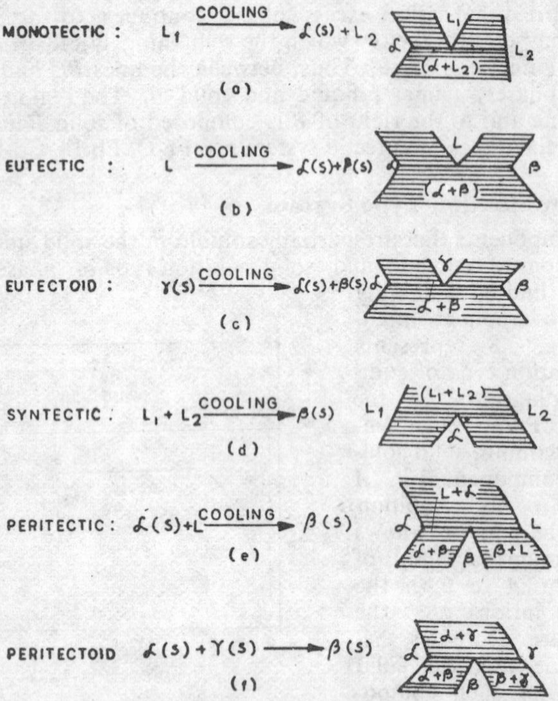

FIG. 5.9. Phase diagrams with important phase reactions

All of these reactions occur at constant temperature in an alloy of a given composition and are represented as following :

Peritectic reaction : $\alpha + L \xrightarrow{\text{cooling}} \beta$

Eutectoid reaction : $\gamma \xrightarrow{\text{cooling}} \alpha + \beta$

Peritectoid reaction: $\alpha + \gamma \xrightarrow{\text{cooling}} \beta$

$$\text{Monotectic reaction}: \quad L_1 \xrightarrow{\text{cooling}} \alpha + L_2$$

$$\text{Syntectic reaction}: L_1 + L_2 \xrightarrow{\text{cooling}} \beta$$

The phase diagrams with the important phase reactions are illustrated in Fig. 5.9. It can be noted from the figure that the reactions monotectic, eutectic and eutectoid involve transformation from one phase to two phases upon cooling whereas the reactions syntectic, peritectic and peritectoid involve transformation of two phases to a single phase during cooling. In these reactions L stands for liquid phase while Greek letters, α, β, and γ denote a solid phase.

QUESTIONS

1. Define the terms phase and system.
2. Distinguish between a homogeneous system and a hetrogeneous system.
3. What do you mean by the term solid solution? How can the solid solutions be classified? Explain the types of solid solutions with suitable illustrations.
4. Discuss the conditions favourable for a substitutional solid solution.
5. (a) Under what conditions a compound will result instead of a solid solution ? Give few examples of intermetallic compounds.

(b) Silver and aluminium both possess FCC crystal structure with almost identical atom sizes (e.882 Å and 2.856 Å dia respectively), yet they do not dissolve completely in each other. Explain.
6. What informations can be gathered from an equilibrium diagram?
7. State phase rule and explain each of the terms included in this relation.
8. Define the following reactions:
   (a) Eutectic;
   (b) Eutectoid;
   (c) Peritectic; and
   (d) Monotectic reaction.
9. Draw cooling curves for single component homogeneous and hetrogeneous systems and distinguish between the two.
10. Explain the cooling of a hypoeutectic alloy for a binary system from liquid to solid state.
11. Melting point of lead is 327°C and that of tin is 232°C. They form eutectic containing 62 pct. tin at 182°C. The maximum solid solubility of tin in lead at this temperature is 19 pct., of lead in tin is 3 pct. Assume the solubility of each at room temperature is 1 pct.

(a) Draw the equilibrium diagram to scale on a piece of graph paper labeling all points, lines and regions (areas).

(b) Describe the cooling of a 70 pct. tin alloy.

(c) Draw cooling curve of the above alloy.

6

HEAT TREATMENT OF METALS AND ALLOYS

6.1. INTRODUCTION

Metals and their alloys are widely used in engineering industries such as metallurgical, electrical, automobile, aeronautical, etc. These materials under service are subjected to various stresses like tensile, compressive, impact, twisting, etc. As a tool material they are to fulfill the requirement of hardness, strength, toughness, wear resistance and machinability. In certain applications they should possess high surface hardness coupled with toughness. In order to satisfy all these requirements, metals and alloys are given a thermal or sometimes a thermochemical treatment in which they are heated and cooled at desired temperature under controlled atmosphere and controlled rate of heating and cooling. This operation is known as heat treatment.

Therefore, heat treatment may be defined as an operation or a group of operations involving heating and cooling of a metal or an alloy in its solid state with a view to achieve certain desirable structure and properties suitable for particular applications.

6.2. OBJECTIVES OF HEAT TREATMENT

Heat treatment may have one or more of the following objectives:

(*i*) to relieve internal stresses set up within the metal due to cold working, welding or casting;

(*ii*) to homogenise the grain composition in alloys;

(*iii*) to improve mechanical properties such as yield strength, tensile strength, hardness, ductility, etc;

(*iv*) to improve grain structure;

(*v*) to secure specific properties such as high surface hardness coupled with tough core, corrosion resistance, etc;

(*vi*) to modify the structure of the material with a view to secure desired electrical and magnetic properties.

6.3. HEAT TREATMENT PROCESSES

Heat treatment processes are broadly classified in two categaries:

(a) heat treatment.

(b) special heat treatments.

Heat treatment consists of simply a thermal action on a metal or alloy. Special heat treatment processes can further be subdivided as chemical heat treatment and thermomechanical treatment (TMT) and respectively combine a chemical action and plastic deformation besides thermal action. Heat treatment proper includes annealing, narmalising, hardening and tempering. All these processes are applicable to ferrous as well as non-ferrous metals and alloys. Since the majority of materials employed in industries are ferrous and as they demand for a variety of heat treatments, the heat treatment processes used in ferrous industries are discussed first and in greater details.

6 4. FUNDAMENTALS OF HEAT TREATMENT OF FERROUS METALS AND ALLOYS

6 4.1. Iron-Iron Carbide Epuilibium Diagram

Iron-Iron carbide equilibrium diagram forms the basis to study the heat treatment of iron and steel, the most important of engineering materials. The pure form of iron which is also known as 'ingot iron' is used for drainage culverts, roofing and ducts, stoves, etc. The total content of impurities present in pure iron is about 0 06 pct. and includes elements C, Mn, Si, P and S. Pure iron has the distinctive property of changing crystal lattice with increase of temperature which is known as "allotropic forms of iron".

Allotropic forms of iron. When pure iron is cooled from its molten state to room temperature and if a cooling curve is drawn simultaneously, four arrest points are observed where temperature remains steady for a while. The cooling curve for pure iron is shown in Fig. 6.1. Freezing starts at 1539°C where liquid iron changes to solid iron with a crystal lattice B.C.C. This form of iron is designated as δ-iron. Upon further cooling at 1401°C, a phase change occurs and the atoms rearrange themselves in a crystal lattice F.C.C. This form of iron is referred to as gamma iron (γ Fe) and is non-magnetic in character. Upon subsequent cooling another phase change results at a temperature of 910°C and the crystal lattice so formed is known as alpha iron (α-Fe). Finally, at 768°C, the α-iron becomes ferromagnetic without any change in crystal structure, though the lattice parameter is changed somewhat. This phase was previously designated as beta iron (β-iron). Since magnetic transformation does not affect the heat treatment of iron carbon alloys, β transformation is overlooked in further discussions.

Iron carbon system. Carban is the most important alloying element with iron. It combines with iron to form solid solutions and/ or intermetallic compound represented by the formula Fe_3C (cementite) depending upon temperatures and composition. Referring to Fig. 6.2 point A represents the melting point of pure iron and the point D which is not known exactly indicates the melting point of cementite containing 6.67 pct. carbon by weight. The iron-carbon diagram is not strictly an equilibrium diagram because at equilibrium,

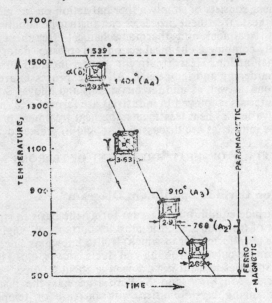

FIG. 6.1. The cooling curve for pure iron.

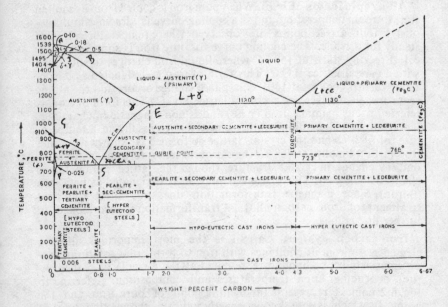

FIG. 6.2. Iron-Iron carbide equilibrium diagram.

phase change does not result. In this case, iron carbide is metastable and tends to dissociate after a long time and even it takes years at about 700°C. However, at room temperature, iron carbide is stable and therefore iron-carbon diagram can be considered as representing equilibrium changes under conditions of relatively slow heating and cooling. The Iron-carbon diagram is commonly known as iron-iron carbide equilibrium diagram since at room temperature, carbon forms Fe_3C with iron.

The iron carbon equilibrium diagram represents three important reactions, namely, peritectic, eutectic and eutectoid.

Peritectic reaction occurs at the temperature shown by the line *HJB* (Fig. 6.2.) where liquid iron and the solid solution of carbon in δ iron with 0.1 pct. carbon change to a single phase solid solution of carbon in gamma iron (i.e. austenite) containing carbon 0.18 pct. The reaction is represented as:

$$\text{Liquid} + \delta\text{-iron} \underset{\text{heating}}{\overset{\text{cooling}}{\rightleftharpoons}} \text{austenite}$$

Eutectic reaction takes place at the temperature of 1130°C represented by the line ECF. At the eutectic point C, liquid changes to ledeburite which is a mechanical mixture of austenite and cementite. The reaction is given as:

$$\text{Liquid} \underset{\text{heating}}{\overset{\text{cooling}}{\rightleftharpoons}} \underbrace{\text{austenite} + \text{cementite}}_{\text{eutectic—ledeburite}}$$

The point *E* in Fig. 6.2, indicates the maximum solid solubility of carbon in austenite. This solid solubility decreases with decreasing temperature and corresponds to the line ES.

The *eutectoid reaction* occurs at the temperature shown by the line PSK. The reaction may be represented as:

$$\text{Austenite} \underset{\text{heating}}{\overset{\text{cooling}}{\rightleftharpoons}} \underbrace{\text{ferrite} + \text{cementite}}_{\text{eutectoid—pearlite}}$$

At this temperature, maximum carbon content can be dissolved in ferrite.

The alloys with less than 2.0 pct. C in iron are usually referred to as steels while those with more than 2.0 pct. are known as cast irons. Further, steels consisting less than 0.8 pct. C are known as hypoeutectoid steels while those containing carbon between 0.8 pct. and 2.0 pct. are called hypereutectoid steels. Similarly, cast irons are classed as hypoeutectic and hypereutectic corresponding to the carbon contents ranging from 2.0 pct. to 4.3 pct. and from 4.3 pct. to 6.67 pct. respectively. In practice, steels are alloys with maximum of 1.7 pct. carbon content.

6.4.2. Critical Temperatures

The temperatures at which a phase change in solid state ccurs, are known as the critical temperatures (Fig. 6.2). The loci of these points are given designations. The curve separating the phase regions of austenite and austenite plus ferrite is designated as A_3. The curve separating the phase region austenite and austenite plus cementite is designated as Acm. Both A_3 and Acm are the upper critical temperature lines respectively for hypo-and hyper-eutectoid steels. The eutectoid temperature line is known as the lower critical temperature line and is named A_1 and $A_{3,1}$ respectively for hypo-and hyper-eutectoid steels.

All these critical temperatures shown in Fig. 6.2 are obtained under strict equilibrium conditions of slow heating and cooling of steels. However, in practice, the equilibrium conditions are seldom achieved. If a hypo-eutectoid steel is slowly heated, the transformation does not start exactly at A_1 or A_3 temperature but at a temperature somewhat more than these values. The critical tempertures observed on heating are therefore designated as Ac points. Thus, all the critical points on heating are indicated by Ac_1, Ac_3, and $Ac_{3,1}$. On the other hand, upon cooling of steels, the transformations take place at a temperature somewhat lower than the equilibrium values and are designated by Ar. Hence, the critical temperatures obtained during cooling of steels may be represented by Ar_3, Ar_1 and $Ar_{3,1}$.

6.4.3. Transformations on Heating

To illustrate the transformation on heating, a hypo-eutectoid steel containing 0.3 pct. carbon that has been slowly cooled under almost equilibrium conditions (Fig. 6.3) may be considered. If such a steel is heated to just below Ac_1 point, no phase transformation occurs. As the temperature is increased just above Ac_1, transformation pearlite to austenite begins. The transformation from pearlite to austenite is continued till the temperature reaches just below Ac_3. Above Ac_3, there exists a single phase solid solution of carbon in γ-iron, i.e. austenite. A two-phase mixture (i.e. ferrite γ-Fe) exists between Ac_1 and

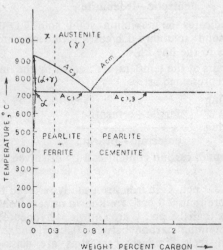

FIG. 6.3. Iron-Iron carbide equilibrium diagram showing heating and cooling of 0.3 pct. carbon steel.

Ac_3. The process of phase transformation involves nucleation and growth of austenite grains. The eutectoid reaction can be represented as:

$$\text{Ferrite} + \text{cementite} \quad \overset{\text{heating}}{\underset{\text{cooling}}{\rightleftharpoons}} \quad \text{austenite.}$$

In case of slow heating of the hypereutectoid steels, the transformation from pearlite to austenite starts at $Ac_{3,1}$ point and completes at Ac_m point. At above the upper critical temperature, there is no phase transformation on further heating of steels for useful heat treating operations. However, the grain growth of austenite takes place.

6.4.4. Transformation on Cooling

If the same hypo-eutectoid steel is cooled slowly from austenitization temperature, no transformation results at just above the Ar_3 point. Just below Ar_3 point transformation from austenite to ferrite begins by allotropic change from γ-iron to α-iron. This transformation is continuous until just above Ar_1 point. As the cooling is continued, transformation from austenite to pearlite occurs at just below the Ar_1 point again by the process of nucleation and growth. The reaction is given as:

$$\text{Austenite} \rightleftharpoons \text{ferrite} + \text{cementite.}$$

Pearlitic structure shows alternate lamellae of ferrite and cementite. This structure remains even at room temperature.

6.4.5. Transformation of Austenite at Constant Temperature

As stated earlier, most of the heat treatment processes take place under non-equilibrium conditions and therefore, iron-iron carbide equilibrium diagram is not so useful to study the heat treatment processes. It has been found that both time and temperature markedly influence the structural changes that occur after the decomposition of austenite and hence, influence the properties of the steel. It is essential to know as to how long it will take for the austenite to begin to transform and how long it will take to complete the reaction, and the nature of the resulting product. The nature of the product changes with the temperature of transformation below the critical temperature. All these data can be expressed in the form of curves by plotting graphs between time and temperature. These diagrams are known as isothermal transformation (I.T.) or the time-temperature-transformation (T.T.T.) diagrams.

A T.T.T. curve for a given steel can be constructed by taking standard sized samples cut from the same stock and heating them to the austenitization temperature. After soaking at this temperature, the samples are withdrawn from the furnace and inserted in a bath of molten metal/salt maintained at certain sub-critical temperature. At different time-intervals the samples are removed one by one and rapidly quenched in water which converts any untransformed austenite to martensite. The samples are then examined microscopically and the hardness is also checked. Microstructures show the extent of transformations of austenite to pearlite. This process is repeated for various subcritical temperatures of transformation. The data are then expressed as time-temperature diagram. In order to condense results, time is presented to logarithmic scale. The loci of points where the transformation begins is disignated as T_s while the loci of transformarion ends is designated as T_f as is shown in Fig. 6.4. It is apparent from the Fig. 6.4. that above Ae_1 (the lower critical temperature) austenite is stable. The region to the left of T_s consists of metastable austenit where as that to

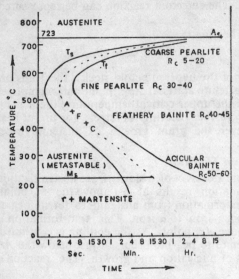

FIG. 6.4. Isothermal transformation diagram for eu'ectoid steel.

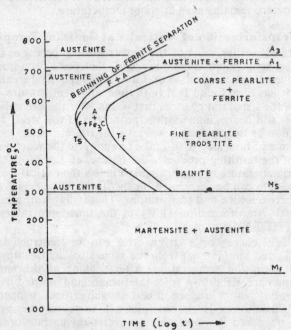

FIG. 6.5. Isothermal transformation diagram for hypoeutectoid steel.

the right of T_f is composed of the transformation product i.e. an aggregate of ferrite and cementite. The area between T_s and T_f obviously consists of a mixture of untransformed austenite, ferrite and cementite. In case of the T.T.T. curves for hypo- and hyper-eutectoid steels, an additional line above the nose is also obtained. This addition line shows the separation of ferrite in hypo-eutectoid steels (Fig. 6.5.) and cementite in hypereutectoid steels (Fig. 6.6.). The other two lines are the same as for eutectoid steel.

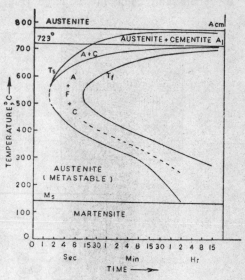

FIG. 6.6. Isothermal transformation diagram for hypereutectoid steel.

The M_s temperature line in T.T.T. diagrams represents the transformation of austenite to martensite which forms upon rapid quenching (as in water) of steels from the temperature above Ac_3.

The T.T.T. curve for steels is of considerable sinificance in that it gives an over all picture of the transformation behaviour of austenite on the basis of which a metallurgist can suggest suitable heat-treating conditions to get the desirable micro-constitùents. For instance, the nature of microconstituents varies with the rate of cooling, time of soaking at austenitization temperature, the degree of under cooling, and other factors.

All the alloying elements, except cobalt, shift the T.T.T. curves to right hand side.

6 4.6. Structure and Properties of Ferrite-Cementite Aggregate

Austenite, upon isothermal cooling at subcritical temperatures in the range Ae_1 to M, transforms to a aggregate of ferrite and cementite. However, the dispersivity of the aggregate varies with the degree of undercooling.

As already mentioned, the transformation of austenite to ferrite-cementite aggregate involves diffusion processes. Initially small nuclei of the transformation product are formed and then they grow at the expense of the parent phase. As the degree of supercooling increases, the rate of nucleation becomes predominant over the rate of growth and therefore, the dispersivity of the aggregate increases accordingly.

If the temperature of transformation is closer to the point Ae_1

(about 700°C), the formation of nuclei is slow. The growth proceeds rapidly to form large pearlite colonies and the interlamellar spacing of ferrite and cementite is large (Fig. 6.7a). At somewhat lower

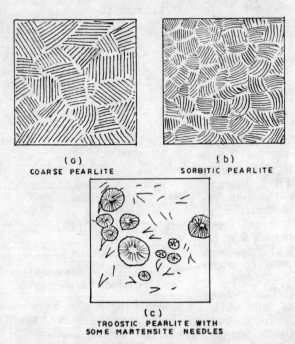

(a)
COARSE PEARLITE

(b)
SORBITIC PEARLITE

(c)
TROOSTIC PEARLITE WITH
SOME MARTENSITE NEEDLES

FIG. 6.7. (a) Coarse pearlite, (b) Sorbitic pearlite and (c) troostic pearlite with some martensite needles.

temperatures of transformation (650°C), the interlamellar spacing of ferrite and cementite is reduced. This structure is commonly known as medium pearlite or sorbitic pearlite (Fig. 6.7b). At still lower temperature of transformation (i.e. near to the nose of the T.T.T. curve), the interspacing between ferrite and cementite is reduced to such an extent that it is difficult to resolve under the conventional microscope and can be observed only under electron microscope. This fine pearlitic structure is named as troostic pearlite (Fig. 6.7c). The structure shows a mixture of radial lamellae of ferrite and cementite.

The structures of the austenite transformed in the temperature range between the nose of the T.T.T. curve and the M_s temperature are different in form from those discussed above, though the constituent phases are the same. If the transformation temperature is in the upper range, the structure resembles some features of fine pearlite and is called the *upper* or *feathery bainite* after E.C. Bain who described this for the first time. The transformation product obtained in the lower bay of T.T.T. curve, resembles martensitic structure and is usually known as lower or acicular bainite. The upper and lower bainitic structures as seen under conventional microscope are shown in Fig. 6.8a and 6.8.b. respectively. The analogue electron microphotographs are shown in Figs. 6.9a and 6.9b. respectively. It is apparent from Fig. 6.9a, that this carbide platelets are oriented parallel to the long direction of ferrite needles which form the matrix. On the other hand, the cementite platelets are usually oriented at an angle of 55° or 60° with respect to the long axis of ferrite needles in the lower bainitic structure (Fig. 6.9b).

FIG. 6.8. Microstructures of (a) upper bainite, and (b) lower bainite as seen under optical microscope.

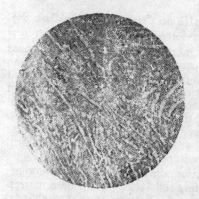 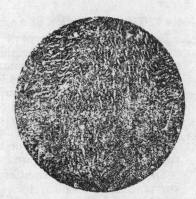

FIG. 6.9. Microstructures of (a) upper bainite, and (b) lower bainite as seen under electron microscope.

Pearlite and bainite mainly differ from each other in the mechanisms of transformation. Pearlite is nucleated by cementite, the formation of which is accompanied by the formation of ferrite whereas bainite is nucleated with ferrite which is associated with the precipitation of cementite.

Transformations below M_s causes F.C.C. austenite to transform to supersaturated B.C.C. ferrite where diffusion is too slow to form nuclei of ferrite or cementite. The transformation is shear like and therefore the structure is highly stressed. The B.C.C. ferrite formed is supersaturated with carbon which introduces tetragonality. This body centred tetragonal structure is commonly known as *martensite*

and resembles needle like structure under the microscope. Transformation to martensite is not a time dependent process and martensite forms only upon continuous cooling of the steel below M_s. Since volume of martensite is more than that of ferrite (BCC), a resultant dimensional expansion takes place. This results in a considerable amount of strain energy due to the resistance of the matrix (the parent phase) to the shape change. As a result of the strain energy factor, martensite has a plate like or needle-like structure (Fig. 6.10). The strain field is also responsible for the high hardness of martensite

FIG. 6.10. Microstructure of martensite.

which increases as a function of carbon content and optimises to Rc 65, when the carbon in steel reaches 0.6 pct.

6.4.7. Transformation of Austenite on Continuous Cooling

From the observation of T.T.T. diagram of eutectoid steel, it is clear that (apart from cementite) martensite is the hardest phase among the various micro-constituents obtained as a result of the decomposition of austenite and it is formed by continuous cooling of steels. Therefore, the basic criterion of hardening steel is to cool it continuously at a fast rate. In practice, majority of heat treatment operations are performed by continuous cooling of steel in certain medium from the temperature, where at least some austenite exists. Therefore, from the views point of studying heat treating operations, continuous cooling curves are more important than I-T curves.

Similar to isothermal-transformation diagrams, continuous cooling curves can be obtained by plotting time-temperature data corresponding to the instant at which transformation starts and ends as shown in Fig. 6.11. The loci of these points are comparable with those obtained in isothermal -transformation of steels. The time-temperature curves obtained by continuous cooling are displaced to lower temperatures and longer times in relation to I-T curves for the same steel.

In Fig. 6.11, curve 'A' represents the slow cooling as in a furnace. Since, the temperature of transformation is nearer to the *Ae* temperature, coarse lamellar pearlite is formed. At still faster cooling rate as in air (curve *B*), the product is finer pearlite. The curve *C* shows a cooling rate so fast that only a part of austenite transforms to fine pearlite whereas rest of the austenite transforms to martensite. Quenching in water (curve *D*) provides sufficiently fast cooling rate so as to suppress any non-martensitic transformation, and transformation starts only when M_s is reached and then continues to form until M_f is reached. In case of drastic quench, some of the austenite may not get enough time to transform to martensite and remain unchanged. This austenite is usually called retained austenite. The coolling rate corresponding to the curve *E* is just enough to produce hardened steel and therefore, it is called the critical cooling rate.

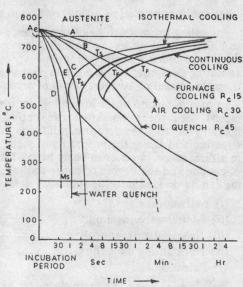

FIG 6.11. Continuous cooling curves superimposed on I-T curves.

A cooling rate slower than the critical will not produce completely hardened steel because a dual phase structure will form which consists of a non-martensitic phase and martensite. This type of transformation is commonly known as split transformation.

6.4.8. Annealing

In general, annealing is referred to the process of softening a hard metal by heating to high temperature and the cooling at a slow rate (generally inside the furnace itself). The purpose of annealing may be one of the following:

(*i*) to soften the steel to improve machinability;

(*ii*) to relieve internal stresses caused by some previous treatment such as forging, rolling, casting or welding;

(*iii*) to refine the grain size;

(*iv*) to remove gases entrapped in steel during casting.

The process of annealing consist of the following steps:

(*a*) heating the steel to the desired temperature depending upon the type of annealing;

(b) holding it for some period at this temperature to allow the necessary structural changes to occur;

(c) cooling the steel at a slow rate as in furnace.

Annealing process can be of two types, i e. (i) first order annealing and (ii) second order annealing. First order annealing differs from the second order annealing in two respect, i.e. (i) the first order annealing does not involve a phase change and (ii) the rate of cooling from the annealing temperature is of secondary importance.

In case of second order annealing treatment, all the three parameters, i.e., the temperature of heating, the time of soaking (or holding) at this temperature, and the rate of cooling affect the structure and hence the properties of steel. Cooling is usually done in a furnace or in air or in some bath. Depending upon the method of cooling and the degree of super-cooling, the second order annealing can be divided into the following categories:

(i) Full annealing;

(ii) Isothermal annealing;

(iii) Spheroidizing annealing;

(iv) Normalising annealing;

(v) Patenting.

Full annealing. The main purposes of full annealing are :

(a) to soften the steel and improve machinability;

(b) to relieve internal stresses caused by preceding operation such as casting, hot working, welding, etc.;

(c) to refine the grain structure.

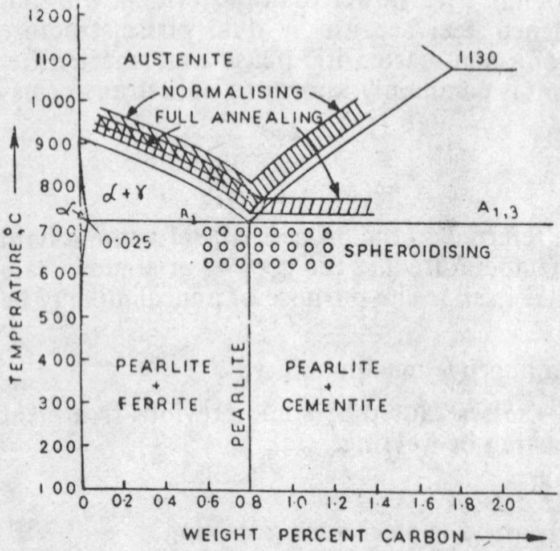

The full annealing operation consists of the followoing steps:

(a) heating the steel 30-50°C above Ac_3 and $Ac_{3,1}$ for hypo-eutectoid steels and hyper-eutectoid steels, respectively, as shown in Fig. 6 12;

(b) soaking at this temperature for a period of time depending upon the section thickness of the article so as to homogenise the structure. The soaking time recommended is approxi-

FIG. 6.12. Iron-Iron carbide showing temperature ranges for various second order annealing treatments.

mately 3-4 minutes for each mm thickness of the article under treatment;

(c) cooling at a slow rate so that the austenite could decompose at a smaller degree of undercooling. The rate of cooling recommended for plain carbon and low alloy steels are 200°C/hr and 100-300°C/hr respectively. The cooling course is shown in Fig. 6.13.

Cooling is done in the furnace itself and the rate of cooling can be adjusted by frequent opening and closing the furnace doors or by controlling the heating of the furnace. If the steel articles are simple in shape, they can be cooled in air after cooling to about 500-600°C in the furnace without any danger of thermal

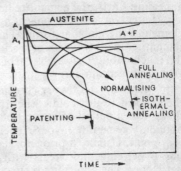

FIG. 6.13. T-T-T diagram showing cooling for second order annealing.

stresses. Complicated in shape are prone to thermal stresses and are therefore, cooled in the furnace down to the room temperature. The approximate annealing temperatures for various steels are shown in Table 6.1. The structure of hypo-eutectoid steel after annealing is shown in Fig. 6.14.

TABLE 6.1. *The Approximate Annealing Temperatures Recommended for Plane Carbon Steels*

Per cent carbon in Steel	Annealing temperature in °C
0.20	860-890
0.40	820-850
0.60	800-830
0.80	760-790
1.00	760-780
1.20	760-780

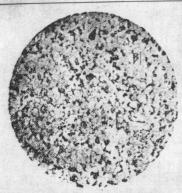

FIG. 6.14. The structure of hypo-eutectoid steel after annealing.

Isothermal annealing. Isothermal annealing involves heating steel articles to the austenitization temperature and after soaking for the desirable period of time they are cooled to 30-100°C below the lower critical temperature. The articles are then maintained at this temperature for the transformation of austenite to occur. The structure so obtained is pearlite which may be coarse to medium depending upon the temperature of transformation below the critical. The principal advantage of isothermal annealing is that a uniform structure is obtained.

The cooling curve for isothermal annealing is shown in Fig. 6.13.

Spheroidizing annealing. In the spheroidizing annealing, the pearlitic-cementite lamellae are changed to globular form. As the annealing starts, the cementite lamellae take unusual shape of a dog's leg. Later on as the anaealing proceeds, the cementite lamellae change to the globular form. The structure consists of spheroids of cementite in the matrix of ferrite. This treatment is used to improve the machinability of high carbon and alloy steels and of certain grades of medium carbon steels.

In general, the hyper-eutectoid steel is heated to 740-780°C and then cooled to just below the lower critical temperature and held there for a period of 2 to 6 hours. In order to spheroidize the grain boundary cementite, hyper-eutectoid steels must be annealed above $A_{3,1}$ point. Usually a prior normalising is preferred before spheroidizing hyper-eutectoid steels with a view to break down the cementite net work. The annealing temperature range is shown in Fig. 6.12.

Hypo-eutactoid steels containng 0.5 to 0.8 pct. C are annealed below A_1. The heat treatment cycle involves heating to not more than 50°C above A_1 and annealed not more than 50°C below A_1 for 2-6 hours. The annealing may be done above A_1 but only a few tens of degrees above A_1. At higher annealing temperatures a greater amount of cementite separates out and transforms to lamellar form rather than globular.

The spheroidized structure possesses the lowest hardness and therefore may not be suitable for certain machining operations such as milling, planing, drilling or reaming. In such cases, a higher annealing temperature can be used so as to get lamellar pearlite together with spheroidised structure. Cementite in the lamellar form increases the hardness of the spheroidised structure.

Normalising annealing. Normalising annealing involves heating the steel (either hypo- or hyper-eutectoid) to a temperature 30° to 50°C above the upper critical temperature (Fig. 6.12) and after soaking for 10 to 20 minutes at this temperature, it is cooled in air. Cooling in air is faster than in furnace and this causes the austenite to transform at lower temperature. Hence, pearlitic structure so produced is more dispersed, i.e., finer. Air cooling also suppresses the separation of excess phase (ferrite in hypo- and cementite in hyper-autectoid steels) partially. Thus, by normalising, greater strength, hardness and toughness can be obtained.

Normalising is preferred to annealing for the following advantages:

(i) because of relatively faster cooling rate, finer pearlite is formed which is stronger and tougher than the coarse pearlite obtained by full annealing;

(ii) faster cooling rate suppresses partially the separation of excess ferrite or cementite both of which tend to reduce tensile strength of the steel;

(iii) instead of cooling in a furnace, cooling is done in air, thus there is saving in energy/fuel and availability of the furnace for production increases.

Normalising is used as an intermediate operation to improve grain size and machinability, and to eliminate structure defects. It may be noted that any process involving air cooling is not always referred to as normalising treatment. For instance, many high alloy steels are air cooled to produce martensite rather than pearlite with a view to harden the steel.

Patenting annealing. Patenting is a special kind of annealing operation used for wires, ropes and springs. The process consists of heating the wire to a temperature 150-200°C above Ac_3 so as to homogenise austenite properly. The wire is then quenched in a salt or lead bath maintained at a temperature of 450-550°C i.e., near the nose of T.T.T. curve (Fig. 6.13). The structure after patenting consists of fine pearlite or bainite or a combination of the two. The speed of the wire through the bath is adjusted so as to prevent transformation to lower bainite or martensite.

The purpose of patenting heat treatment is two-fold. The first is to make the wire amenable to large reductions in cold working without fracture. The second is to improve the strength and toughness obtained after subsequent cold working. As a consequence, the wire can be bent, and twisted with ease. Cold working after patenting produces a fine grain structure.

6.4.9. Hardening of Steel

Hardening is the process of heat treatment by which the steel is made hard by rapid quenching from high temperature. The heat treating cycle consists of heating the steel to 30°−50°C above Ac_3 for hypo-eutectoid steels and to a suitable temperature above $Ac_{3,1}$ for hyper-eutectoid steels. The hardening temperature of steel depends upon its chemical composition, particularly the carbon content which can be appreciated from Fig. 6.15. The hardening temperature for alloy steel varies from 1100°−1300°C. After soaking at this temperature for a period of time depending upon the section thickness, the steel is quenched in water, brine solution or oil. If all the austenite is transformed, the structure at room temperature shows complete martensite provided the rate of cooling is higher than the critical cooling rate (C.C.R.). The heating and holding times for hardening carbon and structural steels are shown in Table 6.2.

Unlike hyper-eutectoid steels, hypo-eutectoid steels are homogenized at above Ac_3 point before quenching. If these steels are heated between the range $Ac_1 - Ac_3$, some ferrite will remain along with austenite and as on quenching only austenite transforms to martensite. Presence of soft ferrite with martensite decreases the hardness of the steel and results in soft spots. On the other hand, if hyper-eutectoid steels are heated to above Acm point for hardening, there will be approaching grains coarsening temperature of austenite. This results in coarse grained martensite associated with warpage and quenching cracks. If the same steel is quenched from above $Ac_{3,1}$, the degree of warpage and quenching cracks is decreased and the structure consists of martensite dispersed with undissolved carbides. The hardness of carbides (about 800 BHN) is more than that of martensite (approximately 650 BHN).

Since, hardening of steel is always accompanied with internal stresses caused by the structural change and high temperature gradient, the steels must be reheated to below the lower critical tempera-

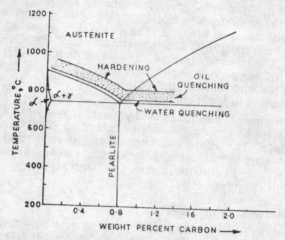

FIG. 6.15. Iron carbon diagram showing hardening range.

ture in order to relieve the internal stresses. This operation of heat treatment is known as tempering and is discussed in detail in section 6.4.10.

TABLE 6.2. *Recommended Heating Times and Holding Times for Structural Steel Parts*

Cross sections mm	Box type oil or gas fired furnaces		Salt bath furnaces	
	heating time in min.	holding time in min.	heating time in min.	holding time in min.
25	20	5	7	3
50	40	10	17	8
75	60	15	24	12
100	80	20	33	17
125	100	25	40	20
150	120	30	50	25
200	160	40	65	35

Quenching media. Various quenching media are being used for hardening of steels depending on their chemical composition. Before discussing the quenching media, it is important to known how cool-

ing proceeds when a steel article is immersed from a high temperature into a quenching medium. As soon as the article is inserted into
the coolant, the skin of the article is chilled and a thin film of vapours
of the coolant is formed on the surface of the article. This thin
vapour blanket prevents further heat transfer from the hot metal to
the coolant due to its poor thermal conductivity. In order to have
cooling fast and continuous, the thin vapour coating must be broken
down. This is possible if the coolant has high boiling point, high
latent heat of vaporization, and low viscocity. Further, the vapour
blanket can be washed off by the surrounding layers of the liquid if
the fluidity of the coolant is high. The most commonly used quenching media are water, mineral oils and salt baths. The cooling efficiency is best in water.

The main aim of hardening steels is to obtain martensitic structure
which forms only where the cooling rate is faster than the critical
cooling rate in the range $Ar_1 - M_s$. However it is preferable to cool
steel at a slower rate in the transformation range $M_s - M_f$ to minimise
the internal stresses built up by structural changes and thermal gradient across the section of the steel. A coolant which can create the
above conditions of cooling is an ideal quenching medium. However,
on such coolant is available commercially which can satisfy the
requirements of an ideal quenchant as is clear from the Table 6.3.

TABLE 6.3. *Recommended Cooling Rates for Small Specimens
in Various Cooling Media*

Quenchant	Cooling rate, °C/See. in the temperature range of	
	650-550°C	300-200°C.
Water at 18°C	600	270
Water at 74°C	30	200
10 pct. NaOH in water at 18°C.	1,200	300
Soap suds	30	200
Mineral oils	100-150	20-50
Compressed air	30	10
Still air	3	1

If an object is complex in shape having thick and thin sections,
quenching in water is not preferred. This is true even if the objects
consist of grooves, holes or sharp corners. Objects of this type require
oils or salt baths as the quenching media in order to prevent warpage
and cracks. The steel articles demanding minimum distortion should
be quenched in oil. A typical example of such articles is gears.

Sometimes, the quenching media are selected on the basis of the
microstructure needed at room temperature. For example, in certain
high alloy steels, a bainitic structure is needed for optimum toughness
(as in austempering). Here, hot oil or molten salt is the preferred
quenching medium.

Cooling methods for hardening steels. The most widely

employed cooling method is the conventional water quenching in which the steel article is directly quenched from high temperature. This causes warpage and quenching cracks to a great extent. The lower degree of warpage and cracks can be achieved by quenching the steel in an ideal coolant, which is seldom available commercially. Neverthless, ideal cooling conditions can be ensured by either of the following two ways.

(i) Quenching in two media.

(ii) Stepwise quenching.

Quenching in two media. Quenching in two media is also called time quenching. This method of hardening is very old and is used since iron smith's era. The process consists of cooling the steel first in water and after holding for a short while (to decrease temperature to 400 to 300°C) transferred into oil or in air. The heat treatment cycle is shown in 6.16. Quenching in water prevents pearlitic transformation, whereas slow cooling in oil or air diminishes the extant of warpage and cracks caused by internal stresses. This is because of the fact that the surface layers that are cooled intensively are tempered due to still high temperature in the inner layers which are not cooled so sharply. Consequently, if the section is heavy, pearlitic transformation results in the core while tempered martensite forms on the surface.

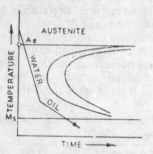

FIG 6 16. Heat treatment cycle for quenching in two media.

In spite of the above advantages, time quenching suffers from a drawback that it needs special care to prevent pearlitic transformation at the surface of the heavy sections. However, the method has been widely used for heat treating tools of plain carbon steels such as taps, dies, milling cutters, etc.

Stepwise quenching. The stepwise quenching involves the heating of the article to the hardening temperature and than its rapid transfer into a hot bath of oil or molten salt. After holding for a desired period of time (depending upon the microstructure desired), it is cooled in air or oil.

The temperature of the hot medium is usually maintained in the lower bay of the metastable austenite region of the C-curve (T.T.T. curve) where the supercooled austenite is quite stable. The step-wise quenching possesses the following advantages:

(i) It is easier to control than time quenching;

(ii) Since temperature gradient across the cross-section of the article is minimised and the transformation to martensite is not drastic, the internal stresses are reduced considerably.

(*iii*) When the article is removed from the bath, it is ductile for a while and therefore can be straightened to eliminate warpage.

Step-wise hardening or cooling can be subdivided in two categories depending upon the microstructure desired at room temperature. These are austempering (or isothermal quenching), and martempering. The heat treatment cycles for both the heat treatment processes are shown in Fig. 6.17.

Austempering is advantage-ous eous over martempering in that the internal stresses are reduced considerably and the quenched articles can be straightened. Austempering is economical for hardening plainc arbon steel only, whereas martempering has limited

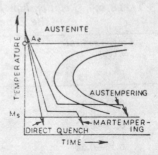

FIG. 6.17. Heat treatment cycle for stepwise hardening.

application for carbon steels of thickness upto 8-10 mm only. However, martempering can economically be used for alloy and tool steels.

Hardenability. Hardenability of steel may be defined as the depth of penetration of hardness. From the earlier discusion it may be noted that martensite is the principal phase in hardened steels. Cooling proceeds from surface to core of the steel when it is immersed into a coolant. Therefore, the temperature drops rapidly on the surface layers but is still high in the core of the article. Consequently, the rate of cooling in the surface layer exceeds the CCR which is responsible for martensite, whereas in the core, either pearlite or bainite is formed due to slow cooling. Thus, hardenability means the depth to which the martensite has formed. Fully hardened articles have the same properties throughout the section thickness. Complete hardening of carbon steels occurs in articles upto 20 mm thickness. The properties vary across the section by variation in the structure from surface to core, as illustrated in Fig. 6.18.

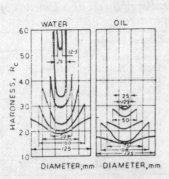

FIG. 6.18. Hardenability curve.

The hardenability is usually measured as the depth of the steel article to which semi-martensite zone (i.e. 50 pct. martensite +50 pct. troostite) has formed. The hardness of the semi-martensite zone varies with the composition of the steel as indicated in Table 6.4.

By the addition of alloying elements in steel the stability of the supercooled austenite increases, which in turn decreases the CCR. Thus, even a slow cooling (as in air or oil) is enough to cause martensitic transformation to a greater depth. In other words, hardenability of alloy steels is more than that of carbon steels.

TABLE 6.4. *Relationship Between the Hardness of the Semi-Martensite Zone and the Carbon Content*

Carbon content per cent	Hardness of the semi-martensite zone, Rc	
	Carbon steels	Alloy steels
0.13—0.22	25	30
0.23—0.27	30	35
0.28—0.32	35	40
0.33—0.42	40	45
0.43—0.52	45	50
0.53—0.62	50	55

6.4.10. Tempering

As quenched steel is very hard and brittle, and accompanied by high internal stresses. This steel cannot be employed in as quenched state because even slight mechanical shock may cause its failure. In order to improve toughness and relieve severe internal stresses the hardened steel is tempered. Tempering is the process of heating hardened steel to below the lower critical temperature and then cooling at any desired rate. As the tempering temperature increases above room temperature, initially some carbon is diffused out of the supersaturated solid solution of carbon in α-iron. Consequently, the α-iron which was supersaturated with carbon becomes ferrite and the carbon which has separated out from the tetragonal martensite forms cementite by combining with iron. This causes volume changes i.e., the expanded lattice is contracted now. Further,

TABLE 6.5. *Superificial Colour of Unalloyed Steels as a Function of Tempering Temperature*

Temperature, °C	Temper Colour
220	Straw yellow
240	Dark straw to light brown
260	Brownish purple
270	Brown
285	Purple
295	Dark blue
310	Light blue
325	Gray
350	Gray to purple
375	Gray to blue
400	Dull gray to deep blue.

the structure now consists of hard carbide particles distributed in the soft ferrite matrix. This structure is responsible for the increase in toughness and impact resistance with the simultaneous decrease in hardness. Any retained austenite gets transformed to bainite (i.e. an aggregate of ferrite and cementite). As the tempering temperature increases, the coarsening of carbide particles also increases resulting in softening of the steel.

Tempering is employed for various tools and work pieces, such as springs, cold chisels, spaners, screw drivers, power press cutters, planning cutters for wood, axles, screw cutting dies, hacksaw blades, etc.

During tempering, the surface of the steel may oxidise. The thin oxide film appears in diffierent colours depending upon the tempering temperature. Table 6.5. shows temper colours and tempering temperatures for various types of tools made from carbon steels.

6.4.11. Dependence of Properties on Grain Size

The properties of an alloy are markedly influenced not only by the nature of the phases present in the microstucture, but also by the size of the grains. For instance, in an annealed steel, the size of grains of ferrite and pearlite has considerable effect on the mechanical properties of the steel. The grains size of the product is dependent upon the grain size of austenite from which the grains have formed. The grain size of austenite also affects the rate of transformation during continuous cooling or under isothermal conditions. Hence, the hardening characteristics of steel are influenced by austenite grain size.

When an originally annealed steel is heated to just above the upper critical temperature, the grains of austenite formed from pearlite are fine initially. On further rise of temperature the grains grow primarily as a function of temperature and secondarily a function of time. On heating upto a temperature of 930°C, if the grain size of austenite increases rapidly, then such steels are called coarse grain steels. On the other hand, if the growth of austenite grains above the upper critical temperature is very slow with the rise of temperature upto 930°C, the steel is referred to as fine grained. The temperature 930°C is selected here because majority of heat-treatment processes involve heating of steels upto 930°C. The steels that are originally fine grained, usually contain inhomogenities such as oxides along the grain boundary region which inhibit the grain growth even at high temperture.

The most commonly used method of determining grain size of steels is the ASTM grain size as recommended by the American Society for Testing Materials in their standard E19-46. The method consists of comparing the structure under examination at proper magnification with the ASTM standard chart. The ASTM grain size charts are formed at 100 X magnification. The grain size is usually expressed as the number of grains per square inch at 100 X according to the expression

$$n = 2^{N-1}$$

Where n is the number of grains/in^2
and $N-1$ is the ASTM grain size no.

Effect of austenite grain size on properties. The grain size of austenite considerably affects the reaction characteristics during transformation and hence, the properties of steel. The effect of austenite grain size on the various properties are shown in Table 6.6.

TABLE 6.6. *Effect of Austenite Grain Size on the Properties of Steel*

Property	Austenite Grain Size	
	Fine	Coarse
Retained austenite	Less	More
Warpage in quenching	Less	More
Internal stress after quenching	Lower	Higher
Toughness	More	Less
Possibility of soft spots in quenching	More	Less
Penetration carburising	Shallower	Deeper
Possibility of quenching cracks	Less	More

6.4.12. Temper Embrittlement

Temper brittleness is usually described as the notch impact intergranular brittleness induced in some steels by slow cooling after tempering above about 600°C and also if they are held for a long period in the temperature range of 400° to 550°C. Temper brittleness may be caused by some elements like, Cr and Mn which enhance the segregation of embrittling elements such as P, Sn, Sb, As, by chemical interaction on slow cooling from 600°C. The embrittling effect can be reduced by reheating the steel to 600°C followed by rapid cooling so as to prevent grain boundary precipitation. Mo also decreases the embrittlement effect.

6.4.13. Sub-Zero Treatment of Steel

In steels like high carbon and alloy, the M_f temperature is usually below 0°C. Such steels when quenched from the hardening temperature to room temperature, some austenite is retained. This retained austenite reduces the hardness, wear resistance and thermal conductivity of the steel and makes its dimensionally unstable. In order to convert the retained austenite to martensite, steel must be cooled below zero (of the order of −30° to −120°C) and held there for 1 to 1.5 hours.

Prolonged holding at room temperature after hardening will tend to stabilise the austenite in many grades of steels. This stabilised austenite is difficult to convert into martensite even after a sub-zero treatment.

6 5. SPECIAL HEAT TREATMENT

Special heat treatment includes surface and case hardening of steels and thermo-mechnical heat treatment.

6.5.1. Surface Hardening and Case Hardening of Steels

There are many machines and automobile parts which are subjected to frequent mechanical shocks and require high wear resistance and hardness on the surface. Gears, for instance, are to work under severe conditions of friction and mechanical shock. The high surface hardness and wear resistance coupled with a tough core can be attained by specialised heat treatments known as surface hardening and case hardening processes.

In the case hardening operation, the properties of the surface layers of steels are altered by altering their chemical composition with respect to core. This results in a hard surface layer above a much softer and more ductile steel core. Because of the change in chemical composition in the surface area, the treatment is also known as chemical-thermal or thermo-chemical treatment. The principal elements that change the chemical composition in the surface layers are the carbon and nitrogen. These elements in their nascent form are absorbed in the steel by the process of diffusion at the desired temperature. When carbon is absorbed, the treatment is termed as carburising, whereas, if nitrogen is absorbed, the process is called nitriding. In certain cases, both nitrogen and carbon are absorbed in the steel and the treatment is known as carbo-nitriding or cyaniding.

Surface and case hardening results in the improvements of the following properties:

(a) Wear resistance under conditions of low compressive loading (upto 68.94 MPa*) as well as high compressive loading (upto 2077 MPa).

(b) Resistance to scuffing or seizing.

(c) Bending or torsional strength.

(d) Bending fatigue strength.

(e) Resistance to pitting or case crushing.

Surface hardening. The basic principle of surface hardening consists of heating the steel article to above the upper critical temperature for few seconds followed by quenching in water. Since the time at high temperature is short, therefore, the penetration of heat is restricted to surface layers only. Thus, after quenching, martensite forms in the surface layers of the article, whereas the structure in the core remains almost unchanged. The structure of the core is usually pearlite or bainite obtained by prior heat treatment operation.

Surface hardening is further subdivided as Induction hardening and Flame hardening based on the means of heating the steel.

Induction hardening. In the induction hardening process, the part to be surface hardened is surrounded by an inductor in the form of a coil or block usually made of copper. The inductor coil comprises several turns of perforated copper tube. A high frequency current

---

*1 MPa (Mega Pascal) = 1 MN/M² (Mega Newtons/Metre²)

passes through the inductor to induce eddy currents through the steel under treatment. The surface layers of the steel are heated due to the resistance offered by it against the flow of eddy currents. After the desired temperature is reached, the steel is cooled by the spray of water through the perforations in the surrounding inductor. The time of holding at the temperature generally varies from 1 to 5 seconds.

The depth of penetration of heat depends on two factors, namely, (i) the power, and (ii) the frequency of current employed. Usually a power input of 0.1-2 KW/Cm^2 of the heated surface is used. The depth of penetration that is required can be calculated from the following expressions:

$$d_c = \frac{20}{\sqrt{f}} \text{—cold state (20°C)}$$

and
$$d_h = \frac{500}{\sqrt{f}} \text{—hot state (800°C)}$$

Where $d =$ depth of penetration, in mm.
and $f =$ frequency in cycles/sec (HZ).

It is clear from the above expressions that in order to decrease case depth, the frequency is to be increased.

The induction hardening offers the following advantages:

(a) It requires very short time compared to the conventional hardening or case hardening;

(b) Since the holding time at hardening temperature is very short, practically there is no chance of scale formation or decarburisation;

(c) Internal stresses are greatly reduced.

Flame or torch hardening. Flame hardening operation involves heating the surface area of the article to be hardened with an oxy-acetylene flame. When the temperature reaches to above the upper critical temperature, the surface is sprayed with water or some other coolent. The depth of the hardness can be controlled by regulating the intensity of the flame and the time of heating.

In general, surface hardening treatment offers various advantages over the other hardening processes. In ordinary hardening, the whole article becomes hard and wear resistant, including the surface layers. In order to improve core toughness, the hardened steel is tempered. However, tempering leads to softening of the surface also. On the other hand, by surface hardening, the articles having hard and wear resistant surface and a tough or plastic core can be produced. Surface hardening method does not require a separate heating furnace. Since the time of holding at the required temperature is very small, there is no danger of oxidation or decarburisation from the surface and the distortion is sharply reduced. Further, due to high compressive stresses in the surface, fatigue limit is improved.

Case hardening. Case hardening treatment consists of heating the steel article to the desired temperature in a medium consisting of carbon or nitrogen element. The articles are held at this temperature for a period of time depending upon the depth of penetration of these elements required. Then the steel is cooled in oil or water. The case hardening processes are carburising, nitriding, carbo-nitriding, and cyaniding.

Carburising. Carburising is the process of increasing the carbon content in the surface region of steel articles. Since the aim is to produce a hard surface combined. With soft and ductile core, the components that are to be carburised, must be of low carbon (0.15 — 0.25 pct.) steel. Increased carbon in the surface layers causes austenite to transfarm into martensite while in the core due to low carbon, austenite transforms to pearlite. A case depth* of the order of 2.0 mm can be attained by this method.

There are three methods of carburising depending upon the form of carbonaceous material, viz.

(*i*) Pack carburising, (*ii*) Liquid carburising, and (*iii*) Gas carburising.

Pack carburising. The articles to be carburised are surrounded by solid carbonaceous material (usually charcoal or coke) contained in air tight boxes. The temperature of the furnace is raised to 900° to 950°C when carbon reacts with the atmospheric air present in the pores of the material and forms carbon dioxide. The CO_2 further reacts with carbon to form CO which in turn decomposes on the surface of the parts and gives nascent carbon and CO_2. The reactions involved may be expressed as following:

$$C + O_2 \rightarrow CO_2 \qquad \qquad \text{... (6.1)}$$
$$CO_2 + C \rightleftharpoons 2\ CO \qquad \qquad \text{... (6.2)}$$
$$2\ CO \quad \rightarrow CO_2 + C(\text{nascent}) \qquad \text{... (6.3)}$$

If the source of oxygen is only the air present in the boxes, then the CO_2 formed may not be sufficient to carry the reaction (6.2) further and quickly an equilibrium sets in.

In order, the reaction (6.2) to proceed further, energizers are added with the carbonaceous material which after decomposition at high temperature gives rise to cabon dioxide. The most commonly used energizers are $BaCO_3$ and Na_2CO_3.

According to reaction (6.3), the nascent carbon formed tends to diffuse in the austenite which is stable at the operating temperature. The increased carbon content in the surface of the steel parts forms an interstitial solid solution with γ-iron. When the limit of solid solubility of carbon in γ-Fe is reached, it forms Fe_3C with iron, according to the following reactions:-

$$2CO + 3Fe \rightarrow Fe_3C(C \text{ in } \gamma\text{-Fe}) + CO_2 \qquad \text{... (6.4)}$$
$$2CO + 3Fe \rightarrow Fe_3\ C(\text{Cementite}) + CO_2 \qquad \text{... (6.5)}$$

---

*It is defined as the distance from the surface to the plane at which the hardness is about Rc 52(Rockwell Rc 52).

The carbon content in the surface layers should not exceed 1.0 pct., otherwise the case will become very brittle due to the formation of cementite network. The time of carburising may be as high as 24 hours depending upon the case depth required (as shown in Table 6.7), and carbon potential* in the gas mixture. After carburising,

TABLE 6.7. *The Approximate Time of Holding the Work to be Carburised as a Function of Desired Case Depth*

Case depth, (mm)	Approximate holding time at carburising temperature in hours
0.40 to 0.70	4 to 5
0.60 to 0.90	5.5 to 6.5
0.80 to 1.20	6.5 to 10.0
1.00 to 1.40	8.0 to 11.0
1.20 to 1.60	10 0 to 14.0
1.40 to 1.80	11.5 to 16.0
1.60 to 2.0	14.0 to 19.0
1.80 to 2.20	16.0 to 22.0
2.00 to 2.40	19.0 to 24.0

the steel parts are quenched in oil. If required, these are to be heat treated again. Solid or pack carburising suffers from following drawbacks:

(*a*) high labour cost is incurred in packing the parts in the boxes;

(*b*) the heat transfer to the components is poor due to the insulating nature of the carburising medium;

(*c*) total time of the process is long;

(*d*) a non-uniform case depth is obtained.

Liquid carburising. Liquid carburising is employed for shallow cases. The method consists in immersing the parts under treatment in a salt bath composed of a mixture of NaCN (40-50 pct.) and alkaline earth salts such as Na_2CO_3. The temperature of the bath is kept at 850°C to 900°C. The salt reacts with the cyanide and forms a cyanide of the alkaline earth metal, which then decomposes at the surface of the parts according to the following reactions:

$$BaCO_3 + 2NaCN \rightarrow Ba(CN)_2 + Na_2CO_3 \qquad \ldots (6.6)$$
$$Ba(CN)_2 \rightarrow BaCN_2 + C \qquad \ldots (6.7)$$

The nascent carbon thus formed (equation 6.7) is absorbed in the austenite. A small amount of nascent nitrogen is also liberated and absorbed by the metal. The case depth depends upon the time of carburising, the temperature of the bath and also its composition.

A salt bath with 20 pct. NaCN may be used for very thin cases of the order of a few tenths of a milimetre. The parts after carburising

Carbon potential. It is defined as that carbon content which a specimen of carbon steel foil acquires when equilibrium conditions have been established between carbon potential of the medium and the carbon content of the foil.

are directly quenched in water. The carbon content of the surface increases with the increase in NaCN content from 10-50 pct. of the bath.

Salt bath carburising is principally applicable to small parts requiring case depths less than 0.5 mm. With a case depth of about 0.4 mm, the hardness that can be obtained is Rc 60.

The advantages offered by liquid carburising over solid or pack carburising are, (i) rapid heat transfer from bath to the surface of the steel parts, (ii) little probability of decarburisation and oxidation, and (iii) minimised distortion.

Gas carburising. Gas carburising is a continuous process of carburising and is particulary suitable for large volume production. The principal source of carbon is methane or propane and natural gas is commonly used.

The process of gas carburising is carried out in a specially designed air tight furnace in which the pressure is more than that of the atmosphere, so that air from outside will not infiltrate. The gases are circulated throughout the furnace chamber by means of fans provided at the bottom of the furnace. The carburising gaseous atmosphere is produced by endothermic combustion using nickel catalyst. The liquid petroleum gas or propane gas is mixed with air in a balanced proportion and burnt in the gas producing unit. The carrier gas consists of a carbon potential 0.35 to 0 5 pct. which can be increased to 0.8 to 0.9 pct. by the addition of propane gas (5-10 pct.) before the gas enters into the furnace chamber. The temperature of carburising varies from 930-950°C. In order to keep the carbon potential in the range of 0.8 to 0.9 pct., the dew point of the furnace is adjusted between −6° to −4°C. The rate of diffusion of carbon in the surface of the steel increases with the increase of temperature and hence, the case depth is increased. The case depth is also a function of time at the carburising temperature and carbon potential in the carburising medium.

The case depth can easily be controlled in this process. Labour cost is also reduced to a considerable extent. However, the process suffers from a drawback of requiring higher skill for the control.

Heat treatment after carburising. In majority of cases, the steel parts are heat treated after carburising. There are two basic reasons for the heat treatment after carburising:

(i) If the steel of the carburised part is originally coarse grained, then due to holding it for a long period of time at elevated temperature, its core will also acquire a coarse grain structure which is undesirable from the view point of toughness and hence, it will require refinement.

(ii) After carburising, the carbon content in the surface region of the steel components may be as high as 1.0 pct., i.e. equivalent to hyper-eutectoid steels. Consequently, a network of cementite often forms which imparts brittleness to the surface. In order to overcome surface brittleness, the cementite network should be broken down. If the steels are originally fine grained, the carburised parts are directly quenched, straight from the carburising medium. In case, some grain coarsening in the core results, the parts are quenched to room temperature from the carburising medium and then reheated to hardening temperature and finally quenched.

If the parts are having exceptionally coarse grained structure and are held for a long period at the corburising temperature, the grain structure in the core cannot be refined even after first quench and a double quench is needed. Double quench usually consists of a direct quench and then requench from a lower temperature (850-900°C). The second quenching is carried out in the same way as in the single quenching, generally from the temperature ranging between 780-820°C.

Depending upon the case depth required for a hardness of at least Rc − 60 at the surface, the following operating conditions are recommended for different methods of carburising:

Conditions for Pack Carburising
Temperature 900°-925°C.

Depth of case hardening (mm)	Method of hardening
0.40	Direct quench
0.40-1.25	Single quench from 800° to 820°C.
>1.25	Double quench. First from 880°C and second from 780°-800°C.

Direct quenching is done from 900°C as recommended. During the first heating for quenching, the carbon concentration is reduced by diffusion. In additon, it breaks up and dissolves carbide network that usually forms when pack carburising is used to give a deep carbon penetration.

Conditions for Salt Bath Carburising
Temperature 850-900°C

Depth of case hardening, (mm)	Method of hardening
1.50	Direct quench (850°-870°C)
0.5-0.75	Requench from 820°C (double quench).
0.75-1.00	Requench from 800°C and double quench.

For double quenching, 900°C is recommended for first heating.

Condition for Gas Carburising
Temperature 900°-940°C

Carburisation is carried out to the required depth and to a surface carbon contant ranging from 0.7 to 0 8 pct. After completion of carburisation, the temperature in the furnace is brought down to 830°C and then the parts are quenched in a suitable cooling medium. Gas carburised parts are usually tempered in the temperature range of 160°-220°C depending on the case hardness required. If a hardness Rc-60 is required, for instance, then the tempering temperature should be kept below 180°C.

Application of carburising. Case hardening by carburising is used for a variety of machine parts such as, gears, cams, piston pins, pump shafts, etc. In certain cases, a portion of the machine part is not to be hardened, it is copper plated and does not get carburised.

Nitriding. Nitriding is a type of case hardening process used for certain alloy steels. It is ferritic thermo-chemical treatment as nitrogen dissolves in ferrite unlike the dissolution of carbon in austenite in the process of carburising.

The process involves heating of steel parts in a nitrogeneous medium in the temperature range of 500° to 590°C. Since the temperature of nitriding is below the lower critical temperature, no phase transformation occurs and nitrogen is absorbed in ferrite which is the stable phase under operating conditions. The source of nitrogen is principally anhydrous ammonia which is circulated around the parts being nitrided. The ammonia gas partially dissociates on the surface of the parts according to the following reactions:

$$NH_3 \rightleftharpoons N + 3H$$
$$2N \rightleftharpoons N_2$$
$$2H \rightleftharpoons H_2$$

The nascent nitrogen gets absorbed in the surface of the steel whereby it dissolves in α-iron upto 0.1 pct. beyond which nitrides of iron and other alloying elements present in the steel are formed. Since iron nitride is not very hard, other nitride forming elements should be present in the steel. The principal alloying elements that form nitrides are aluminium (0.8 to 1.25 pct.), chromium (1.6 to 1.8 pct.), molybdenum (0.15 to 0.25 pct.), and manganese (0.45 to 0.65 pct.). Sometimes Ni (0.72 to 0.8 pct.) or Si (0.25 to 0.35 pct.) may also be used in nitrided steel as nitride forming elements. The nitrides of alloying elements produce extremely hard and wear resistant as well as heat resistant surface. In order to achieve proper toughness in the core, the steel parts are heat treated prior to nitriding since, unlike carburising, no phase change results in nitriding process. The parts are quenched from about 900°C in oil and tempered at about 600° to 650°C before nitriding. The time of nitriding varies with the case depth desired. It takes about 20 hours to produce a case depth of about 0.2 mm.

Properties of the Nitrided Steels

   (i) High surface hardness and wear resistance without risk of galling (*ii*) High resistance to tempering and high temperature hardness.

(*iii*) Due to high compressive stresses in the surface layers, the fatigue limit is increased to a great extent.

(*iv*) Improved corrosion resistance for stainless steels.

(*v*) High dimensional stability.

Applications of nitriding. Nitriding process is widely adopted in automobile and aero industries in order to improve surface hardness of parts like cylinder, shaft, journals, liners, sleeves, etc. It has also been employed for large gears, gauges, forming dies, bearing parts, crank shaft, wrist pins, clutches, spindles of lathe mechines, etc.

However, nitriding process is used only where the cost is not an important factor. The time required in nitriding may be as high as 100 hours to obtain a case depth of the order of 0 8 mm thick. Furthermore, nitriding requires close control of atmosphere by regulating ammonia flow and its dissociation.

Carbo Nitriding. Carbo-nitriding is the process of increasing nitrogen and carbon content in the surface layers of the steel parts. The surrounding medium is a mixture of amonia (15 pct.) with 5 pct. natural gas in the carrier gas obtained by the endothermic combustion of liquid petroleum gas as in gas carburising. The temperature of carbonitriding is usually 650-885°C which is lower than that required for pure carburising but higher than that for nitriding operation. If the temperature is towards the lower range, the absorption of nitrogen is more than that of carbon and vice versa.

The main function of nitrogen in the case is to improve hardenability, and to increase solid solubility of carbon in austenite. It also lowers the lower critical temperature.

The steel for carbo nitriding should contain low carbon and nitride forming elements such as Al, Mo, Cr and V. The presence of alloying elements decreases the critical cooling rate and therefore, higher hardenability combined with minimum distortion can be obtained by oil quenching from the carbo-nitriding temperature. The case depth obtainable is of the order of 0.5 mm.

Cyaniding. Cyaniding is a modification of liquid carburising. Cyaniding comprises the immersion of steel articles in a bath of molten sodium cyanide maintained at 800°-870°C. Sodium cyanide reacts with the oxygen in the atmosphere and forms sodium cyanate which in turn further decomposes to liberate carbon and nascent nitrogen. Both carbon and nascent nitrogen are caused absorbed by the steel components which are then quenched in water or oil. The reactions can be represented as:

$$2NaCN + 2O_2 \rightarrow Na_2CO_3 + CO + 2N \qquad \ldots(6.8)$$
$$2CO \rightleftharpoons CO_2 + C \qquad \ldots(6.9)$$

The time of cyaniding varies from half an hour to 3 hours depending upon the case depth required. Cyaniding is used to preduce a

TABLE 6.8. *Summary of the Characteristics* of Various Surface and Case Handening Processes*

S. No.	Characteristics	Processes					
		Induction Hardening	Flame Hardening	Carburising	Nitriding	Carbonitriding	
1.	Case depth	Deep	Deep	Medium	Shallow	Shallow	
2.	Capacity for contact load	Good	Good	Excellent	Fair	Fair	
3.	Resistance to seizure	Fair	Fair	Good	Excellent	Good	
4.	Freedom from quenching cracks	Fair	Fair	Excellent	Good	Excellent	
5.	Cost	Low	Low	Low to Medium	Medium to High	Low	
6.	Required capital investment	Medium	Low	High	Medium	Medium	

*The common characteristics of all processes are hard and highly wear resistant surface and good resistance to bending and fatigue.

very thin case depth usually less than 0.25 mm which is suitable for parts requiring high wear resistance under conditions of low compressive loading.

A summary of the properties of the various surface and case hardening processes is shown in Table 6.8 given on p. 177.

6.5.2. Thermomechanical Heat Treatment

The presence of heterogeneity in the form of second phase particles, or lattice imperfections like dislocations, vacancies, stacking faults, etc. produces a strong effect on the formation of structure in alloys during phase transformation. For example, steels which are originally of fine grain do not show a rapid grain coarsening with the rise of temperature upto 930°C because of the presence of heterogeneity in the system. Upon cooling such steels, these impurity particles provide sites for quick nucleation. Similar to these impurity particles, other structural defects where the localised energy in high nucleation of a product phase is rapid. The structural defects like dislocations, low angle grain boundaries, etc. can be produced by plastic deformation of a metal or alloy. Plastic deformation before or during the phase transformation can be used to form the optimum structure in a heat treated alloy.

The heat treatment which includes plastic deformation so as to increase the density of lattice defects and thus affects the formation of the structure in the phase transformation occuring during the thermal action is known as Thermomechanical Treatment (TMT).

The process of plastic deformation and heat teratment in TMT may be either combined in a single technological operation (i.e. carried out simultaneously) or made with a time interval of upto a few days one after the other. The important point to be considered is that phase transformation should result under the conditions of increased lattice defects. The TMT process can be applicable to both ferrous and non-ferrous alloys. The main purpose of employing this treatment in alloy steels is to impart ultra high strength coupled with sufficient toughness and ductility in steels. Among the various methods of TMT applicable to steels, the most commonly used is known as ausforming and is discussed here.

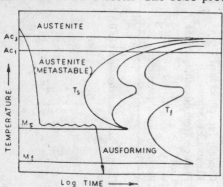

FIG. 6.19. Curve showing heat treatment cycle for ausforming.

Ausforming. The process of ausforming is carried out in lower bay of the metestable austenitic region of TTT diagram, followed by transformation to martensite and light tempering. As a consequence, the dislocation density in martensite is increased and a finer carbide precipitation occurs upon tempering. The complete ausforming consists of the following steps and is illustrated in Fig. 6.19.

(a) Austenitizing the steel above Ac_3;

(b) Cooling to deformation temperature but avoiding split transformation. The deformation temparature is above M_s;

(c) Mechanical working of metastable austenite;

(d) Cooling to room temperature to form martensite;

(e) Finally tempering the steel to get the required properties.

The deformation process of ausforming may be rolling, forging, or drawing. The process is most suitable for low alloy steels, though it can also be used to high alloy steels without improving ductility.

6.6. APPLICATION OF HEAT TREATMENT TO IRON AND ITS ALLOYS

6.6.1. Stress Relief Treatment

It is used to remove coiling stresses in helical springs, and to relieve stresses in castings and machined parts.

(i) **Removal of coiling stresses in helical springs**. Helical springs are produced by coiling the hard drawn spring steel wire over a mandrel. This introduces internal stresses in the metal and these stresses are more, smaller the mendral and larger the diameter of the wire. As a consequence, the loading capacity of the spring is reduced. The coiling stresses can be eliminated by heating the steel spring after coiling for about half an hour at 300°C.

(ii) **Removal of stresses in casting**. When a complex casting is cooled from the pouring temperature, the rate of cooling is different in different sections of the casting. The rate of cooling is faster in the thin walled parts than in the thicker sections. Because of the different cooling rates in different sections of the casting, a substantial amount of stresses are induced in the casting. These stresses are relieved by annealing treatment. This is performed by slow heating of the casting to the critical temperature* and after some time, say about 30 minutes, it is followed by slow cooling. Cast iron for instance, is annealed at about 550°C.

(iii) **Stress relief annealing of machine parts**. When steel is machined and the chips are removed from the surface, large amount of plastic deformation results in the surface layers near the spot where the chip is being formed. The depth to which the metal is deformed from the machined surface depends upon many factors, viz., the shape of the tool, thickness of the chip being formed,

*Here, the critical temperature (tc) is the temperature above which there is no elasticity and below which elastic stresses may occur. Above tc, any stress will result in plastic deformation.

lubrication, strain hardening characteristic of the steel, etc. The stresses introduced due to plastic deformation in the machined surfaces prevent metal to be worked out in subsequent operations. These stresses are relieved by stress relief annealing for 1 to 2 hours. For plain carbon and low alloy steels the annealing temperature varies from 550° to 650°C, whereas, for hot work and high speed steels it varies in the range of 600° to 750°C. The phase transformation does not occur in this treatment though recrystallization may result.

6.6.2. Recrystallization Annealing

When steel is deformed plastically below certain critical temperature called recrystallization temperature, it becomes work hardened. As a result of work hardening it is difficult for the steel to deform further under the application of stresses. In order to have further deformation is needed, the steel has to be annealed at recrystallization temperature (about 600°C). The new stress free grains are formed at the expense of stressed grains. The process is that of nucleation and growth and, therefore, is time dependent. It usually takes about half to one hour for the recrystallization to be completed at the temperature. The holding time is again dependent upon the holding temperature, the holding time being less with a higher holding temperature.

The recrystallization temperature depends upon the degree of cold deformation, and the presence of impurities. The final grain structure is also a function of the original grain strucuture, the degree of cold work and the temperature of recrystallization. Annealing for recrystallization is most commonly employed to cold-rolled, low carbon sheet or strip steel. 18 : 8 stainless steel is also annealed after cold work.

6.6.3. Hydrogen Annealing

Molten steel is liable to pick up hydrogen which may be separated out in the molecular state on cooling the steel to room temperature. This molecular or diatomic hydrogen exerts a pressure of the order of several thousands of atmospheres which in turn causes cracks in the steel. Such defects are generally known as *flakes*. The probability of flackes formation can be decreased by reducing the hydrogen content in steel and is done by annealing the steel in the temperature range of 600° to 680°C for several days, followed by slow cooling.

6.6.4. Isothermal, Annealing

Isothermal annealing is suitable for the treatment of small components of rolled stock or small forgings particularty made of alloy steels.

If an ingot or rolled billet of alloy steel (air hardenable) is freely cooled in air. the core is liable to transform to martensite and therefore cracks are most likely to appear. In order that cracks should not develop and core be transformed to non-martensitic phase, the warm steel is annealed isothermally at about 700°C where the transformation product is pearlite. After the completion of transformation, the steel ingot or rolled billet can be cooled freely in air.

Alloy steels of carburising grade (such as 1 pct. Ni-Cr) are usually heat treated by isothermal annealing after carburising in order to reduce distortion that may occur during carburising. The heat treatment cycle involves:

(a) Austenitization at 930°-940°C.

(b) Cooling to 610 680°C and holding at this temperature for 2-4 hours for transformation to occur.

(c) Cooling freely in air.

The structure thus obtained is usually a mixture of ferrite and pearlite which is very suitable for most machining operations.

6.6.5. Full Annealing

Full annealing is used to eliminate structural defects caused by the preceding processing of steel such as casting, hot working, welding or heat treatment. In cast steels, large austenite grain size may form upon solidification which in turn form coarse grained ferrite and pearlite on cooling to below the lower critical temperature. If the cooling rate is slow enough, excess phase (ferrite in hypo and cementite in hyper-eutectoid steels) is separated out not only on the grain boundaries but also along certain crystallographic planes of austenite. After pearlitic transformation, a mesh like pattern is obtained in the structure. This kind of pattern is known as Widmänstatten structure (Fig. 6.20a). The same structure is usually

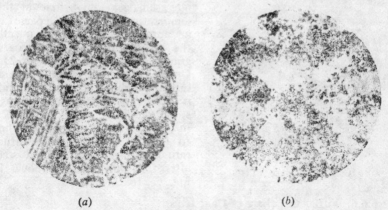

(a)   (b)

FIG. 6.20. (a) Widmänstatten structure, (b) The microstructure of cast steel after annealing.

formed in overheated steels and the heat affected zone in welded steels. Overheating is likely to occur during homogenizing annealing.

The Widmänstatten structure is undesirable because of the following reasons:

(a) It reduces the impact value; and

(b) It reduces the percentage elongation since the strong pearlite is penetrated by ineffective needles of either weak ferrite or brittls cementite, along which cracks can easily be propagated. The structure of the cast steel after annealing is shown in Fig. 6.20b.

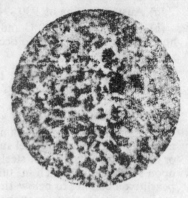

(a)   (b)

FIG. 6.21. (a) Structure of the hot worked hypoeutectoid steel, (b) Structure of the same steel after full annealing.

FIG. 6.22. Lineage structure.

If the hot working of steel is carried out at high temperature, austenite grains get enough time at this temperature to become coarse to an appreciable size. Consequently the pearlite formed is also coarse grained as is shown in Fig. 6.21a. On the other hand, if the temperature at which the hot working ends is sufficiently low then a lineage structure can appear (Fig. 6.22). In both cases, the structure is refined by full annealing. The structure of a rolled hypoeutectoid steel after full annealing is shown in Fig. 6.21b.

6.6.6. Full Annealing of Cast Irons

(i) **Gray cast iron.** Many times, the gray iron castings acquire a chilled surface with a structure of white iron. Such castings must be annealed to improve machinability. The heat treatment cycle involves:

(a) Heating the castings to a temperature between 850°-950°C;

(*b*) Holding at this temperature for a period of 1 to 2 hours;

(*c*) After annealing, the castings are usually cooled in open air.

The *ledeburitic* cementite decomposes at the annealing temperature according to the following reaction:

$$Fe_3C \rightarrow 3Fe + C \text{ (graphite)} \qquad \qquad \ldots (6.10)$$

A higher annealing temperature of the order of 1050°-1150°C can be used for small castings of simple design to reduce the annealing time.

Castings which are complex in shape with thick and thin sections, are annealed at relatively lower temperatures for a longer period of time, otherwise warpage may result in the thin sections. The annealing temperature can vary between 800 and 850°C and the time of holding can be from 2 to 5 hours. It may be noted here that after annealing, the castings should be cooled in the furnace itself at least upto the temperature of 400°-500°C.

(*ii*) **White cast iron.** White cast iron is very hard and brittle due to the presence of much eutectic cementite in its structure. In order to reduce brittleness and improve mechanical properties, white iron castings are given full annealing treatment. Although cementite is stable under the conditions maintained for the heat treatment of steel, but tends to decompose to iron and graphite, and under normal conditions, it takes years to decompose. In the presence of graphitizing elements such as silicon, cementite is no longer stable at high temperature and decomposes according to the reaction (6.10). Thus the annealing of white cast iron results in graphitization of the cementite and the irregular round nodules formed as a consequence of annealing are distributed in the ferrite matrix. This treatment is commonly known as malleabilizing and the cast iron is referred to as malleable cast iron.

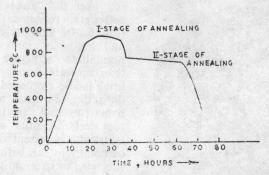

FIG. 6.23. Heat-treatment cycle for malleabilising treatment.

White cast iron castings that are suitable for malleabilizing treatment are annealed in two stages. The first stage consists of heating the castings to a temperature of 900°—950°C. Holding at this temperature results in graphitization of secondary cementite and the original structure of austenite plus cementite becomes austenite plus graphite. The temperature is then allowed to drop down to 760°-720°C for second-order annealing. This temperature range passes through the temperature of decomposition of austenite to an aggregate of ferrite and cementite. The rate of cooling is so slow that the pearlitic cementite decomposes to graphite and ferrite. Complete malleabilized structure shows free graphite (also called temper carbon) nodules distributed in the matrix of ferrite. The heat treatment cycle is shown in Fig. 6.23.

6.6.7. Homogenizing Annealing

Homogenizing annealing is usually employed for low alloy steel ingots and heavy complex castings in order to equalize composition gradient within the separate crystals by diffusion. The annealing treatment is carried out in the temperature range of 1100°-1150°C where diffusion process is quite active. Holding at this temperature homogenizes the composition within the grains and the grain boundaries. The time of the holding should be controlled in order to minimise excessive grain growth, oxidation, and decarburisation.

Holding is followed by the cooling in the furnace for 6 to 8 hours to 800-850°C and then cooling in air. After homogenizing, castings are full annealed to refine the grain structure. Alloy steel ingots are usually homogenized in the temperature range of 1100-1200°C for 10 to 20 hours with subsequent slow cooling.

6.6.8. Normalising Annealing of Steels

When the aim is to eliminate structural defects caused by the preceding operations such as hot working, overheating, or heat

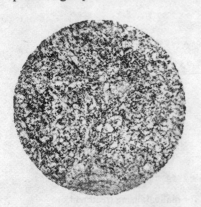

treatment, normalising is preferred over full annealing where better grain refinement is obtained (Fig. 6.24). Comparing Fig. 6.21 and Fig. 6.24, it is clear that normalised structure is finer than annealed structure. Normalising is also employed to break down the cementite network in hyper-eutectoid steels such as tool steels. A prior normalising treatment is essential for high carbon tool steels before they are subjected to spheroidising annealing process. The normalising temperature is about 850°C for tool steels. Normalising is equally

FIG. 6.24. Normalised structure.

important to enhance the machinability of low and medium carbon steels through grain refinement.

In majority of cases, normalising is used for the refinement of structure prior to hardening. If a hypo-eutectoid steel before hardening consists of coarse grains of excess ferrite, then on heating to hardening temperature, the austenite that forms at the interface with excess ferrite will be depleted with respect to carbon content. It takes more time to homogenise the austenite. By the time the austenite gets homogenised, the grains of austenite will become coarse leading to warpage and quenching cracks. On the other hand, quenching without homogenizing may result in soft spots. In order to overcome all these difficulties, normalising is required to reduce excess ferrite and hence the holding time at the temperature is also decreased. Further, the structure of the tool steels before hardening should contain lamellar rather than globular pearlite, since it takes more time to transform globular pearlite to austenite. The usual normalising temperature is 30-50°C above the upper critical point.

6.6.9. Normalising of Cast Irons

Gray cast iron and malleable cast irons with ferritic or ferritic plus pearlitic matrix can be normalised to improve strength, hardness and wear resistance. Gray iron castings are heated at 850-950°C for half to three hours and cooled in quiet air. The castings complicated in design are preferably cooled in furnace until at least 500°C. As the temperature goes to above the $Ac_{3,1}$ point, the ferrite of the matrix is converted to austenite by dissolving carbon from the pearlitic cementite or graphite. This austenite upon air cooling transforms to fine pearlite forming the matrix.

6.6.10. Hardening and Tempering of Steels

(i) **Constructional steels**. Constructional steels are heated to austenitization temperature and then quenched in oil or water depending on the kind of steel (i.e. composition), shape and design of the component. Hardening followed by a tempering treatment is carried out in the temperature range of 500°-700°C depending upon the type of structure and the mechanical properties desired. Constructional steels include both plain carbon and alloy steels.

Plain carbon steels. The carbon content of the hardenable plain carbon steels used for construction work ranges between 0.25 and 0.60 pct. The steels which are used for most general applications contain 0.32-0.39 pct. and 0.47-0.55 pct. carbon. The other elements are Si, 0.15-4 pct.; Mn, 0.5-0.8 pct.; P, 0.05 pct. max. and S, 0.05 pct. max. The light sectioned components such as axles, and bolts are usually made of 0.47-0.55 pct. C and are hardened by oil quenching. For heavy sections water quenching is necessary and this treatment is applicable to parts such as crank shafts for motor-car engines. Water quenching improves hardenability of these parts but introduces warpage and quenching cracks and therefore, this heat treatment is limited to parts simple in shape and design.

Alloy steels. The principal steels for the constructional work are of low-alloy grade Cr-Mo steels. The Cr and Mo may vary from 0.90 to 1.20 pct. and 0.15 to 0.30 pct. respectively. The carbon content ranges between 0.25 and 0.45 pct. The other elements are Si – 0.15 to 0.4 pct., Mn – 0.50 to 0.80 pct., and S and P each 0.035 pct. maximum. These steels are generally quenched in oil but sometimes water can also be used as quenching medium. Cr-Mo steels containing low carbon are quenched in water and if tempered at 200°C, much difference in hardness from surface to core results. If tempering is carried out at 600°C, then the difference in hardness from surface to core is reduced to a large extent.

Parts such as landing gear, and wing assembly of aircraft require high strength, hardenability and are subjected to high stresses (both static and dynamic). These are made of Cr-Ni-Mo steels. These steels are hardened and tempered at 200°C. Quenching is usually done in an oil bath.

Stainless steels. Among the stainless steels, the only heat treatable steels are of the martensite group. Martensitic stainless steels contain chromium from 13-18 pct. These steels are heat treated by quenching from about 1000°C in air or oil. Tempering is usually done at the temperature of 550-650°C. A higher tempering temperature is undesirable because of the precipitation of carbides of chromium which reduce the corrosion resistance. Martensitic stainless steels containing 0.1-0.33 pct. carbon are used as structural members in chemical industries, and steam and gas turbines. It is also used for properller shafts in ships. Steels with high carbon content are used for applications requiring high hardness such as cutlery, valve parts, and ball and roller bearings.

Martensitic stainless steels of weldable class consists of 0.05 pct. C, 12.5 pct. Cr, 5.5 to 6.0 pct Ni and 0 to 1.5 pct. Mo. These steels are quenched from 1000°C in air and tempered at 600°C. In the as hardened condition, the structure contains only martensite. On tempering, there is partial retransformation to austenite which improves impact toughness. When the tempered steels are welded, there is no danger of cracking because of the austenite retained. This property is useful while repairing water turbines. This steel has also been used in cellulose industry and for compressor components.

Spring steels. Springs are made of plain carbon as well as of alloy steels. Springs of plain carbon steels contain carbon from 0.55 to 0.8 pct. The alloy steels used for spring applications are Cr-V and Cr-V-Mo steels.

Plain carbon steels are widely employed for helical springs. The heat treatment can be hardening and tempering or patenting and cold drawing. Thin-section carbon steel spring can be quenched and tempered conventionally.

Watch springs of few tenths of a millimetre in thickness are tempered at 160°-300°C after being quenched. Leaf springs of thickness 1-3 mm are tempered at 300°-400°C.

Maraging steels. Maraging steels are characterised by ultra high strength combined with excellent fracture toughness. These steels are low in carbon, containing 18-25 pct. Ni together with other hardening elements, such as Ti, Al, Mo and Co. The term maraging is used because the steels are aged after annealing. The annealed (or called solution treated) structure consists of martensite which is aged to produce ultra high strength. The structure consists of martensite and the dispersed particles of intermetallic compounds. The martensite formed is soft and tough rather than hard and

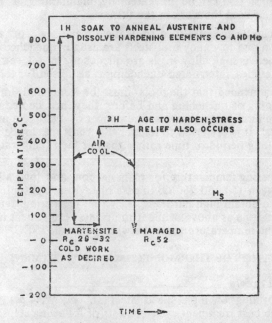

FIG. 6.25. Heat treating cycle of maraging steel.

brittle as obtained by conventional hardening process. The heat treatment cycle for 18 pct. Ni maraging steel is shown in Fig. 6.25. Maraging steels are used for hulls in hydrospace vehicles, motor cases for missiles and low temperature structural parts.

6.6.11. Hardening and Tempering of Tool Steels

Heat treatment of tool steels requires special care to be excercised. Both heating and cooling rates markedly affect the properties of a tool. Most of the tools are made of high carbon and alloy steels. As the carbon or alloy content in steel increases, the thermal conductivity of the steel decreases. Therefore, the heating of the tool for hardening must be slow enough to reduce temperature gradients in the tool section. This can be done by one or two preheatings before heating the tool to the final hardening temperature. Alternatively, the temperature of the work and the furnace is raised slowly to the hardening temperature.

In order to avoid overheating, the temperature of hardening should not be too high and the tool should not be held for a long time at this temperature. Overheating results in excessive grain growth, thereby, produces coarse grain martensite of poor toughness. The probability of quenching cracks is also increased due to overheating. Another reason to avoid overheating is the scale formation and decarburisation that can be prevented by maintaining a protective atmosphere around the work in the furnace.

Cooling can be accomplished in water, brine, oil, or salt bath. Plain carbon and low alloy tool steels are usually quenched in water or brine whereas high alloy steels are quenched in oil, air, or salt baths. Sometimes, interrupted quenching is also used for tool steels.

It is recommended that the tools must be tempered immediately after hardening or quenching and before they are cooled to room temperature in order to minimise the danger of warpage and quenching cracks. It is preferred to temper the tools at lower temperatures for a long period of time rather than at high temperature for a short time.

The tempering temperature for plain carbon and low alloy steels ranges between 150 and 260°C. In case of high alloy tool steels, if the aim is to obtain high hardness, then the tempering temperature range is the same as above, while if the prime requirement is that of toughnss, the temperature varies between 480 and 750°C.

6.7. APPLICATION OF THERMOMECHANICAL TREATMENT

6.7.1. Tool Steels

(*i*) Ausforming of high speed steel (18 pct. W, 4 pct. Cr, and 1 pct. V). The heat treatment cycle consists of following steps:

(*a*) Solutionising (austenitizing) at a temperature of 1200°-1300°C;

(*b*) Cooling to ausforming temperature 450°-550°C and mechanical working.

(*c*) Quenching to room temperature; and

(*d*) Tempering in the temperature range of 400° to 600°C for a desirable length of time.

It has been observed that thermomechanically heat treated high speed steels have considerable improvement in hardness, compared to that attained by conventional heat treatment.

(*ii*) Ausforming of high carbon-high chromium cold worked die steel (C-1.5 pct., Cr-12.5 pct.). Heat treatment cycle consists of following steps:

(*a*) Solutionising at about 1000°C;

(*b*) Cooling to ausforming temperature in the range of 450-550°C and deforming to about 40 pct.;

(c) Quenching to room temperature;

(d) Tempering in the temperature range of 500-600°C; and

(e) Subzero treatment (i.e. heat treatment below 0°C so as to convert any retained austenite to martensite).

(iii) Ausforming of spring steels (i.e. high strength automobile springs). The steels most suitable for high strength automobile springs, such as leaf springs are mainly $Si-M_n$, Cr-V and Cr-V-Mo steels. These steels possess the following composition:

$Si-M_n$ steel : C—0.6 pct., Si—1.8 to 2.2 pct. and $M—_n$0.7 to 0.9 pct.

Cr-V steel : C—0.45 pct., Mn—0.67 pct.,

Si-0.31 pct., Cr—0.98 pct., V—0.21 pct.,

Cr-V-Mo steel : C—0.42 pct., Mn—0.35 pct.,

Si—0.95 pct., Cr—5.00 pct., V—0.40 pct.,

and Mo—1.30 pct.

The heat treatment cycle consists of the following:

(a) Austenitizing at 900°C and 960°C for Cr-V and Cr-V-Mo steels, respectively;

(b) Rolling to about 40 pct. reduction in the temperature range of 500-600°C and 450-600°C for the two steels, respectively.

(c) Tempering in the temperature range of 300-600°C; and

(d) Subzero treatment.

6.8. HEAT TREATMENT OF NON-FERROUS METALS AND ALLOYS

6.8.1. First Order Annealing

Like steels, first order annealing processes such as homogenization, recrystallization, and stress relief are also applicable to non-ferrous metals and alloys. The applications of these processes for non-ferrous metals and alloys are discussed as following:

(i) **Homogenizing annealing**. Alloy castings generally solidify under non-equilibrium conditions. Non-equilibrium changes during crystallization cause the following important defects in the cast alloy:

(a) A brittle phase may appear at the boundaries of the dendritic grains of a solid solution, thereby reducing the ductility of the alloy;

(b) Because of the compositional difference between the dendritic cells and the boundaries, a galvanic cell may form which causes intergranular corrosion of the alloy;

(c) The constituent that forms at the grain boundaries or in the interdendritic region of a solid solution, is the last to solidify and therefore its melting point is the lowest. This reduces the solidus point of the alloy and partial melting may result if the alloy is heated for hot working or for hardening.

In order to eliminate these structural inhomogeneities, the ingots and castings are usually subjected to homogenizing operation consisting of heating the castings or ingots to a temperature where diffusion process is prevalent so that the composition between the dendritic cells and the boundaries evens out. Thus, the ductility, impact toughness and fatigue strength are improved.

Most of the deformable aluminium alloy ingots are homogenized to improve ductility and increase mechanical properties of semifinished products. The annealing is performed at 450-550°C depending on the type of alloy and the kind of product.

Magnesium alloy ingots are homogenized at a temperature of 390-405°C to enable the material to deform in subsequent operations.

The homogenization of aluminium and magnesium alloy shaped articles is not considered a separate operation because it is a part of the hardening operation in these alloys. The main objective is to dissolve the excess phase in the solid solution to the maximum possible extent.

Ingot and shaped castings of alloys of copper, nickel, zinc and titanium have shown little effect on the mechanical properties after homogenizing annealing and therefore, such articles are seldom homogenized. However, exception can be made to some tin bronze castings which show improvement in ductility after homogenizing at 650-700°C by dissolving the non-equilibrium phase $\alpha + Cu_{31}Sn_8$ eutectoid.

(*ii*) **Recrystallization annealing.** Recrystallization annealing is the most important operation for non-ferrous metal sheets, strips, tubes, etc. It may be the starting operation before cold working (with a view to improve ductility), as an intermediate operation between various passages of cold deformation (to over come the strain hardening effect) or as the final operation to get the desirable structure and properties.

The structural changes that occur during recrystallization annealing of non-ferrous alloys are similar to those in steels. The approximate temperatures (in °C) of recrystallization annealing of non-ferrous metals and alloys are as follows:

Copper	500—700
Brasses and Bronzes	600—700
Cu-Ni-alloys	700—850
Nickel	700—800
Nickel alloys	800—1150
Aluminium	300—500
Aluminium alloys	350—450
Titanium	670—690

The holding time at the above temperatures may range from 10 to 60 minutes.

(*iii*) **Stress relief annealing treatment.** The processes like hot working, welding, heat treatment, etc. can introduce internal stresses which must be relieved. The treatment applied is known as stress relief annealing treatment or the low temperature annealing treatment and is carried out below the recrystallization temperature. The stress relief treatment can be used to anneal cold rolled sheets and stampings made of copper, nickel, titanium or deformable alloys, but is widely used with brasses containing more that 20 pct. Zn. In the work hardened condition, compressive as well as tensile stresses are introduced in brass articles. If the articles are exposed to humid atomsphere, corrosion takes place along the grain boundaries. The cohesion of the grains is thereby reduced to such an extent that cracks are developed. Since this phenomenon occurs mainly during the wet season, it is generally termed as "Season cracking " The season cracking can be eliminated by heating the worked articles in the temperature range of 275-320°C for about $\frac{1}{2}$ to 1 hour directly from after forming.

6.8.2. Second Order Annealing

Second order annealing treatment involves a phase transition and is therefore, seldom applicable to non-ferrous metals and alloys because most of the commercial non-ferrous metals and alloys do not undergo a phase change. Though there are some alloys that involve a phase change in the solid state but if they are subjected to second order annealing, undesirable changes in their properties result.

The annealing treatment that is applicable to the majority of non-ferrous alloys is known as hetarogenizing annealing. Many alloys form a single phase solid solution at high temperature and by lowering the temperature one or more phases in the form of precipitate are separated out from the parent phase. The base metal forms the matrix while the excess phase is usually a compound. Those alloys which exhibit a precipitation phenomenon by lowering the temperature can be given the heterogenizing annealing treatment. Examples of these include alloys of aluminium (duralumin), magnesium (Mg-bronze), copper (Cu-Be), nickel (nimonic), etc.

These alloys are also characterised by the fact that the crystal lattice of the matrix phase does not change whether the excess phase dissolves in or is precipitated from it. This clearly indicates that annealing process simply alters the concentration of the components in the matrix phase, and the size and shape of the precipitate particles in the matrix.

The purpose of heterogenizing annealing is to soften the alloy partially or fully. or to improve corrosion resistance. Full softening is applicable to all heat-hardenable aluminium alloys (duralumin, etc.). The principal aim of full softening is to improve ductility of the alloy before mechanical working like bending, flanging, etc. The process consists in heating the alloy until its excess phase is completely dissolved, followed by very slow cooling, which provides equilibrium conditions and therefore, the excess phase is separated out according to the equilibrium composition in the form of coarse precipitate particles. A greater interparticle spacing is responsible for full softening.

Most of the full heat treatable aluminium alloys are fully annealed by heating them to 380-420°C for 10 to 60 minutes, followed by cooling at a rate always slower than 30°C/h. The softening effect is not only due to the change in composition of the solid solution and the coarsening of percipitate particles, but is also due to recrystallization effect.

Partial softening of heat-treatable aluminium alloys is done below the temperature of full annealing. Because of the lower temperature of annealing, the time of annealing is more but total time is shortened by cooling the alloy from the annealing temperature in air or even in water in some instances. Since the cooling is somewhat faster, a higher dispersivity of precipitate particles ensures partial hardening of the alloy. Heterogenizing annealing is also applicable to other metals and alloys such as $(\alpha+\beta)$ brass.

When the aim is to improve corrosion resistance of an alloy, the heterogenizing annealing causes uniform distribution of the excess phase within the grains rather than a large portion at the grain boundaries and less in the grains. For example, the maximum resistance to stress-corrosion in a Al-Mg alloy is ensured by a two-phase mixture in which the β-phase (Al_3Mg_2) is uniformly distributed in the grains of aluminium solid solution. The annealing temperature for this alloy is about 320°C.

6.8.3. Hardening of Non-ferrous Alloys

The major changes in mechanical and other properties which may be induced in a non-ferrous alloy system by heat treatment are usually a result of producing structures in metastable equilibrium. For example, consider a case of decomposition of a supersaturated solid solution where the basic reactions are of the following form:

α-saturated   rapid cooling α-supersaturated   . . . (6.11)
(high temperature) $-- --\rightarrow$ (low temperture)

α-supersaturated   ageing α-supersaturated$+\beta'$ . . . (6.12)
(low temperature) $--\rightarrow$ (low temperature)

α-Supersaturated$+\beta'$ further α-saturated$+\beta$ . . . (6.13)
    $----\rightarrow$ (low temperature)
(low temperature)   ageing

The transition from the supersaturated solid solution of reaction (6.11) to the final stage reaction (6.13) may take place by a number of metastable intermediate states. The structural changes that result between these stages have quite interesting and important effects on the properties of the alloy. Such reactions commonly occur in the alloys of Al, Mg, Cu and Ni.

The most widely studied system is the Al-Cu alloy system. The hardening treatment given to non-ferrous alloys can therefore, be discussed by considering a typical example of Al-Cu alloy.

With regard to mechanical properties, aluminium alloys are only second to steels and are widely employed as structural material after steels. The high mechanical properties are obtained through heat treatment operations. The heat treatment of aluminium alloys can be explained by taking the system Al-Cu. Solubility of copper in solid solution in aluminium decreases from 5.7 pct. at a temperature of 548°C (i.e the eutectic temperature) to 0.5 pct. at room temperature. A higher hardening effect can be obtained at an optimum copper percentage of 4.0 or more in aluminium.

The hardening treatment consists in heating the alloy to about 500-550°C depending upon the composition and holding there for a sufficient period to dissolve all the excess phase. This process is known as solutionizing treatment. The holding is followed by quenching to obtain a supersaturated solid solution of copper in aluminium. The cooling is so rapid that copper atoms can not diffuse out of the aluminium solid solution. If the alloy is aged at a temperature of about 150°-200°C, fine dispersion of coherent precipitate particles in the aluminium matrix are obtained. More is the dispersion of precipitate particles, less will be the interparticle spacing and hence higher the mechanical strength. As the ageing time or temperature is increased, precipitate particles will become coarse which causes a decrease in strengthening effect.

A typical example of Al-Cu alloy is duralumin (Cu—4.0 pct., Mg —1.5 pct., Mn—0.5 pct. and rest Al) which is heated to about 500°C for solutionizing treatment.

Copper containing 2 to 2.5 pct. beryllium is also percipitation handenable. The heat treatment of Cu-Be alloy consists in quenching the alloy in water from a temperature of 760°-780°C followed by ageing at a temperature of 310°-330°C for a period of 2 to 2½ hours. The Cu-Be alloy is also known as beryllium bronze and is used as non-sparking tool in petroleum and chemical industries, and in Navy. Because of the precipitation hardening effect, the electrical conductivity of copper is not decreased to a great extent.

Wrought Mg-Al alloys containing 7.8 to 9.2 pct. Al in Mg are solutionized at 410°-420°C for 12 to 16 hours and then cooled in hot water or air. Hardening is followed by ageing at 170°-180°C for 16-24 hours.

6.9. FURNACES FOR HEAT TREATMENT SHOP

Heat treatment of metals and alloys consists of subjecting them to a definite temperature cycle. The temperature of heating may vary from 100°C (for tempering) to about 1000°C (for hardening, carburising, etc). The time of heating and cooling cycles may vary from few seconds (for induction hardening) to a few days (for malleabilising).

Depending upon the wide variations in temperature, time of heating, size and shape of the articles, the furnaces can be classified in a number of ways, such as (i) according to use, (ii) according to type of work, (iii) according to source of heat, etc.

The most important type of classification is based on according to the type of work i.e. (i) batch type, and (ii) continuous type.

In the batch type of furnaces, the temperature in the working chamber varies according to the required heating cycle. The operation of a batch type furnace comprises of following steps:

(i) Charging of a batch of parts in the furnace.

(ii) The parts are heated to the given temperature.

(iii) Soaking the parts at temperature for a certain period of time depending upon the composition and corss-section of parts and the type of heat treatment carried out.

(iv) Subjecting the parts to some heat treating operations (annealing, heating, normalising or hardening).

(v) Whole of the batch of stock is withdrawn from the furnace.

This process is repeated for different batches. One batch of parts may differ from another in weight, size, grade of steel and the type of heat treating required. Batch type furnaces are usually employed in heat treating, tool making and maintenance shops of machine building plants where limited number of parts are to be heat treated. If the changes are large (i.e. the volume of work is more) each heat treating operation should be performed in a specified furnace, such as annealing furnace, hardening furnace etc.

In continuous furnaces, the charge is fed through one end of the furnace and is discharged at the other end. These furnaces are used where mass production is envisaged and only one specific operation is carried out in these furnaces.

Batch type furnaces are used for job order purposes. They can be used for a variety of operations, namely, annealing, hardening, etc. These furnaces may be heated by some conventional fuel like coal, coke, oil or gas or they may be heated electrically. Electric furnaces are the best among all. They are simplest in design and fabrication and are free from gas pollution. A desired constant temperature ean be maintained with ease in electrically heated furnaces. The types of batch furnaces used for the heat treatment are discussed below.

6.9·1· Batch Type Furnaces

(i) **Box type batch furnaces.** In the box type furnaces, a batch of work is introduced and removed after the operation, from the same gate as shown in Fig. 6.26. Charging can be done manually for light jobs while for heavy jobs, mechanical means can be used.

If the parts beings heat treated are large, then the bottom or the hearth of the box type furnace can be made movable by putting it on the wheels (Fig. 6.27). The loading in done by removing the bottom

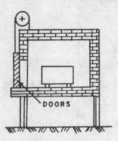

FIG. 6.26. Box type furnace
with fixed bottom.

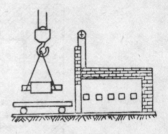

FIG. 6:27. Box type furnace with
movable bottom.

from the furnace and is replaced back into the furnace after loading with the work.

For large and heavy parts, pit type furnace (as shown in Fig. 6.28) can also be used. The parts are then hung in to the furnace chamber. This furnace is also equally suitable for small parts which can be loaded in basket.

In case, the shope floor area in an industry is not enough, a modification to movable bottom type furnace (called elevator type furnace) can be substituted. The elevator type furnace consists of heating chambers suspended at a height of several metres. The hearths with loaded parts are raised into the furnace chamber by means of hydraulic hoists. These furnaces are specially suitable for malleabilizing treatment and the heat treatment

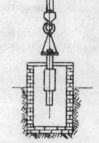

FIG. 6.28. Pit type
furnace.

of transformer steel (i.e. steel with very low carbon and silicon upto 4.0 pct.).

Electrically heated muffle type furnaces have been widely employed in metallurgical and other industries. Muffle furnaces are used for heat treatment of small parts and tools, heating for the heat treating operations like bright annealing*, hardening, and case hardening. These furnaces consist of a rectangular working chamber made of a special refractory material. The muffle is surrounded by electrical resistance element (usually nichrome or kanthal) as shown in Fig 6.29. The close end of the muffle is provided with a hole for inserting a thermocouple to measure the temperature of the furnace. The muffle

---

*Bright annealing: The term bright annealing is applied to an annealing operation in which an oxide does not form on the surface of the steel article.

is further surrounded by refractory material (usually fire bricks powder) which is finally lined with steel jacket.

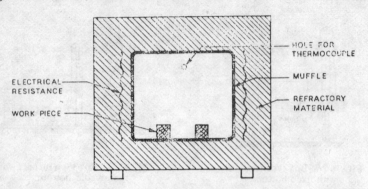

FIG. 6.29. Muffle furnace.

The other kind of electrically heated furnaces is a salt bath furnace like muffle furnaces, which are also used for hardening, and case hardening of small articles of steel. They are particulary suitable for final heating of the tools which are heated to a temperature of around 1200°-1300°C. At such high temperature, the probability of oxidation and decarburisation of the tool is minimised by heating it in a salt bath. A salt bath furnace comprises a pot made of steel or cast

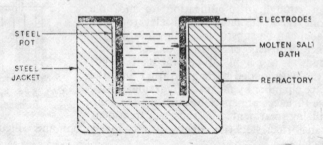

FIG. 6.30. Salt bath furnace.

iron. The heating element in the form of thick strips is inserted in the pot as illustrated in Fig. 6.30. The salt is put into the pot and becomes molten when the current is passed through the resistor. The temperature of the bath is controlled by regulating the power input. The parts to be heated are immersed directly or in a basket in the bath when the desired temperature has reached. The time of holding in the bath depends upon the type of heat treatment being carried out.

6.9.2. Continuous Type Furnaces.

In continuous heat treating furnaces, the parts to be heat treated are pushed in the forward direction through the furnace by some mechanical means, such as a pusher or conveyer belt. The principal types of continuous heat treating furnaces are described below.

(*i*) **Rotary hearth furnaces.** Rotary hearth furnaces consist of a hearth which rotates along its vetical axis. These furnaces are used when there is shortage of space on the shop floor.

(*ii*) **Pusher type furnaces.** Pusher type furnaces comprise a long horizontal hearth. The work can be directly loaded or may be contained in fixtures/boxes and then loaded on the hearth. The parts are pushed by a pusher operated hydraulically and is so designed as to move through a predetermined distance at a certain frequency.

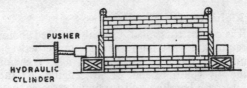

FIG. 6.31. Pusher type furnace.

Pusher type continuous furnaces are being used for annealing, normalising, hardening, gas carburising, etc. The schematic diagram of a pusher type furnace is shown in Fig. 6.31.

(*iii*) **Conveyor furnaces.** As the name implies, conveyor furnaces consists of an endless conveyor belt supported on two rolls and moves at a slow rate. The work to be heat treated is loaded on the belt directly and is discharged after the treatment either in a box (opened to air as in normalising) or in a quenching tank (as for hardening). Conveyor furnaces are widely employed for hardening and tempering of steel articles on large scale.

(*iv*) **Rotary furnaces.** Another type of continuous-type furnaces is a rotary furnace which comprises a steel drum rotating at a slow rate around its horizontal axis. In many cases, the horizontal axis of the drum in inclined with the earth's surface. The furnace chamber is provided with ribs at right angles to the furnace axis with a view to move the parts being heat treated. These furnaces are used to heat treat small parts for hardening, tempering, gas carburising, etc.

6.10. APPLICATIONS OF HEAT TREATMENT TO TYPICAL AUTOMOBILE AND OTHER PARTS

6.10.1. Pistons of Air Craft Engine

The old material used for pistons of air craft engine, diesel engine or motor cycle was cast iron. Due to heaviness in the casting, cast iron has been replaced by light aluminium alloys in many countries. The two important alloys of aluminium that are being used for pistons are:

   (*i*) Cast aluminium-silicon alloy; and

(*ii*) 'Y' alloy.

(*i*) **Cast Al-Si alloy**. Composition Si—12.5 pct., Cu—0.9 pct., Mg —1.0 pct., Ni—0.9 pct., and rest Al.

Heat treatment. The alloy is solution treated at 510°-525°C and artificially age-hardened at 100°-200°C.

(*ii*) **'Y' alloy**. Composition Cu—4.0 pct., Ni—2.0 pct., Mg—1.5 pct., Si—0.6 pct. (max.), Fe—0.6 pct. (max.), and rest Al.

Heat treatment. The alloy is solution treated and quenched in hot water from 500-525°C and aged either at room temperature or by precipitation treatment at 100-200°C.

6.10.2. Crank Shaft

Crank shaft is one of the most critical stressed components in a vehicle. It requires a very high wear resistance between crank shaft main and connecting rod pins and the bearings. Wear on the bearing determines the overhaul period of an engine. At the fillet of the crank shaft, alternate bending and torsional stresses may cause fatigue failure of the crank shaft. There are two possible materials to satisfy the above requirements. These are case hardenable/surface hardenable steels or forgeable steel and ductile cast iron (also known as nodular or spheroidal cast iron).

For mass production, crank shafts made of steels are commonly surface hardened by flame or induction heating. Nitriding process induces better wear resistance and fatigue resistance than surface hardening but is a costly process and therefore should not be used where mass production of crank shafts is not required.

6.10.3. Transmission Gears

Transmission gears are to work under severe conditions (such as high unit stresses and high velocities) and are also likely to be subjected to mechanical shocks. The widely employed material for this purpose is alloy steels of case carburising grade. The Suitable alloy steels include straight nickel steels with 0.3 to 0.5 pct. and 3.5 to 5 pct. Ni steels, nickel-molybdenum (Ni—1.8 to 3.5 pct.), nickel-chromium (Ni—1.5 to 3.5 pct. and Cr—0.6 to 1.5 pct.) and Ni-Cr-Mo steeles. These materials are suitable for heavy duty automobile gears such as bus and truck gears, air craft gears, worm gear and aircraft landing grears. The heat treatment involves carburising followed by hardening and tempering so as to develop a surface hardness of the order of Rc 58-62 and a core strength of 110-140 kg/mm^2. Gears are hardened immediately after carburising (at about 900°-950°C). Quenching is followed by tempering at about 180°-200°C.

6.10.4. Low Power Transmission Gears

Gears that are to work under low stress are commonly made of plain carbon steels usually containing about 0.5 pct. C. quenching is carried out in water or oil from a temperature of 820°-840°C which is followed by subsequent tempering (or drawing) at a tempereture of 520°-550°C to obtain a hardness of the order of 220-250 BHN. In order to increase the surface hardness of gears, they may be subjected to surface hardening.

6.10.5. Balls and Rolls of Bearings and the Races

These components are usually made of low carbon steels which may or may not contain alloying elements. The usual alloying elements are Ni and Cr. The components are carburised in the temperature range of 930°-950°C followed by oil quenching. The carburised parts are then hardened at about 800°C followed by tempering in the temperature range of 100-200°C for 1 to 2 hours depending upon the size of balls, rollers, and races.

6.10.6. Components of Areo-Engine and Helicopter such as Areo-Engine Compressor Blades, Impeller, Gnide Vanes, and Engine Starter Turbine Disc.

The components of aero-engine and helicopter usually require low fatigue cycles. This requirement together with a creep strength in the temperature range of 175°-250°C can better be satisfied by medium strength aluminium wrought alloys. Typical alloy forgings which are being manufactured at foundry and forge division of HAL from imported extrusions have the composition of Cu—2.5 pct., Mg —1.5 pct., Ni—1.2 pct., Fe—1.0 pct., Ti—0.1 pct., and balance Al. The heat treatment of this alloy consists in solutionising at 525°C for $1\frac{1}{2}$ hours followed by water quenching to room temperature. The quenched alloy is then aged at 200°C for 20 hours and cooled in air.

6.10.7. Heat Treatment of Aircraft Wings and Skin

The structural components of aircraft such as wings and skin are being made of aluminium-zinc alloy containing 5.5 pct. Zn, 2.5 pct. Mg, 1.5 pct. Cu, and rest Al. India is importing this alloy in large quantities to meet the demands of our aerospace industries. The components are solutionised in the temperature range of 470°-490°C and quenched in water to room temperature. The alloy is then aged at about 125°C for 24 to 28 hours and cooled.

6.10.8. High Speed Steels

The general composition of high speed tool steel is C—0.7 —1.0 pct., W—18 pct., Cr—4 pct. and V—1.0 pct.

Heat treatment of high speed steels (HSS) involves two processes namely hardening and tempering.

The hardening cycle consists of the following steps:

(i) Preheating the tools first in the temperature range of 540°-650°C and then between 845°-870°C. The purpose of preheating is two-fold, i.e. (*a*) to prevent severe thermal shocks caused by placing cold tool in hot furnace, and (*b*) to minimise the danger of cracking or warping that may result due to phase transformation at about 760°C.

(*ii*) Final heating is done at about 1200°-1290°C depending upon the cross-section of the tool and is carried out in a molten salt bath.

(*iii*) Soaking the tool at the hardening temperature for 2 to 5 minutes depending upon the section thickness. Longer soaking time should be avoided to minimise decarburisation, incipient fusion at the grain boundaries or the formation of angular carbides.

(*iv*) Quenching from the hardening temperature by either (*a*) a molten salt bath at 600°-650°C and then in air or (*b*) an oil bath, till the temperature comes down to about 450°C and then air cooled to room temperature or (*c*) an oil bath to room temperature and requenched to −80°C.

Tempering is done in the temperature range of 550°-600°C. Sometimes double tempering is also required.

6.10.9. Heat Treatment of Steel Castings

Steel castings are usually classified as plain carbon, low and medium alloy and high alloyed types. The carbon content in plain carbon steel castings usually amounts to 0.2 to 0.6 pct., while silicon and manganese contents lie within few tenths of a per cent. Mild steels are usually used where moderate strengh, ductility and impact resistance are required. These steels can be given surface hardening treatment if wear resistance is required.

Steel castings are usually heat treated to improve structural properties. The usual heat treatments given are annealing and normalising. Sometimes normalising is followed by tempering treatment.

Annealing. Steel castings are slowly heated to the annealing temperature depending upon the grade of casting steel. The recommended heating rate is 100°C/hour. The time of soaking at annealing temperature can be determined by calculation (i.e. 1.5 to 2 minutes for each mm of a maximum section thickness of the casting). After annealing, the castings are slowly cooled (usually in the furnace) to a temperature not exceeding 300°C. Further cooling can be conducted in open air. Heavy castings are annealed at 900°-1000°C for 5-10 hours.

Normalising. Steel castings containing low carbon are usually normalised instead of annealing. In some cases, even high carbon steel castings are normalised to improve mechanical properties. Such castings are usually reheated after annealing/normalising to a lower temperature and cooled slowly, the operation is called high temperature tempering or drawing. The usual temperature of tempering is 600°-650°C.

6.10.10. Heat Treatment of Gas Turbine Blades

The conventional materials used for gas turbine blades are super-alloys. A newly developed nickel base super-alloy is Nimonic PE-16 used for gas turbine blades. The heat treatment of this alloy involves the following steps:

(a) Solution annealing at 1100°C for 1 hour and air cooling;

(b) 40-50 pct. reduction in thickness by cold rolling;

(c) Ageing at 900°C for one hour followed by air cooling;

(d) Further reduction in thickness to about 30 pct. by cold rolling;

(e) Heating at 900°C for 1 hour and cooling at a rate of 40°C/hour to 750°C; and

(f) Final ageing at 750°C for 16 hours followed by cooling at a rate of 40°C/hour to 650°C and then air cooling.

6.10.11. Heat Treatment of Springs and Connectors used in Electrical Field

The conventional alloy that has been used for springs and connectors at present is Cu-Be alloy. This alloy is precipitation hardened. More recently a new alloy of copper containing 9.0 pct. nickel and 6.0 pct. tin has been developed and found to be most suitable for springs and connectors in heat treated condition. This alloy is cast and heat treated thermomechanically.

QUESTIONS

1. What do you mean by allotropy? What are the different allotropic forms of iron?

2. Define the term steel. How does steel differ from cast iron?

3. What is plain carbon steel? How is it classified?

4. Define the terms:

   (a) Austenite, (b) Ferrite, (c) Pearlite, and (d) Cementite.

5. Distinguish between hypo-eutectoid, and hyper-eutectoid steels.

6. Define the term critical temperature. What for the terms A_1, $A_{1,3}$ A_3 and A_{cm} stand?

7. Draw $Fe-Fe_3C$ equilibrium diagram and lebel all the phases in the diagram

8. Determine the relative amounts of the structural constituents present in an annealed steel containing (a) 0.3 pct. carbon, and (b) 1.2 pct. carbon.

9. What is the effect of degree of undercooling on the structure and properties of ferrite-cementite aggregate.

10. Differentiate between the mechanisms of pearlitic and bainitic transformations.

11. Differentiate between the upper bainite and lower bainite with regard to structure and properties.

12. Draw T.T.T. diagram for a 0.6 pct. carbon steel and describe its isothermal transformation.

   (i) at a temperature just below A_3 and (ii) at a temperature just below A_1.

13. Annealing of hypo-eutectoid steel involves heating above the upper critical point whereas annealing of hyper-eutectoid steel involve heating above the

lower critical point but below A cm. Explain, why?

14. The structure and properties of a normalised steel are found to be superior to that of an annealed steel. Why? Explain.

15. Usually stells are annealed below the lower critical temperature in order to improve machinability. But the steel so annealed is difficult to machine by machining operations like milling, planing etc. Suggest suitable heat treatment to improve machinability of steel required for above the operations.

16. What for is patenting annealing used commonly? Write the annealing cycle for patenting trertment.

17. Define the term critical cooling rate.

18. What do you understand by the term hardening of steel? Schematically show the heating ranges of hypo-eutectoid and hyper-eutectoid steels.

19. Enumerate the various requirements for an ideal quenching medium.

20. Schematically show the heat treating cycle of quenching in two media and step wise quenching methods.

21. Hardenability of alloy steels is higher than that of plain carbon steels. Explain, why?

22. What is the necessity of tempering treatment after hardening?

23. Distinguish between surface hardening and case hardening methods.

24. What is the principle of induction hardening?

25. What is gas carburising? What are the advantages of gas carburising over pack and liquid carburising?

26. Heat treatment is generally necessary after carburising. Why? Explain.

27. Write the mechanism of nitriding process. What are the favourable requirements for nitriding steels?

28. What are the salient features of nitriding? Write the applications of nitriding process.

29. How does cyaniding differs from liquid carburising?

30. State heat treatment cycle for ausforming treatment with schematic representation.

31. What is hydrogen annealing?

32. What is Widmänstatten structure? Under what conditions [does it form? How can it be eliminated?

33. What is malleabilising treatment? State the heat treatment cycle with schematic representation.

34. What are maraging steels?

35. What are the important requirements for tools?

36. Write a critical note on heat treatment furnaces?

37. What is temper embrittlement ?

38. What is season cracking ? How is it eliminated?

39. State the heat treatment cycle of aluminium-copper alloys.

40. Suggest suitable materials, their composition and heat treatment for the following applications:

(a) Crank shaft, (b) Transmission gears, (c) Piston ring, (d) Aricraft wings and skin, (e) High speed steel.

7

ORGANIC MATERIALS

In early civilizations wood has been used as an industrial material. It was employed principally as a construction material and it is still used for the same purpose. Wood and other organic materials such as canvas, manila fibre and okum made possible the construction of a sailing ship. The organic materials are the innumerable substances which are based on carbon-chemistry. Organic materials can be classified broadly in two groups i.e. (*i*) natural and (*ii*) synthetic. The natural materials include wood, coal, petroleum, natural gas, natural rubber, animal fibre and food, whereas synthetic organic materials include the larger group of solvents, adhesives, metal and wood finishes, synthetic fibres, rubbers, plastics, explosives, lubricants, dyes, soaps, cutting oils, zeolites and a numberless others.

Organic materials are becoming important in engineering at a very fast rate. These materials now-a-days are holding the most useful and competitive status in the industries. Its specific properties such as strength, anticorrosiveness, light weight etc. are of great importance for the consideration of its application in various industries and other purposes.

7.1. WOOD

Wood is the most classical naturally occurring organic material which is used in various fields such as buildings, bridges, industries, furniture and as a domestic fuel. From engineering standpoint, wood is the most important portion of the tree. Basically wood consists of two types of cells: (*i*) long hollow cells whose axes run parallel to the length of tree and (*ii*) cells radiating from the central axis of the tree. These cells are bonded together by a natural resin called *lignin*. Therefore, behaviour of wood can be considered similar to the bundle of thin walled tubes cemented together. The growth of the tree is directly related to the growth of cells growing rapidly during the spring and early summer. However, the cells laid down during this time are not so strong and thick walled as the cells laid down in the later period of the year. Towards the end of the summer and early fall, growth of cells ceases. A cross-section through a tree shows the rings of annual growth, the dark portion of each ring represents the summer growth.

7.1.1. Seasoning of Wood

Processing of wood for making it suitable for constructional purposes is called seasoning of wood. When wood is seasoned, water leaves the cell walls causing shrinkage. Most of shrinkage takes place at right angles to the lenght of the cell and the amount of shrinkage depends upon thickness of the cells. Because of the cell geomerty, the greatest shrinkage occurs across the grain, tangentially to the rings of annual growth and the least occurs longitudinally.

Ideal seasoning of wood aims to produce a moisture content in stable equilibrium with the moisture content of the atmosphere in which the wood is to be used. In this way the dimensions of wood are stabilized prior to its actual use. When the moisture content or relative humidity of the atmosphere varies, the equilibrium moisture content of the wood also varies resulting into expansion or shrinkage depending upon the rise or fall of the moisture content, respectively.

Green wood is tougher than the seasoned wood and thus can bend and deform whereas seasoned wood can not bend or deform. By seasoning of wood many mechanical properties are improved. Both strength and hardness are improved with decrease in moisture content. However, the toughness may get reduced.

7.1.2. Mechanical Properties of Wood

The structure of wood is like bundles of thin walled tubes. Thus, many characteristics of wood behaviour can be explained on this basis. The important mechanical properties of wood include (*i*) flexural loading, (*ii*) tensile loading, and (*iii*) compressive loading.

(*i*) **Flexural loading**. Wood usually reacts very favourably when subjected to flexural loading. Under flexural loading, failure occurs commonly by compression or tension in the outermost fibres. Beams carrying flexural loads also fail by shear force acting along the grain near the centre fibre. Failure can also occur by compression across the grain at regions of concentrated normal stress beneath a concentrated load or at the support points. The limit fibre stresses range from 400 kgs/cm^2 (for white cedar) to about 1000 kgs/cm^2 (for black locust). Since knots exert a weakening effect in tension, beams should be positioned with the knots in compression if possible.

(*ii*) **Tensile loading**. Tensile loading of wood is difficult to accomplish without involving shear stresses along the grain at the end connections. Since the shear strength along the grain is low, the ability of wood to be loaded in pure tension is limited by this consideration. Therefore, due to low shear strength, wood cannot be used under tensile loading. Maximum shear strength along the grain in the air dry condition varies between 55 kgs/cm^2 for balsam fir to about 200 kgs/cm^2 for black locust. The tensile strength of wood along the grain is probably higher than the modulus of rupture in bending. The modulus of elasticity of wood varies from 0.6×10^5 kgs/cm^2 for cedar to 1.7×10^5 kgs/cm^2 for black locust in the air-dry condition.

The properties of green wood are approximately 25-50 pct. lower than those of wood in air-dry condition. The effect of loads applied for a long time as compared to short time loading is important. For instance, under long-time loads, beams fail at stresses of less than two-third the ultimate strength. The other factor influencing the properties of wood is temperature. Prolonged high temperatures definitely have a harmful effect on the properties.

(*iii*) **Compressive loading.** Wood also responds very favourably when subjected to compressive loads acting along the grain. Failure of short columns under compressive loads occur by compression of the fibres or by shear along the grain. Failure of long columns can also occur by buckling of the colomn. The compressive loads along the grain run from 200 kgs/cm^2 for white cedar to 550 kgs/cm^2 for black locust. Compressive strength across in the grain is low, as it would be in a bundle of tubes. For this type of loading the values of stresses in the air dry condition run between 16 kgs/cm^2 for bars wood to 180 kgs/cm^2 for some varieties of hickory.

7.1.3. Preservation of Wood

Since wood is an organic material of natural origin, it can be attacked by living organisms such as insects and fungi. It is also susceptible to fire damage. Fungi causes discolouration, decay, rotting or staining. Fungi causing discolouration and staining do not attack the cell walls or lignin which are responsible for the strength of wood. However, some fungi attack either the cellulose or lignin resulting the wood not usable. These types of fungi require moisture, some air, and proper temperatute for their living and growth. Thus, the best way to prevent the fungi attack is to have the absence of moisture in the working atmosphere. Thoroughly seasoned wood is not attacked by the organisms unless it is used in surroundings when its moisture content rises above 20 pct. To prevent the fungi attack, a coating of antiseptics such as zinc chloride, creosote and penta chlorophenol is quite effective.

Insects are responsible for serious damage to woods and their structures. Perhaps the most widespread attack is caused by white ants (subteraneous termites). In addition to this there are also dry wood termites and massive borers. Protection against white ants is effected by proper inspection of structural members with the help of an ice pick or other sharp instrument. If, infestation is discovered, soil poisons can be used to control the attack. Chlordane and DDT both can be used effectively.

Protection against dry-wood termites can be effected by inspecting the wood before use, sealing exposed surfaces with paint and screening of ventilators and access ways to cellars and air spaces. If infestation is detected, it can be controlled by blowing poison dusts into the wood which has been attacked.

Marine borer attack can be prevented by using metal sheathing, asphalt sheathing or concrete sheathing around submerged wooden structures. Once the continuity of the cover is broken, attack is no longer prevented. Protection against marine borers is so difficult that frequent replacement of unprotected damaged members is sometimes the easiest solution.

True fire-proofing of wood can not actually be achieved. However, pressure impregnation with solutions of borax and ammonium salts improves the fire resistance of wood. The wood so treated chars when subjected to flame, but does not readily burn.

7.1.4. Wood Products

A large number of products are derived from trees and wood. Some of these are chemicals such as methyl alcohol, turpentine, rosin and cellulose which are obtained by chemical as well as mechanical methods. Cellulose is produced in the form of pulp and is one of the most useful wood derivatives. It is used for making cellophane, artificial silk, plastic filler, paper and paper board. Other wood products of interest are plywood, laminates, and impregnates. These possess superior properties compared to natural wood.

(*i*) **Manufacture of cellulose.** For making cellulose, the logs are first cut to the desired length (50 cms to 100 cms) and the bark is removed by a claw knife or by tumbling the logs in a large barrel where the operation is assisted by high-pressure jets. From these debarked logs, pulp can be made mechanically or chemically. In mechanical method, the pulp is made by forcing the log against grinding wheel. In chemical method, first the logs are cut into small chips about 5 mm thick and running at 45° to the grain. The chips are then digested in a tank with steam, water and chemicals which dissolve lignin. Three kinds of chemical pulp can be produced, viz., (*a*) sulfite pulp made by digesting with $Ca(HSO_3)_2$, (*b*) soda pulp made by digesting with NaOH, and (*c*) kraft pulp made by digesting with Na_2SO_3. Pulp produced by mechanical method is cheaper and absorbs ink better than chemical pulp. However, chemical pulp has longer fibres and the papers produced are stronger. The pulp obatined from chemical process should be washed thoroughly to remove entrapped chemicals. The pulp produced from either process is screened to remove foreign materials and undisintegrated large pieces of wood. One part of pulp is then mixed with 24 parts of water and used for making paper or laps. Laps are thick, blotter like sheets of pulp which can be handled and stored easily than pulp suspensions.

(*ii*) **Paper.** Most papers consist of a high percentage of wood fibres. Only the more expensive ones such as writing paper and blue print paper contain appreciable quantities of cotton cellulose fibres. Newsprint, the most abundantly produced form of paper contains only wood pulp and filler materials. The use of rag fibres improves the strength and other properties of paper. Paper making consists essentially of reassembling the fibres of wood or cotton in the form of a continuous sheet by mixing the various types of fibres with large volume of water, and with appropriate fillers (talc, clay, and gypsum) and sizing agents (rosin, alum). This mixture is flown on to a moving belt of fine wire screen for removing the water by draining and sucking. In this way, a weak and wet sheet of paper form is lifted from the end of the screen. This weak sheet is passed through pressure rolls to reduce the water content to about 70 pct. and then passed through heated rolls with as speed a high as 600 metres per minute. These rolls reduce the water contents to only about 8 pct. after which the paper is calendered or polished and finally reeled.

(iii) **Plywood**. For making plywood, unbarked logs into convenient sizes are placed in lathe where a knife running the full length of the log removes a continuous strip of *veneer*. Short lengths having large defects are cut and removed from the strip by a shear blade. The strip free from large defects is cut into convenient lengths. The *veneers* are sorted, stacked and dried in an oven for approximately 10 minutes. Minor blemishes are cut from the *veneer*, and plugs of round wood having the same size as the removed area are cemented there. The *veneer* then passes through a roller coater which applies bonding material. After coating, the sheets of veneer are stacked so that the grains in one ply runs at right angles to the grain of adjoining ply. The stack is then pressed hot or cold. Cold pressing is used with case in or soyabean glues which are water resistant but not waterproof. Hot pressing is necessary for thermosetting resin bonding agents which are used for waterproof plywood. After the bond is set, the plywood is removed from the press and then the edges are trimmed and the surfaces are sanded to make them smooth. The grade of the plywood is marked on the edge and then it is shipped or stored.

Plywoods are superior to natural wood because the strength and shrinkage tendencies of the final product are less directional and the pieces having large continuous surfaces are easily available in plywood. In addition to this, a high quality surface can be made available at low cost in plywood because of using cheap core materials.

(iv) **Laminates**. These are small pieces of clear wood cemented together which are free from usual defects. Wood is also pressure-impregnated with strong waterproof synthetic resins. This improves the strength and water resistance of wood and stabilizes its dimensions against changes in moisture content of the surroundings. Somewhat similar effects are achieved by simultaneous application of heat and pressure so that lignin and the natural resins of wood are temporarily softened and redistributed. This produces a stronger and more dense material. Laminates and impregnated or compressed wood products are much more expensive than natural wood and are only used if the service requirements justify the cost.

7.2. COAL, PETROLEUM AND NATURAL GAS

The organic natural resources available in the earth's crust may be solid (coal), liquid (petroleum), or gas (natural gas). Each of these materials is a mixture of large number of hydrocarbons. Some specific hydrocarbons such as methane is found in all the sources. Particularly, some petroleum hydrocarbons are always found in natural gas deposits and natural gas is always found in petroleum. The main difference between petroleum and natural gas is that petroleum consists of greater proportion of liquid hydrocarbons while natural gas consists of greater proportion of gaseous hydrocarbons. On the other hand, coal contains a large amount of fixed carbon along with many hydrocarbons and other constituents. Coal is mainly utilized as a fuel in industry and homes.

7.2.1. Petroleum

The word 'petroleum' means rock oil, signifying oil found in sedimentary rock deposits. Petroleum became an industrial material in 1860's, the period that gave us cheap steel and paper from wood. At that time, whale oil was the principal illuminant. As it became less available due to scarcity of whales, the less popular coal oil (kerosene made from coal) had to be substituted. Kerosen is also a product obtained from petroleum which was first distilled from petroleum in 1860 in Southern Ontario.

Later, another very improtant group of products known as petro‐ chemicals was developed from petroleum and gas. Though only a small proportion of petroleum production goes into petrochemicals but this group of products serves a vast spectrum of applications even far beyond the familiar plastics and rubber. The history of petrochemicals dates back to 1916, when a discovery was made to make propyl alcohol from petroleum. The synthetic plastics and rubbers in limited production were included in the list of petrochemi‐ cals in 1930.

Crude petroleum represents a mixture of wide range of oil and gas components which differ from source to source. These have be con‐ verted to a crude oil of fixed characteristics before their refining. The first refinery operation is the separation of crude oil into various 'cuts', using distillation method. For flexibility of operation, two other basic refinery processes i.e. (i) cracking (breaking up the larger molecules into shorter gasoline molecules) and (ii) polymerization (polymerizing small gas molecules into larger molecules) are needed. Other refinery processes are incorporated with these either to improve product quality or to produce special products such as gresses, coke, or chemical intermediates.

Refining of petroleum consists of mainly three steps, i.e. (i) distilla‐ tion, (ii) catalytic cracking, and (iii) polymerization.

(i) **Distillation**. This is the first step in reducing the multitude of hydrocarbons in petroleum to usable products. After separating the crude oil into distilled fraction, these can be further refined by frac‐ tional distillation taking advantage of differences in their boilding points. The light fractions including heavy gas and oil are separated by distillation at atmospheric pressure. The heavier fractions are distilled under vaccum conditions (50-100 mm Hg) as the temperature required for their distillation at atmospheric pressure would be so high that the products may be damaged resulting in polymerization and excessive formation of coke.

Petrochemicals are produced from light fractions such as ethane and butane, while gasoline is made from both lighter fractions and the heavier gas oils.

(*ii*) **Catalytic cracking**. Cracking is the process by which fractions boiling in the gasoline or light naphtha range are produced from heavier fractions. In this the larger molecules are divided into fragments of lower molecular weights basically by heat, but with the assistance of pressure and catalysts (a material which promotes a chemical reaction without being consumed). Without the catalyst, excessive amount of methane and ethane are produced by cracking.

Petroleum hydrocarbons are cracked at temperatures above 342°C. However, higher temperatures are required to crack larger molecules. The resulting cracked product is a mixture containing fractions from gas to tar and coke with almost the same boiling range as the crude from which it is made. But the cracked material will contain perhaps twice as much material boiling in the gasoline range, that is pentance (C_5H_1) and heavier. Kerosene, lubricating oils, waxes, or asphalts are not suitable for cracking. Gasoline, diesel fuel and furnace oil are the products which are cracked.

Straight-run distillate gasoline made of the pentane, hexane, heptane, octane, etc. can not be burned in modern automobiles, though these were used in the past. A special type of cracking process used to upgrade the quality of gasoline is called reforming which produces greater amounts of naphthene and aromatics, converting hexane, for example, into benzene. The products of the reforming process may also be converted into petrochemicals.

(*iii*) **Polymerization**. Cracking and reforming processes produce large amounts of gaseous hydrocarbons. These light fractions may be put through a 'polyunit' to produce polymer gasoline. This operation is the reverse of cracking

Gasoline, petrol and diesel are the light products from petroleum which are used in automobiles. Lubricating oils, kerosene, furnace oil, greases, petroleum waxes, petroleum asphalts, insulating oils, and petroleum coke are special refinery products which serve various purposes in a variety of industries.

7.2.2. Solvents

Industrial solvents used for the cleaning of metals and paint stripping are petrochemicals with small molecules that enables them to penetrate into surface coatings. There are three types of solvents i.e. (*i*) paraffins (*ii*) aromatics and (*iii*) chlorinated solvents, their solvency power being in the increasing order.

(*i*) **Paraffin solvents**. These are simply members of the paraffin family such as diesel fuel or gasoline. These have limited solvency.

(*ii*) **Aeromatic solvents.** This group includes chemicals such as bengene and xylene.

(*iii*) **Chlorinated solvents.** Trichloroethylene (C_2HCl_3), methyl chloride (CH_3Cl), carbon tetrachloride (CCl_4) etc. are paraffins with the hydrogen atoms partially or wholly substituted by chlorine atoms.

7.2.3. Petrochemical Intermediates

There are the chemicals manufactured from petroleum and natural gas, which are further processed into finished products. They are the raw materials for most rubbers, plastics and a large number of other chemicals for industry. Petrochemical intermediates may also be manufactured from coal rich in aeromatic hydrocarbons. The most important one is ethylene which is used to manufacture ethylene glycol (engine antifreeze), many plastics and rubbers. The chief feed stocks used for cracking into ethylene are ethane and propane, but butane, naphthas and gas oils may also be used. In principle, any organic chemical can be made from any fraction of petroleum or natural gas.

Other olefin intermediates are acetylene, propylene, butylene, iso-propylene and butadiene. Most of these are used in the production of rubber, among other products. Nylon may be produced by buta-diene. Acetylene can be converted into such plastics as polyvinyl chloride (PVC) and orlon.

Next to the olefins, the most important group of intermediates is the aromatics, chiefly the BTX trio-benzene, toluene, and xylene. Of the cyclic naphthalenes, the most significant intermediate is cyclo-hexane, used in the production of nylon.

Insecticides, detergents, solid rocket fuel, photographic films, pharmaceuticals, solvents, explosives and alcohols are a partial listing of some of the end uses of the olefin, aromatic and naphthene intermediates mentioned.

7.3. ORGANIC POLYMERS

Polymers are defined as the high-molecular weight interaction products of monomers or of related polyfunctional molecules. The process by which these polymers are obtained is known as polymerization. Polymerization is a chemical process in which two or more similar chemical compounds join to make one compound. The products are known as polymer products. By this method we can get gaseous, liquid or solid polymers depending upon the number of unsaturated molecules taking part in the reaction.

When thousand of such unsaturated molecules join together, semi-solid or solid or polymers result. For example, polyethylene is the result of joining thousands of ethylene molecules into one giant molecule. Butyl rubber and paratone are solid and semi-solid polymerization products of isobutylene.

Thus a polymer may be defined as a number of repeating chemical units held together by covalent bonds. But in case of crystals or liquids, the repeating units may be held together by ionic or hydrogen bonds or even by weaker forces such as dipole interactions. Rayon, nylon, dacron, terylene, teflon, rubber, paints, and quite a large number of products are polymer products by different chemical processes.

Most of the industrial polymers are plastics and elastomers. Plastics are characterised by their plastic deformation under stress, whereas elastomers or rubbers are capable of withstanding extensive elastic deformation. However, some plastics are highly elastic and any rubber may also be deformed plastically under certain conditions. Further, it is also common to copolymerize a plastic monomer with a rubber monomer to overcome the brittleness of some plastics.

The plastics can be further classified into two groups: (*i*) thermoplastics, and (*ii*) thermosets. The thermoplastics can be softened repeatedly with heat and will reharden when cooled. The examples are polyethylene and polystyrene. Thermosetting plastics harden or 'cure' with heat and then can not be resoftened by heating. Typical thermosets are bakelite, epoxy, silicones and rubbers.

7.3.1. Polymerisation and Its Mechanism

There are two general methods of polymerisation:

(*i*) Addition polymerisation; and

(*ii*) Condensation polymerisation.

(*i*) **Addition polymerisation**. In this method, the polymer is produced by adding a second monomer to the first, then a third monomer to this dimer, a fourth to the trimer, and so on until the long polymer chain is terminated. For examale, polyethylene is produced

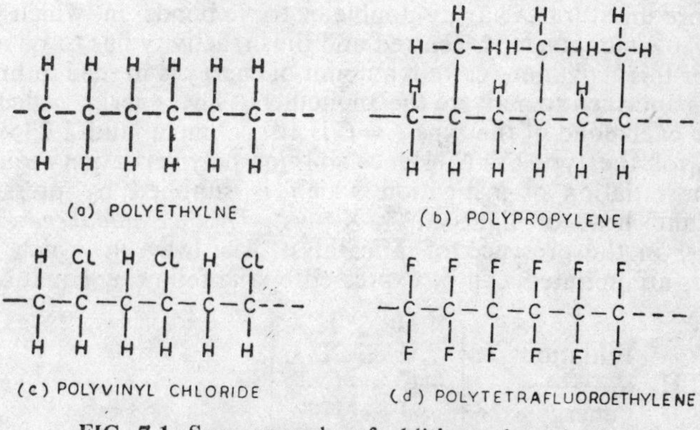

FIG. 7.1. Some examples of addition polymerisation

by the addition polymerisation of ethylene monomers as shown in Fig. 7.1. Addition polymerisation always results in a thermoplastic.

In general there must exist at least one double bond in the monomer for the addition polymerisation reaction. Polyethylene is the simplest polymer formed by the addition reaction. Ethylene molecules are unsaturated consisting of double bonds between the carbon atoms. During the addition reaction, the double bond is shifted to form saturated hydrocarbon chain. An addition polymerisation reaction may take place in three different ways i e. (a) step reaction, (b) chain reaction and (c) ionic reaction.

(a) *Step reactions.* In this case the reaction occurs step by step and goes on repeating till the end product is obtained. For example, polyethylene glycol is formed according to the following overall reaction:

$$n \begin{array}{c} CH_2 \\ | \\ CH_2 \end{array}\!\!\!\diagdown O + H_2O \rightarrow HOCH_2.CH_2 \left\{ -OCH_2.CH_2 \right\}_{n-1} -OH \qquad ...(7.1)$$

(b) *Chain reactions.* Chain reactions are of maximum importance in the chemical products. For example, polyethylene, polyvinyl chloride, polystyrenes etc. are the result of chain reaction. General mechanism of this type of reaction can be expressed as

$$R + R \rightarrow R \overset{R}{R} \rightarrow R\ R\ R \rightarrow R_n \qquad ...(7.2)$$

(c) *Ionic reactions.* These are not very common in industrial products. Preparation of polyisobutylene with BF_3 catalyst is an example of this type.

Characteristics of addition polymerisation. The reaction of addition polymerisation does not initiate by simply bringing the monomers together. There are many characteristics such as starting or initiation, propagation, transfer, termination and kinetic factors which help in completion of the reaction. The monomers taking part in addition, reaction are unsaturates having double or triple bonds in which the reactivity of monomers is centred and thus reactivity has to be activated. For this activation, certain amount of energy is needed to break the bonds and then to activate the monomers. The energy needed to dissociate each bond of the type $C=C$ is 10^5 cal/mole and 1.23×10^5 cal/mole for the type $C \equiv C$. Hence addition polymerisation requires energy for initiation or instigation which is supplied by pressure, catalyst and heat or light $(\alpha, \beta, \gamma, X\text{-rays})$ *This activation energy is much lower* in the presence of a catalyst. The way in which the monomers are initiated, can be expressed by the following equation:

$$n\ C_2H_4 \xrightarrow[\text{energy}]{\text{Initiation}} \begin{bmatrix} H & H \\ | & | \\ -C- -C- \\ | & | \\ H & H \end{bmatrix}_n \qquad ...(7.3)$$

Addition polymerisation is of two types, i.e. (a) homopolymerisation and (b) copolymerisation.

(a) *Homopolymerisation.* This is a polymerisation process in which one and only one identical monomer is involved to produce polymer. For example, if two different monomers i.e. R and S take part into reaction than homopolymers are formed of the following type:

$$\overset{R\quad R}{R \rightarrow RR \rightarrow RRR \rightarrow \ldots\ldots \rightarrow R_n} \qquad \ldots(7.4)$$

or
$$\overset{S\quad S}{S \rightarrow SS \rightarrow SSS \rightarrow \ldots\ldots \rightarrow S_n} \qquad \ldots(7.5)$$

The most common examples of homopolymerisation are the formation of polyethylene, polyvinyl chloride and polystyrene.

(b) *Copolymerisation.* The polymerisation process involving more than one kind of monomers to produce a polymer is called copolymerisation. Many monomers do not polymerise among themselves, but copolymerise with other compounds. The reactions of R and S monomers may produce the products of the following type:

$$RS \; RS \; RS \; RS \qquad \ldots(7.6)$$

or
$$RR \; SS \; RR \; SS \; RR \qquad \ldots(7.7)$$

For example vinyl chloride and vinyl acetate copolymerise to give a product chloride-acetate copolymer which has quite different properties from homopolymers polyvinyl chloride or polyvinyl acetate. In general, copolymer plastics are observed to have better physical and chemical properties.

Polyvinyl chloride is normally hard, tough and soluble in solvent. Its softening point is 80-90°C. However, its copolymers have better heat stability and solubility in the solvents. The vinyl polymers are used in surface coatings, spray, coatings textile fabric coating, rain wear, tubing etc.

Copolymerisation has great applications in the manufacture of buna-S rubbers, which is a copolymer of butadiene and styrene. Many fibres are also made of copolymer. Now-a-days synthetic textile industries are dependent upon this type of plastics only.

(ii) **Condensation polymerisation.** This process occurs in the combination of a compound with itself or other compounds, accompanied by the elimination of some simple compound such as water, hydrogen, hydrochloric acid or sodium chloride as a result of the polymerisation. The molecular formula lacks certain atoms present in the monomer from which it is made. Important groups which take part in polycondensation reactions are anhydride, amino, amide, aldehyde, carboxyl, hydroxyl, chloride or others. A monomer must contain two or more of such groups. For example, in a monomer of aminoacid $NH_2(BH_y)_n COOH$, amino (NH_2) and carboxyl $(COOH)$ two groups are present. When phenol and formaldehyde monomer are polymerised, water is expelled, and the resulting product is a polymerised phenol-formaldehyde (*bakelite*). Condensation products may be either thermosets or thermoplasts.

Phenol is chemically related to benzene (C_6H_6). The polar (—OH) group of the phenol, however, interacts with the resonant benzene structure. Three of the five hydrogen atoms of the benzene ring at three active points (Fig. 7.2) become loosely attached i.e. these three active hydrogen (H) atoms may take part in the reaction. In formal

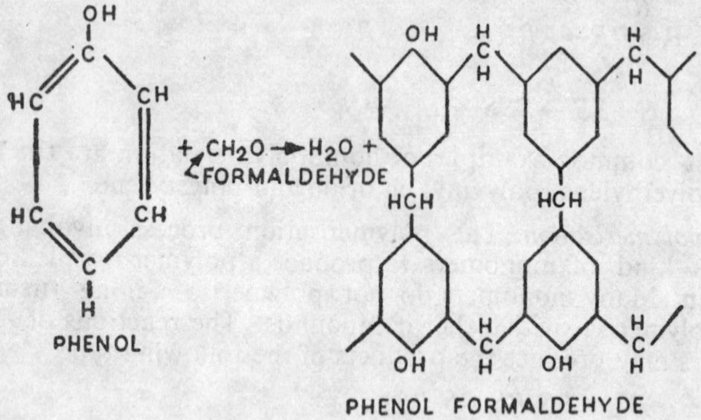

FIG. 7.2. Formation of phenol formaldehyde by condensation polymerisation.

dehyde, oxygen (O) is active atom to take part in the reaction. For reaction, two hydrogen atoms from two phenol molecules (one from each) combine with the oxygen from formaldehyde and form water which gets separated as by-product. The rest results into formation

Difference between Addition and Condensation Polymerisation

S. No.	Addition polymerisation	Condensation polymerisation
1.	It requires unsaturated monomers which combine in succession to give a polymer.	In this chemical groups (one or more) are important. These chemical groups of different monomers combine and result in a polymer.
2.	Addition reaction makes use of all monomers to yield a polymer without any resulting by-product.	A by-product is always obtained along with the polymer.
3.	It is a kinetic chain reaction.	It involves intermolecular reaction
4.	In this, polymers are formed quickly 10^{-2} 10^{-6} second).	This reaction is completed in different independent steps taking a definite period of time (usually hours and days).
5.	When two growing polymer chains start addition reaction, the product formed stops to grow and this situation is called termination of polymerisation.	In this case when two growing polymers react, the reaction propagates instead of termination due to the reactive points of newly formed molecules.

of a large molecule of phenol-formaldehyde plastics. The water form-ed gets vaporised or removed from the system.

Condensation polymerisation is also very important in industries. Phenolic plastics, amino plastics, polyesters, polyamides and epoxies are all condensation products.

Under suitable conditions polymerisation is a unidirectional process which necessitates the conditions to be carefully controlled. Little change in it may cause the reversal called depolymerisation of the process. Depolymerization may also be considered as break-up of large molecules which is of particular interest in petroleum refineries for the production of most valuable gasoline and a large number of products. Depolymerisation is also termed as degradation.

7.3.2. Additives to Polymers

These are the ingredients added to polymers in order to improve or alter their properties, such as for plasticizing them, protecting them from deterioration or change of any other property. The additives are normally of two types. i.e. (i) *plasticizers* and (ii) *reinforcing fillers*. *Plasticizers* are non-volatile solvents which make the brittle plastics softer and more plastic. For example, un-plasticized PVC (polyvinyl chloride) is used as rigid pipe, but when plasticized, it makes an excellent flexible garden hose. However, the polyolefins such as polyethylene, polystyrene, Plexiglass and the thermosets are normally not plasticized. Reinforcing fillers such as carbon black and clay are added to rubbers for portection against the depolymerisation effects of ultraviolet radiation. Polyethylene pipe is almost invariably blended with carbon black.

7.3.3. Natural Polymers and Their Derivatives

Asphalt, cellulose, shellac, natural rubber, casein and starch are natural polymers of vital importance to industry. Starch is used mainly as a paper-product adhesive. Natural rubber corresponds to polyisoprene and it is used for various industrial applications. Shellac is an excretion of the lac bug and is used in the form of projective and decorative coating. It can be compression molded and is one of the materials used for phonograph records. Casein is the chief pro-tein in milk. Its industrial importance is declining, but it is still used as an adhesive and for small molded articles.

A considerable quantity of thermoplastic materials can be made from cellulose, which is itself a thermosetting plastic. Cellulose nitrate (or celluloid), discovered about 100 years ago, was the first of the synthetic polymers to be introduced. It is used in paints and finishes, combs, tooth brush handles, and billiard balls. Its chief disadvantage is its high in flammability.

Cellulose acetate has a crystal clear transparency and permeability to water vapour and gases. It is used as an adhesive, packaging film, and photographic film. Permeability makes it an excellent choice for the packaging of fruits and vegetables.

Cellulose acetate butyrate is molded into pipes, telephone housings, small tool handles, and automobile steering wheels. These uses are important due to its resistance to oils, greases and perspiration. Several other synthetic polymers are made from cellulose.

7.3.4. Synthetic Polymers

Most of the industrial polymers are (i) plastics and (ii) elastomers. *Plastics are synthetic resins characterised by plastics deformation under stress.* Plastics are further classified as (a) thermoplastics, and (b) thermosets. *The elastomers are rubbers capable of extensive elastic deformation.*

Plastics. In general the term 'plastic' is applied to all those materials which are capable of being molded. However, it also includes a large group of synthetic organic materials which become plastic by the application of heat and are capable of being formed to shape under pressure. Plastics replace materials like glass, wood, and metals in construction and are used to make coatings and filaments for weaving. Initial modulus of elasticity of plastics ranges from 10^8 to 10^9 dynes/cm^2. They also possess deformability characteristics of the order of 100 to 200 pct. at high temperatures. The deformations is partly temporary and partly permanent.

7.4. PROPERTIES OF PLASTICS

Various properties of different plastics differ considerably. Most important properties are mechanical and deformation properties.

7.4.1. Mechanical Properties

Tensile and compressive strengths are much below the metals. The modulus of elasticity of non-flexible plastic is almost equal to that of concrete. The favourable strength/weight ratio increases the suitability of plastics considerably. The ductility depends on the resins and the materials which are mixed in the finished product. In some respects ductile plastics have response to service conditions equivalent to metals. The elastic limit increases with increasing tensile loading and decreases with high temperatures. Fatigue loading causes failure at lower stresses than static loading. Creep phenomenon also develops when loads are applied for longer duration.

7.4.2. Effect of Polymer Structure on Properties

Different organic stuructures produce different plastics. With the change in the structure and type, mechanical properties vary considrably as indicated in Table. 7.1.

7.4.3. Deformation of Plastics

Deformability in plastics is a usual phenomenon specifically at higher

TABLE 7.1 Properties of Some Plastics

S. No.	Kinds of plastic	Tensile strength kgs/cm²	Elongation per cent	Modulus of elasticity kgs/cm²	Temperature limit °C	Electrical resistance Ohms cm.
1.	Thermosetting Plastics					
	(a) Phenol-formaldehyde (bakelite)	500-700	0.5-1.5	7×10^4	120	10^{11}-10^{12}
	(b) Cast Epoxy	850	—	3.3×10^4	150	10^{16}-10^{17}
	(c) Polyster	300-700	—	10.5×10^4	150	10^4
2.	Thermoplastics					
	(a) Cellulose Acetate	450	15-50	5×10^4-25×10^4	95	10^{11}-10^{12}
	(b) Polystyrene	500	1-2	3×10^4	95	10^{17}-10^{19}
	(c) Teflon	300	—	—	260	10^5
	(d) Low Density Polyethylene	100	200-750	1.5×10^3	95	10^5
3.	Others					
	(a) Nylon	650	90	3×10^4	150	10^{13}-10^{14}
	(b) Polycarbonate	700	15-60	2.5×10^4-3×10^4	120	10^{16}
	(c) Polyvinyl	70-600	—	upto 10×10^4	90	—

temperature. Fig. 7.3 represents the characteristic behaviour of thermoplastic materials under tensile test. The load deformation curve shown in Fig. 7.3 is true for most of the plastics. Region *O-P* of the diagram is approximately linear and obeys Hooke's law. In this region deformation is very small and is relieved on removing the load and thus the material is considered to be elastic in this region. This elastic deformation is due to bending or stretching of the interatomic bonds between atoms of the plastic molecules as Fig. 7.4(*a*). This type of deformation is practically instanteneous and no permanent displacement of molecules takes place relative to one another.

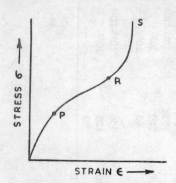

FIG. 7.3. Stress-strain curve for thermoplastic materials.

The deformation taking place between *P-R* region (Fig. 7.3) represents the elongation of a coiled portion of the molecular chains in tension as Fig. 7.4(*b*) where the deformation is reversible but not immediately. It will take some time to return to its original position. The mechanism of this deformation is slippage as Fig. 7.4(*c*), and not intermolecular. This deformation is much prominent in rubbers. This is also considered ultimately under elastic limit. Region *R-S* of the curve (Fig. 7.3) represents the extension of the material beyond the elastic limit where the molecules are displaced with respect to one another. Hence, the slipage between the molecules does not have the tendency to slip back to original position. Such deformations are not recoverable and thus a permanent deformation results.

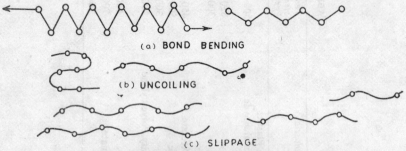

FIG. 7.4. Extension types of plastic molecules.

The intermolecular forces in plastic molecules are quite small and further weaker under constant increasing tensile load and finally causes the slip between the molecules resulting into permanent deformation. When slippage occurs between the molecules, three significant phenomenon occur in plastic deformation: (a) deformation, (b) orientation of molecules, and (c) increase in crystallinity. The align· ment of the molecular chains (particularly of the continuous chains) is greatly improved which increases the proportion of *crystallinity*. Improvement of these qualities results in increase of strength of the material. This increased strength may be attributed to the following facts:

(a) Intermolecular bonding force is increased due to locking effect.

(b) Molecules get aligned in the direction of load-greatly affecting the mutual attractive forces. This increased strength of the oriented material is represented by the upward trend of the curve (Fig. 7.3) at point S. The tensile strength of oriented plastics is about 10 times the unoriented one.

7.4.4. Effect of Polymer Structure on Plastic Deformation

Deformation does not take place without slip. The slip tends to occur under tensile stress and structure of the polymer has a direct bearing to resist the slip. Every polymer offers certain resistance to slip and the degree of this varies from structure to structure of the polymer. For example, polyethylene and polyvinyl chloride (PVC) have different structures. Former has a simple one offering poor resistance whereas the latter has large obstructions offered by chlorine atoms along the chain. Hence polyvinyl chloride is tough and strong. This effect is more pronouned in polystyrene.

7.5. ADVANTAGES AND LIMITATIONS OF PLASTIC MATERIALS

Plastics have a good combination of a number of properties, rather than extremes of any single property. Many plastics are used for specific purposes due to their special properties.

Advantages. (i) From plastic resins articles can be made rapidly with close dimensional tolerance and excellent surface finish.

(ii) They possess the favourable properties such as lightness in weight, moisture or corrosion resistance and dielectric strength due to which these are preferred sometimes over metals.

(iii) Plastics can be made either transparent or in various shades of colours.

(iv) They absorb vibrations and sound.

(v) It is easier to fabricate plastics than metals.

Limitations. (i) Plastics possess comparatively low strength, low heat resistance and low dimensional stability.

(ii) They are softer, less ductile and more susceptible to deformation under load and embrittlement at low temperatures.

(iii) Comparatively these are costlier than other materials.

(iv) Many plastics are inflammable.

7.6. RAW MATERIALS

The raw materials used for manufacturing plastic compounds are various agricultural products and a variety of minerals and organic materials such as coal gas, natural gas, petroleum, lime stone, silica, sulphur etc. Other ingredients such as colour, pigments, solvents, lubricants, plasticizer and filler materials are also used. Wood powder, flower, cotton, rag fibres, asbestos, powdered metals, graphite, glass, clays, and diatamaceous earth are major materials used as fillers in the products such as outdoor chair seats, plastic cloth, garbage cans, machine housings etc. The fillers are usually employed to reduce manufacturing cost, minimize skrinkage, improve heat resistance, provide impact strength or impart other desired properties to the product. Plasticizers or solvents are used with some compounds to soften them or to improve their flowability in the mold. Lubricants also improve the molding characteristics of the compound. All these materials are mixed with the granulated resins before molding.

7.7. TYPES OF PLASTICS

Plastics may be broadly classified as thermosetting and thermoplastic.

7.7.1. Thermosetting Plastics

These are formed to required shapes by heat with or without pressure, resulting in a permanently hard product. In the first instance heat makes the material soft but on additional heat or by adding special chemicals, the plastics are hardened by polymerisation and can not be resoftened by heat. Polymerisation in such cases develops a continuous frame work picture where slip cannot take place between molecules. The whole structure is one large mass (molecule) because the primary covalent bonds are present throughout. In this case plasticity does not change with temperature because of their permanent setting. Thermosetting plastics are normally stronger than thermoplastic resins and thus can be used under the conditions of high temperature also. Methods used for processing thermosetting plastics are compression or transfer moulding, casting, laminating and impregnating. Examples are: (i) Phenolic resin (phenol formaldehyde or bakelite) used for manufacturing coating materials, laminated products, grinding wheels, metal and glass bonding agent and various other items of common use; (ii) amino resins (urea formaldehyde and melamin-formaldehyde) used for making table ware, ignition parts, knobs and electric appliances housings, circuit breaker parts and buttons, in the field adhesives and for laminating wood or paper. The other plastics of this group are furnace resins, epoxides and silicones (silicon based).

7.7.2. Thermoplastics

Thermoplastic materials do not undergo any chemical change

while molding and do not become permanenty hard with the application of pressure and heat. These plastics remain soft at elevated temperatures and are hardened only by cooling. They can be remolted repeatedly by sucessive applications of heat, as in the melting of paraffins and their plasticity increases with temperature. This group includes a large number of compounds such as polyvinyl chloride (PVC), polystyrene, cellulosics (acetate, acetate-butyrate, ethyl cellulose), polyethylene, polypropylene, polysolfones, ABS plastics (a crylonitrile, butadiene and styrene are combined for high degree of hardness, great flexibility and toughness), polyimide, nylon, acrylic acid, vinyl resins etc. These are used for different applications depending upon the requirements. Thermoplastic materials are processed principally by injection or blow-molding, extrusion, thermoforming and calendering.

7.8. ELASTOMERS

These are distinguished by their special characteristics of getting elongated on application of the force and returning back to their original positions on removal of the force. Thus these materials are

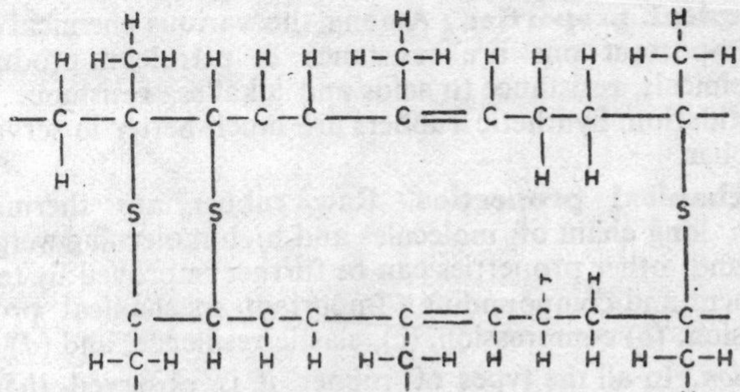

FIG. 7.5. Vulcanisation of rubber.

always in elastic limit. All rubbers and rubber like materials may be called *elastomers*. The displacement caused between molecules is too little that the elastomer regains its shape on release of the force. This elastic property associated with elastomers is due to their structure and not because of cmoposition. The rubbers are usually addition polymerised from unsaturated monomers such as butadiene and cross linked (vulcanised) with sulphur at approximately every 500th carbon atom. Increased cross-linking gives increased stiffness and reduced elongation. The structure of cross-linking is shown in Fig. 7.5.

7.8.1. Vulcanisation of Rubber

The curing reaction by which rubber reacts with the setting reagents (chemicals) is termed as *vulcanization*. By vulcanisation, properties of rubbers are changed considerably. Rubber molecules

222 MATERIALS SCIENCE AND MANUFACTURING PROCESSES

form a cross-linking on reacting with sulphur atoms, known as the vulcanizer. The effectiveness of vulcanisation can be enhanced by the use of accelerators which are organic chemicals.

7.8.2. Properties of Rubber

Toughness, wear resistance, low permeability, flexibility, abrasion resistance and resistance to various organics and inorganic chemicals among the are important properties of rubber. Various properties of rubber can be classified under three groups, i.e. (*i*) physical, (*ii*) chemical, and (*iii*) mechanical.

(*i*) **Physical properties.** Its specific gravity depends upon the composition and can be considered approximately equal to 1 0. Out of the various physical properties, low permeability of fluids and electrical properties are of great importance. Low permeability to fluids (like water) makes it water proofing material and resistant to a large number of chemicals. Because of its good electrical insulation properties it is used as insulating material. Rubbers are available having low as well as high specific resistances which are also affected by temperature. Electrical conductive rubbers are used in de-icing equipment of air-craft and for anesthetic hoses.

(*ii*) **Chemical properties.** Among the various chemical properties, the important one are resistance to petroleum products and organic chemicals, resistance to acids and alkalies, resistance to sun light or oxidation. Synthetic rubbers are much better in service than natural rubber.

(*iii*) **Mechanical properties.** Raw rubber are thermoplastic resins with long chain of molecules and high molecular weight. Its plasticity and other properties can be further improved by temperature treatment and compounding. Important mechanical properties are (*a*) tension, (*b*) compression, (*c*), elastic resilience, and (*d*) drift.

(*a*) *Tension.* In all the types of rubber it is observed that resistance to deformation first decreases with increasing tensile load and

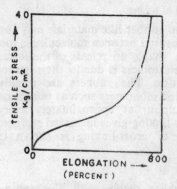

FIG. 7.6. Typical stress-strain curve for a polyisobutylene rubber.

then decreases. The natural of load-deformation curve is shown in Fig. 7.6. However, in case of rubbers, Hooke's law is not valid i.e. elastic strain is not proportional to stress. There is a definite time lag between the stress and the corresponding strain. A typical feature of stress-strain is *S-curve*. The linear middle portion of the stress-strain curve is due to the development of crystallinity in the rubber during stretching. Except the hard rubber, all rubbers show a maximum possible strain of several hundred per cent (shown in

Fig. 7.6). Modulus of elasticity for the softest rubber, soft-hard rubber and hard rubber are 11,100 and 10,000 kgs/cm², respectively. This characteristic of rubber depends upon various factors such as temperature, time during which rubber is exposed to the temperature, loading, compounding, and curing.

(b) *Compression.* Elasticity under compression loads is very impartant in case of rubbers. Modulus of elasticity in compression state is practically the same as that in tension. It can work as a spring also if lateral expansion is allowed.

(c) *Elastic resilience.* This is the property of a material to absorb energy elastically. This is shown on the stress-strain curve by the area under the curve within elastic limit. Rubbers are suitable materials to withstand shock-loads due to their good elastic resilience which is more than three times than of high strength steel.

(d) *Drift.* It is a phenomenon in which permanent distortion of the material takes place while subjecing for long time under load. Thus it is some what similar to creep phenomenon of metals. Increased temperature and vibrating loads increase the drift of rubbers.

7.8.3. Types of rubber. The more important rubber monomers are isoprene, styrene, isobutylene, acrylonitrile, butadiene, and chloroprene. The polymers are usually addition polymers. Natural rubber corresponds to polyisoprene. Synthetic polyisoprene is also produced, but is not identical to natural rubber.

(i) **Natural rubber.** Low hysteresis and high strength are the specific features of natural rubber. However, it is readily attacked by solvents, gasoline, and minute quantities of ozone in air. When rubber is vulcanised and reinforced with carbon black, tensile strength lies in the range of 250-320 kgs/cm² and elongation 550-650 pect. It is mainly used for larger tires for heavy vehicles and air-craft tires.

(ii) **Styrene-butadiene rubber SBR.** This is the synthetic rubber, used for car tires, rubber hose and tubing, and conveyor belts. Tensile strength after vulcanising and compounding with carbon black is 180-250 kgs/cm², and elongation 500-600 pct. This is the most important synthetic rubber and most of the goods are made from this rubber.

(iii) **Butyle rubber.** This is a copolymer of isobutylene and a small amount of isopren or butadiene. Permeation of gases through butyle rubber is only 10 pct. of the permeation through natural rubber, hence the use of this rubber for inner tubes and liner is recommended. It is also used as mastic sealant, especially for curtain-wall construction of buildings and has occasional uses as a solid fuel for rockets. This is a low density rubber of low strength and high elongation.

(iv) **Nitrile rubber.** This is copolymer of butadiene and acrylonitrile. Such rubbers have excellent adhesion to metals and resistance to oils and solvents. It is used for gasoline hose and hose linings, air-craft fuel tanks, printing rollers, and O-rings. An interesting use is that of nozzles for aerosol cans to resist the fluorinated hydrocarbon gas which pressurises the can.

(v) **Ethylene-propylene rubber (EPR).** These rubbers are made from low priced monomers which yield a very light-weight rubber. Ethylene propylene rubber has excellent resistance to aging, ozone, and chemicals, and possesses good electrical properties. It is incompatible with other rubbers.

(vi) **Polysulphide rubber (Thiokol).** It is a rubber of low mechanical strength but with outstanding resistance to solvents and low permeability to gases. Polysulphide rubber adhesives have excellent adhesion to metals. The uses of thiokols are all specific one, including rocket fuel, aircraft fuel tanks, gasket etc.

(vii) **Polychloroprene rubber (Neoprene).** It is resistant to oils and paraffins, ozone, and abrasion. It is not highly inflmmable. It is mostly used in electrical cable covering. It is also used for making gaskets, hose, engine mounts, bearing pads in bridge construction, protective clothing (gloves and aprons), conveyer belts and adhesives.

(viii) **Fluoro elastomers.** Fluorine containing rubbers are associated with low strength, high dielectric strength and high dielectric constant. Most of these rubbers are saturated and therefore are not vulcanised. Like the fluoro-plastics they may be used at both high as well as low temperatures. Kel-F, viton, fluorel and other fluoro elastomers therefore, have specific applications including aerospace field.

(ix) **Silicone rubbers.** Silicone rubbers may have fluorine, nitrile, or phenyl group in the monomer. Unlike most rubbers, these are unaffected by ultraviolet radiation or ozone. Like other silicone products, the silicone rubbers are resistant to heat, cold, and solvents. Their tensile strength is quite low at room temperature, but at higher temperatures they are the strongest of the elastomers. Silicone rubbers can be vulcanised at room temperature. This feature, together with temperature limit of 250°C or higher has made possible the use of silicone rubber as a tooling and mold material.

(x) **Polyurethanes.** Polyurethanes are produced by reacting a di-isocyanate (complex aromatic compound containing nitrogen) with an alcohol. Molded polyurethane articles are usually two component systems that are mixed and poured to cure in a mold. A typical polyurethane rubber has a tensile strength of 350 kgs/cm^2 higher than natural rubber, high elongation, high hardness, great tear strength and remarkable abrasion resistance. All these properties make its use as an excellent tire material. This is comparatively more expensive than other standard rubbers. However, polyurethane tires have proved their worth on the wheels of lift trucks and other ware house trucks. Other uses of polyurethane include long-wearing shoe heels, printing rollers, oil seals, diaphragms, vibration mounts, gear, pump impellers, duct liners, gasket, football, helmets etc. In some of these applications polyurethane compets with metals.

(*xi*) **Reclaim rubber**. This is scrap rubber. It is a convenient raw material as it is already blended with required antioxidants and other additives. It is used in large amounts in rubber goods because of its low cost.

7.9. FABRICATION OF PLASTIC OBJECTS

A variety of methods have been used for the fabrication of plastic objects, use of which depends largely upon the properties of the resin (i.e. thermoplastic or thermosetting) and the geometry of the finished product. Most of the processes are similar to metal fabricating processes. The processes of commercial importance are discussed as below:

7.9.1 Compression Molding

It is analogous to hot pressing of powdered metals. A definite amount of thermosetting resin, filler and other ingredients are placed in a mold cavity of the desired shape and both male as well as female portions of the die are heated (usually by steam). Preforms in the form of tablets can also be used, in which case preheating is done by high-frequency dielectric heating, or infrared heating lamps. Preheating results in several advantages such as, reduced time cycle during molding, increased die life, reduced pressure requirements, and more uniform product. Molding temperatures usually range from $130°$ to $180°C$, with pressures varying from 100 to 600 kgs/cm² depending upon the kind of raw materials and object.

Thermoplastic objects must be cool enough at the time of withdrawal so that no distortion is caused on removal of the objects from the mold. Compression molding process is not conomical for shaping thermoplastics due to expensive alternate heating and cooling cycles.

7.9.2. Injection Molding

It is analogous to die casting of metals. Thermoplastic molding compound is loaded into a hopper from which it is fed into an upper cylinder of the molding machine. One stroke of piston takes the proper amount of compound from the upper to lower cylinder as shown in Fig 7.7. A ram in the lower cylinder forces the charge forward into a heating chamber. Here the granular powder becomes plastic and is forced as a viscous liquid through a nozzle into the mold cavity. The mold is water coold which keeps it below the melting range of the compound. Pressure is maintained on the plastic until it has cooled sufficiently to solidify. The mold is then opened and the object is removed. The process is used principally for thermoplastic resins, though a modification known as jet molding has been developed for thermosetting materials.

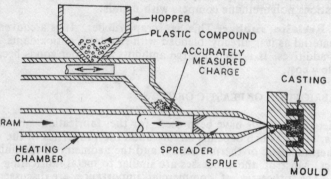

FIG. 7.7. Schematic diagram of injection molding.

7.9.3. Jet Molding

It differs from injection molding in that the mold cavity must be heated to cure the plastic forced into it. The hot nozzle by which the plastic is initially softened before being forced into the mold is hot only for a short time before and during the time the mold is being filled. It is quickly cooled after this part of the cycle to present curing of the plastic remaining in it. As in injecting molding, here also the pressure is maintained until the plastic in the mold hardens. Jet molding finds only limited use because more complex designs cannot be worked out as the process provides less flexibility.

7.9.4. Transfer Molding

It is a modification of compression molding and is shown in Fig. 7.8. It is used for making parts of thermosetting resins in which the design involves delicate or complex shapes. If such objects were made by compression molding, application of pressure to the solid powder in the mold cavity might result in breakage or distortion of delicate mold sections, or mis-

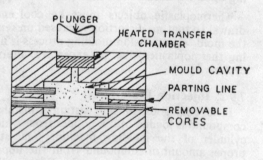

FIG. 7.8. Schematic diagram of transfer molding.

alignment of inserts. To avoid these difficulties, the solid resin compound is first placed in a transfer pot, when it is heated until it melts. It is then forced into the heated mold cavity, distributing the pressure evenly on all surfaces, and avoiding difficulties described above. As in compression, molding pressure is maintained until curing is complete, at which time the mold is taken apart and the object is removed.

7.9.5. Extrusion Molding

It is also similar to the hydraulic extrusion. A mechanical screw is used in place of hydraulic ram, which forces the solid thermoplastic compound through a heating zone where melting occurs. The viscous liquid is then extruded through an orifice of required section on to a conveyor. The length coming from the extrusion-molding machine is commonly cooled by blowers, water spray etc. It is used for manufacturing continuous thermoplastic shapes, such as sheets, filaments, rods and tubes.

7.9.6. Casting

It is mainly useful for thermosetting plastics and to some extent for thermoplastic resins. In this process, first the steel mandrel having the required shape and size is dipped into molten lead. A thin shell of lead freezes on the steel and on withdrawing the mandrel, a thin lead mold is obtained. Plastic is poured into the mold and cured for several days at temperature near 70°C. The cured plastic is then knowcked from the mold and the lead is remelted for recycling. The process is useful for making rods, tubes, cylinders, and special shapes such as screw driver handles, gears and gear blanks.

7.9.7. Drawing

It is a term applied to processed analogous to deep drawing and stretching in sheet metal working. Drawing involves either stretching a sheet of thermo-plastic material over a form, or forcing the sheeting by means of a plunger through a die.

7.9.8. Blowing

It is similar to the process of glass blowing. Sheets or extrusions of thermoplastic materials are forced into hollow, closed molds by air or steam pressure.

7.9.9. Laminating

It is used to combine sheets of various materials such as paper, cloth, glass fibres, and wood with plastics. In one method absorbent materials are passed into a resin-solvent solution. Afterwards the solvent is evaporated from the impregnated sheets by heating. The heat also effects a partial cure. Absorbent materials, such as wood veneer, are commonly superficially coated with resin by a roll-type glue spreader, brush, spray or by dipping. The plys are then stacked and cured between two steel sheets.

7.9.10. Foamed Plastics

These may be thermosetting or thermoplastic materials which have been expanded to a sponge like structure during processing. This is accomplished by incorporating chemicals which decompose with the liberation of gas at a critical stage of fabrication. Another method is to dissolve a gas in the plastic under conditions that allow the gas later to come out of solution to form bubbles. The foams are useful for cushioning, packaging and thermal insulation.

7.10. FABRICATION OF RUBBER OBJECTS

In the raw condition, rubber is composed of molecules of great length and molecular weight. Although it is thermoplastic in this condition, its plasticity can be improved by working or *masticating* the rubber in air at room temperature. This has the effect of partially oxidising the rubber, resulting in fragmentation of the large molecules into more plastic smaller ones. This *mastication* is carried out in a plasticator which operates on the same principle as the extruder. Synthetic rubbers do not respond to mastication, and plasticity must be controlled during manufacture. For various objects, different processes are used.

7.10.1. Extrusion

Extrusion of rubber is similar to the extrusion of plastics. The machine used for extrusion of rubber is sometimes called a tuber which is used for extruding continuous lengths of tread and side wall stock for tires. The continuous strips are later cut into proper length to make one tire. Other common extrusions are tubing and moldings of various shapes.

7.10.2. Calendering

This process is used for making continuous sheets of rubber or impregnating fabric with rubber. The rolls are hollow in order to provide temperature control. If the two rolls in contact with the fabric move at the same circumferential speed as the fabric rubber is pressed into the voids of the fabric and the operation is called skim coating. If the circumferential speed of the rolls is faster than the speed of the cloth, the process is called frictioning and the rubber compound is wiped into the voids of the fabric.

Prior to calendering, the fibres are usually solutioned. Solutioning involves soaking the fibres in a rubber solution followed by drying. Solutioning provides a better base for the calendered stock.

7.10.3. Molding

Molding of rubber parts is accomplished mainly by compression molding and transfer molding. One of the final steps in rubber tire manufacture is vulcanizing, in which the tire is both vulcanized and shaped for heating in a compression mold.

7.10.4. Dispersions

Dispersions of rubber are known as *latex* solutions. Latex is the form in which the rubber is collected from trees before it is coagulated into the plastic solid. Latices are also made by grinding dry rubber so finely that the particles remain in water suspension. The compounding ingredients can be more easily mixed with the liquid latex than with solid rubber. Coagulation of latices is achieved by acid and salt solution.

7.10.5. Dipping and Electrodeposition

Both are used to produce shapes such as gloves, face masks, and balloons from latex. Dipping is accomplished by immersing a form, sometimes precoated with coagulated chemicals, into the latex. The form may be dipped several times until the desired thickness is attained. Electrodeposition consists of plating of charged rubber particles in much the same way as metals are deposited from solutions.

7.10.6. Foam Rubber

Foam rubber parts are made from latex which has been beaten into a forth of entrapped air. Other methods of producing foam are similar to those used for plastics. Foams are cast in open or closed molds depending upon the product being made and the type of foam used.

7.11. TIRE MANUFACTURE

Automobile and truck tires are the most important rubber products. For making tires, the raw rubber is first cut in the form of *bales* in rough and wedge shaped pieces. The small wedges of rubber are then put into a plasticator for *mastication* and softening. The ribbon of rubber from the plasticator is cut into small and conveniently handled lengths, which are aged for a number of hours and mixed with the recipe ingredients in a mixer to make the master batch. These pieces are bended and fur mixed on rubber mills. Afterwards the rubber goes to warm-up mills and is used for making one of the various tire components. Some of the rubber is extruded. A different stock is used for coating the fabrics which are later made into *plys*, *breaker*, strip, *chafing* strip, and *bead* covering. Rubber-coated fabric is made by the calendering process already described in section 10.2.

The components of the tire are dssembled on a tire building machine which is a collapsible drum. This drum can be rotated to facilitate application of ply to the drum surface. The plys are laid down in a proper sequence and then locked into place around the *beads*. Finally the *breaker* strip, *tread* and *side wall* stock are put firmly in place over the layers of coated fabric. The drum is then collapsed and the tire resembling a barrel open at both ends, is removed. The tire is next conveyed to the vulcanizing unit which has a flexible heavy rubber cylinder attached to a spindle in the mold. The tire is placed over the rubber cylinder and spindle. As the mold closes, steam expands the cylinder and tire into a *dough nut* shape. Heat softens the heavy *tread* and *sidewall* stock of the tire and steam pressure forces the plastic rubber into the *tread* design cavities which are cut into the mold. In about 15 minutes *vulcanization* is complete, the mold is opened and the tire is removed from the spindle.

7.12. ORGANIC COATINGS

Protective coatings are essential for various equipments and machines against their service conditions. The protective coatings serve against corrosion, high temperature exposure and weathering. In addition, this gives better appearance also. It improves the visibility and reflectivity. There are various types of organic coatings, i.e., paint, varnish, shellac, water paint, enamel, and lacquer. The basic difference lies in the type of vehicle in each of them.

7.12.1. Paint

It is a pigmented coating using a vegetable oil (linseed oil) working as a binder as well as drying oil. In addition, it contains turpentine as a thinner. Drying is affected by the oxidation action. Sometimes magnesium silicate ($MgSiO_3$) is added to impart improved resistance to cracking of the paint film.

7.12.2. Varnish

In this a synthetic or natural resin is used in place of pigments. The tung-oil is generally used which gets partly oxidised and partly polymerised at high temperatures. The resin is dissolved in the oil and a drier is sometimes added at the time of thinning.

7.12.3. Enamels

These are mixtures of paints and varnishes. In water paints, thinner used is water. Oil-resin combination is normally used as binder. Water paints have the advantages like (*i*) no fire hazard, (*ii*) water is odourless, and (*iii*) exaporates quickly. Hence the enamels are very useful for home decorations.

7.12.4. Shellac

It is a solution of a natural resin in an alcohol. It gets hardened by the evaporation of the thinner. It is not water resistant. It is mainly used in wooden furniture industry as sealer.

7.12 5. Lacquers

These are solutions of nitrocellulose in volatile organic solvents. Plasticizers and other resins are used to improve the quality of the film. Pigments and dyes are also added sometimes depending upon the requirements. Lacquers are coated on the surface by spray technique. On evaporation it lowers down the temperature by 8-10°C below the room temperature and therefore to avoid this fall in temperature, it is heated to about 70°C before spraying. When sprayed, it cools down to 20-25°C by the time it recaches the surface to be coated. Higher temperature helps in avoiding condensation and improving flow-characteristics.

7.12.6. Vehicles

The protective coatings contain a vehicle which consists of a film forming ingredient and a diluent. The film forming agents (or binders) include unsaturated compounds which solidify by polymerization or oxidation or bath along with thinner. The film forming agents form the films and hold the particles of the pigment together. Pigments change the physical appearance and sometimes chemical properties also.

Organic coatings are flexible, cheap and can be easily applied. The service environment in this case is very important. The organic coatings loose their life under high temperature service condition. Similarly the effectiveness decreases with abrasive wear and the oxidation conditions requiring periodic recoating.

QUESTIONS

1. Why is seasoning of wood necessary?

2. Give a brief account of mechanical properties of wood.

3. Why is preservation of wood required? Give different methods for preservation of wood against various attacks.

4. What are the different products that can be manufactured from wood? Give a brief account of their use and processing.

5. What is "petroleum"? What are the various steps involved in the processing of petroleum? Outline the importance of each step.

6. What are the various products desired from crude petroleum?

7. What is an organic polymer? Discuss the mechanism of polymerisation.

8 What are the different types of polymers? Give a brief account of these with examples.

9. Compare and contrast addition and condensation polymerisations.

10. What are the natural polymers and their derivatives? Give their uses.

11. What are synthetic polymers? Discuss their various mechanical properties.

12 How does the deformation of plastics take place? Explain it with the help of a typical diagram.

13. What are the advantages and limitations of plastic materials?

14. What are the various raw materials used for making plastics?

15. What are the types of plastics? Discuss their applications giving examples.

16. What are elastomers? Discuss the various properties of rubbers.

17. What are the various types of rubber? Give their application with examples.

18. Discuss the general methods for fabrication of plastics.

19. Discuss the various methods of fabrication of rubber articles.

20. What is "vulcanisation"? Describe briefly the process of tire manufacturing.

21. What are the various organic coatings? Give their specific applications.

8

INORGANIC AND SILICATE MATERIALS

There is a great variety of inorganic and silicate materials employed for various engineering and industrial purposes. There is good number of silicate materials occurring in nature, which are useful for making refractories as well as directly for construction work. Another category of inorganic materials are synthetic which include cements, glass, refractories, ceramics, etc.

8.1. ROCKS AND BUILDING STONES

A rock is a naturally occurring mass of solid material which may consist of one mineral such as quartzite and marble or may be composed of many minerals such as granite (usually composed of quartz, felspar and mica). In comparison with a mineral, a rock is usually not homogeneous. Although a rock may consist of one mineral, it is composed of mineral fragments, lumps, or complete single crystals which may be loose, or may be consolidated to a hard mass either by pressure of the overlying material, or by infiltration of cementing materials. In both cases the rock may be considered granular to some extent. Thus not only a hard rock but also a relatively loose sediment is considered to be a rock.

8.1.1. Origin and Formation of Rocks and Minerals in the Earth's Crust

The major portion of the earth's crust consists of silicates and silica. It might be expected that homogeneous concentric shells of rocks should have been formed from the molten silicate slag in earlier stages of the earth's history. However, agglomerations of various rocks (even basic rocks) and the minerals occurring in the earth's crust are complicated and fortunately, the minerals occur in local concentrations. Rocks and minerals are classified as (i) *igneous*, (ii) *sedimentary* or (iii) *metamorphic* deposits, depending upon the process of formation.

(i) **Igneous deposits**. These are formed from a solidifying molten material called *magma* in the beginning (thousand million years ago). This magma in various regions must have melted and solidified again and solidified masses have sunk to the hotter regions or have been heated again by hotter magma moving upward. This process is still repeated today. At some depths (40-100 kms) where pressure drop occurs, a large mass of magma may be formed (pressure drop lowers the melting point of the rocks) and when the pressure increases again, magma can be squeezed upward, dissolving rock above it, and solidifying again either due to increase in pressure or cooling.

The compounds with the higher melting points solidify first and either sink to the bottom or float to the upper part of the magma depending upon their densities. Deposits formed in this way are called segregations and can be very rich in ores. However, segregation process takes thousands of years, and often the minerals are not allowed to settle but instead are forced upward in simultaneously hardening regions of the magma or the regions hardened before. In the latter case a semi-fluid mass of molten minerals and rocks is squeezed into fissures.

As the temperature of magma falls and solidification continues, the heavy basic rocks such as *basalt* and *gabbro* solidify first, and then the more common acid silicate such as granite. After solidification of the bulk of the granite, the remaining liquid is strongly enriched with gases, steam, silica and many metals that have not formed compounds earlier. Since gases do not dissolve in the solidified mass, the pressure increases inspite of the decreasing temperature due to which liquid is always forced into fissures of rocks solidified earlier. When the temperature falls below 600°C, *pegmatic veins* are formed which are rocks of well crystallised minerals and ores such as quartz, potassium felspar, various ores of less common metals, various gem stones, etc.

The remaining mixture containing gases, water, silica and compounds of the most common industrial metals is a superheated solution which penetrates the surface rocks and sediments and solidifies at temperatures between 350 to 150°C forming veins of quartz and various metal compounds. Among the metals to be found in veins are lead, zinc, copper, arsenic, antimony, bismuth, and uranium compounds, and elemental gold, silver, and mercury.

When the magma succeeds in breaking through the earth's crust, a volcanic erruption is caused and a molten magma known as *lava* flows over the earth's surface. Because of the more rapid cooling and the pressure drop, the magma solidifies as a glassy mass. *Pumic* or porous rock is formed when a large quantity of gas under pressure is dissolved in acid magma. Because of the pressure drop the gas forms a large number of gas filled cells in the glassy mass when it comes to the surface. Basic magmas which cool slowly may form the coarse-grained crystalline rock '*gabbro*', but if the same magma cools rapidly, e.g. when it is forced to the surface in a volcanic erruption, it forms the finer grained rock '*basalt*'.

Igneous rocks can be divided into three parts according to crystallisation:

(a) *Plutonic rock*. Crystallisation of plutonic rock takes place inside the surface of earth, minimum distances from earth's surface being about 35 metres. It takes long time in cooling and hence, the size of the crystals are large. Granite, cyanide, diorite, gabbro, etc. come under this group. Plutonic rock is mostly used for building construction.

(b) *Hypabassal rock*. The crystallisation of this rock takes place very near to the earth's surface, i.e. between 30 and 35 metres. This rock gets less time for cooling and hence, their crystals cannot be easily identified. Crystals of such rock are very fine. Dolome falls under this group.

(c) *Volcanic rock*. Magma comes out due to volcanic eruption. Molten material starts solidifying immediately after cooling and hence it does not get time for crystallisation. Top layers of this group of rock are smooth and shining but these are fine crystals in internal layers. Basalt is important in this group.

(*ii*) **Sedimentary rock.** The surface of the earth crust after cooling of magma is very hard but the continuous action of the seas, rains, ice, wind, varying temperatures, and animal and vegetable life gradually break down the rocks and minerals formed from magma. Because of difference in solubility, various minerals and rocks can be leached by water and settled again in other places in concentrated forms and various layers of different sedimentary deposits are superimposed. These deposits are often formed before a certain magmatic deposits; thus magmatic veins etc. can occur in sedimentary deposits, and various superimposed layers can be mixed or interrupted. The layers are also deformed by sagging and folds caused by enormous pressure difference in the earth's crust. Sand, graval, sand stone, clay, limestone, dolomite, phosphate rock, gypsum, borates, sulphur, etc. are the examples of sedimentary rocks.

(*iii*) **Metamorphic rock.** Metamorphic deposits are formed from igneous or sedimentary deposits by changes in the mineralogical or chemical composition or in the structure which is affected without complete melting and without the influence of atmospheric surroundings. Recrystallisation without melting can occur, as a result of increasing pressure and temperature which in turn is caused by a growing layer of sedimentary deposits. This form of metamorphism is known as *regional metamorphism*, since it is often developed over large areas upto thousands of square kilometres in extent.

If a directional pressure or shearing stress occurs locally, the minerals in the rock are subjected to granulation and pulverisation. New rocks formed by this process are usually flinty and fine grained. Uncrushed fragments usually lie with their long axes parallel to the direction of the shearing stress. Extensive recrystallisation may also occur since melting points are lowered and solubilities increased at the points of greatest pressure. At the latter points the crystals may melt, until solidification takes place at the lowest pressure. The result is usually a more or less laminar structure. Examples are gneiss and slate. Metamorphism resulting from directional stress is called *dynamo metamorphism*.

Metamorphism also takes place when a high temperature magma penetrates into surrounding deposits of magmatic or sedimentary origin. This form of metamorphism is called *contact metamorphism*. It occurs only in restricted zones adjacent to bodies of igneous rocks. Because of the high temperature of the magma, the surrounding deposits can be recrystallised. For example, quartzite is formed from sand stone, and marble and calcite are formed from calcareous sediments.

Hydrothermal solution of gaseous constituents of magma, such as water and compounds of boron, fluorine, and chlorine, can also penetrate the surrounding deposits and react with constituents of the latter to form orher minerals and rocks. Formation of topaz $[Al_2SiO_4(OH,F)]$ from felspar in granite is an example of content metamorphism.

Although rocks and minerals are used as raw materials for the production of portland cement, lime, and ceramics, they are not widely used in massive form for building. At one time some rocks and minerals were commonly used as building stones, but they have been replaced by other materials which have better properties and are more conveniently handled, such as steel, concrete, and clay products. However, in India, in some places where the good quality stones are available and the cost of clay products such as bricks is high, stones are also used for masonry work. For example, hilly regions and Rajasthan are still making extensive use of stones for masonry work. Other use of stone in buildings is in the form of ingredient of concrete. In general, now-a-days the use of stone in masonry work is restricted to decorative constructional details.

8.1.2. Stones for Masonry Construction

There are four varieties of stones which are commonly used for masonry construction, i.e. granite, limestone, marble and sand stone. These stones are normally stronger than the mortar used for their joining. Durability of the stone depends upon conditions of exposure and service. Porous stones lack in durability if exposed to moisture and freezing temperatures. On the other hand, if it is used in a warm or dry climate, paosity will not alone cause deterioration. Stone lacks durability if it reacts chemically with its surroundings. Hardness is an important property in stone exposed to abrasion and wear.

(*i*) **Granite**. About 4000 to 3000 years BC granite was already marketed as a building stone by the ancient Egyptians who also used slabs of granite in the Pyramids of Cheops. Granite is the collective form for numerous rocks. Consisting of a crystalline aggregate of potash felspar, quartz and one or more ferro-magnesium silicate minerals (usually biotite and hornblende). The name granite is based on the granular structure of this rock and is derived from the Latin word *granum* which means grain. Commercially the name granite is also used for other rocks which have a granite-like structure, for example, diorites, dolerite, etc. The colour of granite ranges from pale pink-grey through salmon colour to flesh like red depending upon the colour of felspar in it (felspar is yellow, red and white). Granite is the most durable of all stones (compressive strength of granite is about 1500 kgs/cm²) because relatively it is nonporous, inert to industrial and other atmosphere, hard and wear resistant. Particularly with higher percentage of silica, granite is very strong. Granite is a very heavy and hard stone and hence its dressing is difficult. However, it responds poorly for fire resistance due to different coefficients of expansion of three ingredients (quartz, felspar, and mica) contained in granite. Due to its difficult dressing, it is rarely used for ordinary building work. Granite is mainly used for the construction of bridges, light houses, walls of docks and harbour, and other marine works. Smaller pieces of granite are used for railway ballast. In India, granite is found in Karnataka, Rajasthan, Andhra Pradesh, Tamil Nadu, Orissa, Himachal Pradesh and Madhya Pradesh.

(ii) **Lime stone.** This is the mineral having a formula, $CaCO_3$ along with small quantities of impurities (Al_2O_3, SiO_2, $FeCO_3$, $MgCO_3$ etc.) which result variations in properties and appearance. Siliceous limestone is tough and durable, and thus used for building construction but silica has bad influence if the lime stone is used for purposes other than masonry work. Other varieties of lime stone are used for the manufacture of lime, cement, calcium carbide etc. In India lime stone is found in most of regions such as Bihar, Orissa, Assam, Madhya Pradesh, Uttar Pradesh, Himachal Pradesh, Andhra Pradesh, Karnataka, Rajasthan, Gujarat, etc.

(iii) **Marble.** Having compressive strength of about 1000 kg/cm² marble is a metamorphic rock and its parent rock is lime stone. Marble differs from lime stone in that it has developed greater crystallinity than lime stone as a result of the action of pressure and temperature in the earth's crust. It is less porous, more durable and harder than lime stone, and takes a high polish. It is available in many colours such as white, grey, black, green, yellow, etc. Dressing and carving can be done easily on marble stones and thus mainly selected for construction of beautiful buildings. Taj Mahal and Moti Maszid have been constructed from marble. White marble is found in Makrana (Jodhpur) and black marble is found in Jaipur. Marble is also found in other places of Rajasthan, Madhya Pradesh, Karnataka, Uttar Pradesh, and Andhra Pradesh.

(iv) **Sand stone.** Having compressive strength of about 500 kgs/cm² sand stone is sedimentary rock and consists of conglomeration of sand particles held together by a natural mineral cement such as lime stone or hydrated silica. The durability and strength of sand stone depend on the strength of the mineral cement bond. Durability of sand stone is not good due to its porosity and chemical reactivity. Sand stone may be white, yellow, grey, red, green, and deep blue in colour. Sand stones of finer grains are considered better as good net work can be done on fine grained sand stone. Large grained sand stones are normally hard and are used for ashlar work. Soft sand stones are used for carving work. Paving, flooring, roofing, etc. can be done by splitting sand stone. Sand stone is found in a large number of places such as Chunar, Mirzapur, Fatehpur Sikri, Banaras and Mathura in Uttar Pradesh, Gwalior and Jabalpur in Madhya Pradesh, Karnataka, Tamil Nadu, Bihar, Orissa, etc.

Other varieties of stones used in construction are gneiss, basalt, dolerite, quartzite, serpentine and slate.

(a) *Gneiss*. This is a hetero-geneous coarse crystalline sedimentary rock in which the crystals are arranged more or less parallel in the form of bands or streaks which are rich in a particular mineral. Gneiss usually has the composition of granite-diorite or black granite (gabbro), but gneisses of quite different compositions are also known. Depending upon the composition these rocks are known as granite gneiss, gabbro gneiss, hornblende gneiss, etc. Because of its layer structure gneiss like slate has a lower compressive strength, lower hardness and a lower resistance to weathering than granite. Gneiss can be split into small pieces easily and hence they are used for roads and floors of buildings It is mainly mined in the form of crushed stone which is used as ballast under roads and railways. In India it is found in Tamil Nadu, Karnataka, Gujarat, Kerala, Andhra Pradesh and Bihar.

(b) *Basalt*. It is an igneous rock comprising an extremely fine grained aggregate of crystalline sodium-calcium felspar and one or more ferro-magnesium silicates of the pyroxene group. Usually augite, olivine, apatite, and magnetite are common associate minerals. As early as 2500 BC, basalt was used in ancient Egypt for pavements and revetment of lime stone buildings. Basalt is the principal rock underlying the ocean, and consists of same mineral constituents as granite, but in different proportions. Basalt is heavier and harder than granite. Its compressive strength is very high. It is shaped with difficulty and is not commonly used for masonry. Basalt is usually crushed and in this form widely used for road construction, rail-road ballast, or as an aggregate in cement concrete. It is found in Maharashtra and Bihar.

(c) *Dolerite*. It is an igneous rock which usually has the same composition as basalt. Its granular structure, however, is somewhat coarser. Dolerite usually occurs in the form of sills and contains intrusions of materials from surrounding deposits. Dolerite often occurs very near to basalt stratigraphically. This is also very hard and durable stone and is used in the same way as basalt. It is found in Madhya Pradesh and Maharashtra.

Both dolerite and basalt rocks are known commercially as traprock. Ajanta and Elora caves have been made in traprock.

(d) *Serpentine*. It is a hydrated magnesium silicate available in red and other different colours. The stone takes good polish and its

238 MATERIALS SCIENCE AND MANUFACTURING PROCESSES

dressing is easy. It is used normally for interior decoration works. It is found in Singhbhoom district of Bihar.

(e) *Quartzite.* This is of metamorphic origin formed from siliceous sand stone by high pressure, usually accomplished by high temperatures, resulting into deformation and compression of quartz grains to form a perfectly close fitting mosaic. Sometime silica penetrates the sand stone in the form of a hydrothermal solution, to fill all intergranular spaces. The granular and porous structure of sand stone has disappeared almost completely in quartzite which often has a vitereous appearance. Quartzite can be extremely hard (as hard as quartz) and breaks as readily as through the grains around them or through the cement. Colour of these rocks is often similar to the colour of the sand stones from which they are formed. It is a crystalline stone but its dressing is difficult due to excessive hardness. It is used as an aggregate in cement concrete. Kutubminar of Delhi has been constructed from this stone. It is found in Tamil Nadu, Madhya Pradesh, Karnataka, Uttar Pradesh and other places.

(f) *Slate.* Slate is the general name for microcrystalline silicate rocks that can be split along parallel surfaces into smooth surfaced sheets of identical character. The major portion of the microcrystals consists of quartz, mica and clay minerals such as illite and chlorite. Slate is a hard material with low porosity and high transverse strength but can be easily splitted in the cleavage direction. Because of the micro-crystalline structure of slate, it forms sheets with smooth surfaces. High quality slate is practically impervious to moisture and has a very good resistance to weathering. Slate with a high content of $CaCO_3$ has a relatively low durability. The colour of the slate, which depends on the composition, may be black, grey, green, blue, purple, or red. Black and grey colours in slate are caused by carbon, and the red is caused by ferric oxide.

Thin sheets of slate are principally used for roof covering. Thicker sheets of slate are used as flag stone and small quantities are used for billiard table, acid resistant tables, electrical switch board, black board and sanitary ware.

Slate wastes (chips etc.) are crushed and heated upto 1200°C to form an expanded cellular product, which is used as a light weight aggregate for concrete. Granules of coloured slate are used as a decorative additives in various artificial building stones. Slate waste is also used as filler in clay-rubber, paints, linoleum, etc.

Slate is found in Andhra Pradesh, Haryana, Uttar Pradesh, Himachal Pradesh, Bihar, Karnatak, Rajasthan, Gujarat etc.

8.2. REFRACTORIES

A refractory material is one which can withstand the action of high temperature, heavy load, corrosive fluids, thermal shock and remains unmelted and undeformed. High temperature is a relative term but in general a material melting above 1500°C can be regarded as refractory material. Basically refractories can be classified into three categories depending on their chemical nature i.e. acid, basic and neutral refractories.

8.2.1. Acid Refractories

These are acidic in nature and thus are resistant to acidic materials but are attacked by basic materials. These are composed of acidic materials such as aluminium silicates and siliceous materials. These include silica refractories, fire clay refractories, high alumina bricks etc.

(i) **Fire clay refractories**. The principal ingredient is kaolinite (Al_2O_3. $2SiO_2$. $2H_2O$) containing 18-45 per cent Al_2O_3 with a minimum of glass forming substances. It is made from fire clay by hand moulding, repressing of extruded wire-cut bricks, and dry pressing. The mouldability is improved by adding a little amount of plastic clay. The firing temperature applied depends mainly on the nature of the clay and the purpose for which the brick is made. The bricks are first dried and then fired in kiln. At about 200°C all the water molecules get expelled. Finishing temperatures may be anywhere between 1100°C and 1400°C, being low for the bricks used as casting pit refractories and high for the bricks used for blast furnace hearths and the roofs of open hearth checkers. Fireclay brick's strength is low, but it is not intended to carry structural loads. Its primary function is to confine flames and hot atmospheres and to protect structural members from excessive temperatures. Its softening temperature is about 1650°C. They can not withstand thermal load beyond 1300°C. One of the most important reasons for their wide use is their low cost. Fireclay is mostly available in Bihar, Bengal, Madhya Pradesh, Andhra Pradesh, Orissa, etc.

(ii) **High alumina bricks**. These are similar to fireclay bricks but contain over 50 per cent Al_2O_3. With increased amount of alumina content, increase in softening temperature and reistance to slag attack are obtained. These refractories can be made by melting diaspore or bauxite with clay in an arc furnace and casting it in blocks. Large blocks can be built up in this way, and they have given excellent service in glass tank furnaces. However, refractories can be made from these materials without recourse to actual melting.

(iii) **Corundum refractories**. By milling pure alumina to an extremely fine state, slip casting, and firing to 1800°C, products of virtually zero porosity can be obtained which are particularly useful as laboratory wares. Bricks are more often prepared by grinding 98 per cent purity fused alumina, and mixing it with a small amount of bond clay. These bricks are fired at 1600-1700°C to obtain the best properties.

(iv) **Mullite and sillimenite refractories**. This class of refractories is made from naturally occurring sillimenite, kyanite or andulusite (each consisting of $Al_2O_3.SiO_2$) on ignition or possibly topaz [$Al_2SiO(F.OH)_2$]. All of these are converted to mullite (3 Al_2O_3. $2SiO_2$)on hard firing (1550°C); and at the same time silica is liberated. The manufacturing technique is similar to that employed for making semi-silica bricks. i.e. crushing the calcined mineral, blending it with minimum quantity of plastic clay and sulphite lye, and pressing bricks by pneumatic ramming or semi-dry high pressure moulding. Firing should be at high temperature, although fired strength is developed at 1300°C and higher. Control of firing shrinkage can be obtained by used of suitable mixtures of calcined and raw kyanite with clay, because raw kyanite expands on calcination and converts to mullite.

(v) **Silica refractories.** Quartz or ganister is used as a source of silica. This is mixed with 2 per cent lime in a water suspension. After forming the required refractory shape the product is fired, during which time a reaction occurs between lime (basic) and silica (acidic) to form the glass bond which cements the silica particles together. Silica bricks tend to undergo slight permanent expansion upon pralonged exposure to high temperatures. Therefore, combustible filler material such as strips of card-board should be used in expansion joints to accommodate this expansion. Tendency of silica bricks to expand is useful in producing a good fit in furnace arches; it is used as the lining material for acid open hearth and acid bessemer converters, and for roofs of basic furnaces.

(vi) **Siliceous or semi-silica refractories.** This name is commonly applied to clay-bonded silica bricks. They may be made from naturally occurring sand clay mixtures, or from batches prepared from ground ganister bonded with a refractory clay. These are used for constructing steel furance plants.

8.2.2. Basic Refractories

Basic refractories are composed of basic materials such as magnesia (MgO), dolomite, etc. Examples of such refractories are magnesite, dolomite and chrome-magnesite. These are attacked by acidic slags but are resistant towards basic slags.

(i) **Magnesite.** This alone is a good refractory material. The first step in making magnesite refractories is calcination of naturally occurring magnesite at about 1700°C by which a stable product MgO is obtained. Calcined magnesite is used as refractory material. This calcined magnesite is crushed and ground in a series of crushing and grinding mills to obtain the required amounts of coarse and fine fractions. This graded magnesite is mixed with bonding agents such as iron oxide, water and sulphite lye, and the mixture is moulded into bricks and simply dried at about 300°C and finishing temperatures of 1400-1600°C are used. Sometimes alumina is added to improve the resistance to thermal shock. It finds considerable application in basic open hearth and arc steel furnaces.

(ii) **Dolomite refractories.** Dolomite refractories (CaO.MgO) are highly basic in nature and have proved a good and cheap substitute for magnesite bricks. They can withstand high temperature load (about 1700°C) and also a very good mechanical load. The only drawbacks are low resistance to thermal shock and poor quality because of lime content which causes disintegration of bricks on absorbing water at room temperature or below. The latter defect can be removed by providing tar coating which would not allow bricks to come in contact with water and CO_2 or by mixing a stabilizer such as serpentine ($MgO.SiO_2$) with dolomite and then by calcining the resultant mixture. Calcium silicate of di or tri type is formed which is not at all attacked by water or CO_2. The calcined material is mixed with water and shaped into bricks and finally dried and heated to about 1600°C. These are mainly used in basic steel making processes and other processes where the slag formed is basic in nature.

(iii) **Chrome-magnesite refractories.** Chrome-magnesite bricks containing about 70 per cent chrome and 30 per cent magnesia are much superior to the magnesite or chromite bricks because these refractories are also quite resistant to thermal shock. In this chrome (70 per cent) is present in the coarse fraction (7-25 mesh) and magnesia in the form of fine fraction. Bricks made from the mixture with the addition of little amount of water are dried and fired at temperatures 1350-1640°C. Higher temperatures are preferred as there is very little difficulty encountered with firing shrinkage or expansion.

8.2.3. Neutral Refractories

These are the materials which are neither acidic nor basic in nature and hence applicable in both mediums. This group includes a wide range of materials such as chromite, silicon carbide, zirconia, carbon etc.

(i) **Chrome refractories.** At one time these refractories were used in good quantity in steel plants. But now-a-days their use is not very common. Such bricks were made by grinding chrome ore with water and little gum. and then moulding, drying and firing (1500-1700°C). They were liable to give trouble during the firing because of softening. To overcome this difficulty, sufficient magnesia is added to react with serpentine or other gangue material to form forsterite. Another drawback in chrome refractories is that certain types show an abnormal expansion when heated under reducing condition which give rise to crumbling. The chromite refractories have very good mechanical and thermal properties. They are used in steel and copper industries particularly in the furnaces.

(ii) **Silicon carbide**. This is formed in an electric furnace by heating together coke, sand, salt and saw dust. The salt helps in volatilizing the various impurities in the coke and sand, whilst the saw dust gives a degree of porosity which enables the carbon monoxide formed by the reaction between coke and sand to escape;

$$SiO_2 + 3C \rightarrow SiC + 2CO \qquad \qquad ...(8.1)$$

Silicon carbide decomposes in the temperature range of 2200-2700°C before its melting and does not react with hydrogen, nitrogen, or carbon monoxide. Above 1000°C it oxidises in air, but the SiO_2 formed by this reaction tends to prevent further oxidation. It is a very hard material (hardness 9 on Moh's scale) and its density is 3.22. Bricks can be made from the crushed and graded product from the fusion furnace. A small proportion of clay or bentonite is added as binder, and the bricks are fired to a high temperature say 1500°C. Silicon carbide refractories are valued for their thermal conductivity, high thermal shock resistance, and high hot strength. They are also resistant to coal ash as well as acid and neutral slags. They are attacked, however, by basic slags. Silicon carbide refractories are used for various muffle furnaces, recuperator tubes, walls of boiler furnaces, etc.

(*iii*) **Graphite refractories**. Natural graphite is mined in various localities such as Orissa, Rajasthan, etc. It is also manufactured by heating coke to a high temperature in an electric furnace. It has a relative density of 2.1 to 2.5 and a sublimation temperature greater than 3500°C and possesses various specific properties such as (*a*) it burns slowly, (*b*) chemically inert, (*c*) good conductor of heat and electricity and (*d*) negative coefficient of resistivity. When bonded with clay, it has refractory application and is used particularly in the form of crucibles for containing molten metals. Carbon bricks can take up high temperatures and thus they are mostly used in (*a*) lining the blast furnaces, (*b*) non-oxidising atmospheres and (*c*) chlorination reactors.

(*iv*) **Zirconia (ZrO_2) and zircon ($ZrO_2.SiO_2$) refractories**. Zirconia has a melting point more than 2700°C and a relative density of 5.8. Zirconia refractories are manufactured from ZrO_2 mixed with a binding material like alumina or colloidal zirconia and fired at about 1700°C or higher temperatures. Zirconia refractories can bear temperatures as high as 2500°C and offer great resistance to thermal shock and basic slags. High price of zirconia prevents it from being used as general engineering material, but is used in the special circumstances when temperature required is very high. Zirconia is used for the manufacture of crucibles for melting the noble metals and also used in glasses, enamels and glazes. It is also used as an addition to magnesite bricks to improve their thermal shock resistance. Promising results have been given by steel pouring nozzles made from zircon.

8.2 4. Heat Insulating Refractories

Insulating bricks are generally classified into three groups, according to the maximum temperature at which they retain their insulating properties, i.e.,

    (*i*) Low temperature insulation upto 900°C.
    (*ii*) Medium temperature insulation upto 1200°C.
    (*iii*) High temperature insulation over 1200°C.

The low temperature insulating materials are largely made from diatomite, asbestos, and vermiculite, although some of the pure diatomites can be used for medium temperature insulation. Porous fire clay bricks are used for medium temperature insulation. High temperature insulation bricks are usually made from highly refractory, finely ground materials, rendered porous by frothing, or by including combustible matter that can afterwards be oxidised away.

8.2.5. Properties of Refractories

(i) Apparant porosity and bulk density.

(ii) True relative density.

(iii) Cold crushing strength.

(iv) Permeability to air.

(v) Contraction and expansion on heating.

(vi) Refractoriness withhout load.

(vii) Refractoriness under load.

(viii) Thermal shock resistance.

(xi) Slag resistance.

8.3. CERAMICS

The word 'ceramic' is derived from the Greek *Keramos* which means the potter's earth or clay and therefore, the materials made from naturally occurring clay or earth may be considered as ceramics. However, in modern applications, the term *ceramic* is extended to a wide range of inorganic and non-metallic materials processed or used at high temperatures. Ceramics are usually hard and brittle in nature and exist in the form of amorphous (non-crystalline) or glassy solids. The atomic bonding in these materials is of a mixed ionic and covalent character. They can be made in single crystal forms, though more common structures are amorphous or glassy. Ceramic materials include a wide range of silicates, oxides, and combination of silicates and oxides. Some carbides, borides and various refractory hydrides, selenides, etc. are also considered as ceramics. Thus from the engineering view point, a wide variety of substances such as glass, brick, stone, concrete, abrasives, porcelein enameles, dielectric insulators, non-metallic magnetic materials, high temperature refractories, etc. may be included in ceramics.

The common characteristic feature of all these materials is that they are compounds of metal and non-metals, and the mode of deformation of ceramic materials is highly dependent on structure. However, these materials can be deformed by viscous flow processes under proper conditions of stress and temperature. A low temperature, where viscous flow is negligible and plastic flow is impossible, the behaviour of glasses and ceramics with stress is elastic. One of the chief uses of these non-metallic materials is as an insulator, both thermal and electrical. There are many other inorganic materials possessing specific properties may not be called exactly ceramic materials, e.g. agglomerated materials, rocks and building stones, etc.

8.3.1. Clay Products

Clay is the basic raw material used in the manufacture of ceramic articles. It is a finely grained rock which is sticky in wet condition. For potters, brick makers, and other interested in ceramic products, clay is considered to be a plastic substance or a substance which can be made plastic by suitable treatment and water, whereas for chemists and physicists, clay is an admixture of certain mineralogical species. A definition of clay given by American Ceramic Society is that "clay is finely grained rock which when suitably crushed and pulverised, becomes plastic when wet, leather hard when dried, and rock like permanent mass when fired."

The various steps involved in making the clay products are compounding, shaping, drying, glazing and firing.

(i) **Compounding of clay.** The first step in making clay products is to compound the refined clay with various ingredients required to control fusion temperature, plasticity of the wet clay, shrinkage, strength, colour and porosity. In some clay products, control of particle size and their distribution is an important consideration.

(ii) **Shaping of clay.** The shaping of clay can be accomplished by using a very wet mixture of creamy consistency known as slip. The slip is cast into porous moulds of plaster of paris which absorb enough moisture from the slip to cause a thick layer of solid material to form on the mould walls. After the object achieves porper wall thickness, the mould is inverted and the excess slip is dumped out. Absorption of water by the plaster of paris makes the object shrink away from the mould walls, thus facilitating the removal of casting. Plaster cores are used if closer control of inside dimensions is required. Examples of ceramic products made in this way are sanitary ware for bathrooms, large electric insulators, and household items such as teapots and lamps.

Objects can also be made by working clay in the plastic condition. Clay containing about 20 per cent moisture can be extruded, forced, into moulds, or shaped on potter's wheel. Building bricks and various kinds of tiles are examples which are made by extrusion. Long extruded lengths are cut to proper size as the extrusion is squeezed from the mill. Air entrapped by the plastic mix should be removed before extrusion otherwise it will expand during firing producing internal voids.

(iii) **Drying.** The objects made from clay are dried before firing. Direct heating of wet objects to a high temperature will result in the production of large quantity of steam which will cause voids, distortion, and weakening of the product. Drying is conducted either naturally in the air or artificially in kilns.

(iv) **Glazing.** Some clay products are coated with glazing com-

pounds before firing. These substances have lower softening temperatures and form a hard glassy surface during firing. Glazing is done
on various clay products such as sanitary ware, floor tile, chemically
resistant porcelein, electric insulators, etc Glazes produce a wear
resistant nonporous surface which is easy to keep clean.

(v) **Firing**. Ceramic objects are carefully stacked to prevent
sagging and to insure uniform heating during firing. If the object is to
be glazed or highly vitrified by firing, care is taken to prevent fusion
with neighbouring pieces. In the beginning when temperature rises
slowly toward 120°C, surface moisture on the clay particles is driven
off. Excessive heating rates during this period will cause swelling
and rupturing of the product. Between 290°C and 540°C chemically
combined water is driven off, and organic matter is burned away. At
about 900°C, in some products having low softening temperatures,
fusion commences. The temperature is raised above this point until
the desired degree of vitrification is achieved, accompanied by an
increase in strength and decrease in porosity. Use of excessive higher
temperatures is avoided because they cause slumping and distortion.
Cooling should be allowed at controlled rates to allow the volumetric
changes occurring due to crystal transformations without any damage.
Rapid cooling gives rise to non-uniform temperatues throughout the
objects due to which severe stresses are resulted causing cracking.

8.3.2. Building Bricks

Building bricks are the most important and extensively used
product of clay. Building bricks are supplied in various grades which
are based on differences in compressive strength, water absorption,
and freezing and thawing resistance. With increasing firing temperature strength increases with decrease in porosity and the brick
becomes darker in colour. Building bricks in general can be classified
into two groups, i.e (i) face bricks and (ii) common bricks. Face
bricks are darker, more dense and stronger than common brick,
because of the higher buruing temperatures in the former case. On
the other hand face bricks do not absorb as much water as common
bricks. Face bricks are more resistant to frost damage and are therefore used to face buildings. Common bricks absorb about 15 per
cent water on a weight basis, whereas face bricks absorb only about
10 per cent. Common bricks have a compressive strength of about
300 kgs/cm², whereas face bricks can withstand about 450 kg/cm²,
in compression.

Among other clay products of interest are building tiles, sewerage
and drainage pipes, chemically resistant procelein, and fired procelein
enamel, etc.

8.3.3. Properties of Ceramic Materials

The ceramics find wide applications in various fields due to their
many favourable properties such as chemical resistance, electrical
resistivity, thermal resistivity, compressive strength, etc. Important

properties of various ceramic phases may be grouped as physical, chemical, mechanical, electrical, thermal, etc.

(*i*) **Physical properties**. At low temperatures the ceramics exhibit shrinkage caused by drying and thus a decrease in volume is accomplished. Simultaneously loss of moisture and evolution of CO_2 take place resulting into compactness of material and thereby increasing the density. However, the changes in texture, porosity, elasticity and plasticity occur mainly at high temperatures. At elevated temperatures changes in specific gravity, volume (expansion or contraction), porosity, strength, weight and colour take place. Other physical properties like optical, electrical, thermal, hardness, etc. also change. Ceramic materials exhibit a wide range of crystal structures. For example, MgO is of cubic structure, mica is of layer structure and asbestos (hydrous magnesium silicate) has a linear structure. The structures are often of low symmetry, which may lead to the effect of *piezoelectricity* (the formation of a electro-static charge upon elastic deformation). Quartz (one crystalline form of SiO_2) is an example of such a case which is used in electronic oscillators.

(*ii*) **Mechanical properties**. Strength of finished ceramics is of great importance. In some cases high strength ·may be desirable whereas in some cases the reverse may be desired. Though the strength of raw materials is not important, it is of great importance in moulded condition as well as when dried and finally fired. In dry materials the strength is caused mainly by the attractive forces between the molecules which is attained by the compactness of the crystals. The compactness can be achieved by larger proportion of colloidal or fine particles. Some agents such as bond clays or ball clays and other may be mixed with materials before moulding to increase the strength.

The strength of various ceramic materials varies on firing depending on the raw maetrials used, manufacturing process and the conditions employed. The building bricks, for example, have varied strength depending upon the amount of glass and the final porosity which have developed under the conditions of firing.

(*iii*) **Chemical properties**. The chemical changes in ceramic materials take place in contact of water, acids and alkalies both at low and high temperatures. At ordinary temperatures water does not react with silicate phases but reacts quickly with lime, magnesia, calcined dolomite and other alkali oxides. Acids are quite reactive and they bring changes in chemical composition, physical form and sometimes even decompose ceramic materials. For example, ceramics are decomposed by heating with concentrated sulphuric acid; dolomite, magnesite, etc. are decomposed by hydrochloric acid; and raw bauxite can be readily attacked and dissolved both in sulphuric and hydrochloric acids. Phosphoric acid can effectively attack precipitated silica at low temperatures. Phosphoric acid in combination with silica forms crystalline substances, $SiO_2.P_2O_5$ with four polymorphic forms, i.e. two at low temperatures which are attacked by water and two at high temperatures which are stable and are not at all attacked by water or any acids. Silica materials which are not attacked by most of the acids, hydofluoric acid has very severe and penetrating attack on silica materials.

In addition to the attack of various chemicals, ceramic materials on heating undergo chemical changes with respect to composition, size distribution, rearrangement of atoms, dissociation-association, decomposition and displacement.

(iv) **Electrical properties.** Conductivity of a material is due to the movement of free ions or electrons and the absence of free electrons in ceramics is responsible for their poor heat as well as electrical conductivity. Due to these properties, ceramic materials find their extensive applications as thermal and electrical insulators. Some of the ceramic materials are also used as semi-conductors.

Since ceramic materials possess high resistance, they become heated quickly and thus the ionic bonds get agitated and consequently ionic diffusion becomes very fast at high temperatures. As a result, conductivity rises rapidly upto 1000°C and then becomes constant. In the molten state, the conductivity of ceramics is very high. Ordinary glass and silicates are insulators at ordinary temperatures but very good conductors in the molten state.

Ceramic materials such as fire clays and porcelein have good dielectric capacity which makes them suitable for cores in transformers, and dielectric medium in condensers.

The factors on which the electrical properties depend are composition of the material, texture of the material, size and density of the material, temperature, etc.

(v) **Thermal properties**. The most important thermal properties of ceramic materials are: thermal capacity, thermal conductivity and thermal shock resistance. These properties of ceramics vary from material to material and from condition to condition. For example, specific heat of fire clay bricks at 1000°C is 0.265 and 0.295 at 1400°C. Carbon bricks have a specific heat of about 0.812 at 200°C and 0.412 at 1000°C. Similarly thermal conductivity varies with conditions, for example, thermal conductivity of fire clay brick at 450°C is 1.6 and 2.8 at 940°C.

Thermal shock resistance is the ability of a material to resist cracking or disintegration of the material under the condition of abrupt or sudden changes in temperature. Due to the ability to withstand shock at high temperature, many ceramics are used for high temperature services. Thermal stresses may arise due to various reasons such as anisotropic coefficient of thermal expansion and change in temperature producing thermal stresses between the grains. A rapid change in temperature leads to thermal gradients and differential expansion, which are aggrevated by the low thermal conductivities of ceramics. Rapid cooling is usually more injurious than a rapid heating because the former brings the surface in tension where small flows grow into cracks. Further, differential effects also arise from nonuniform com-

TABLE 8.1 Properties of Some Ceramics at Room Temperature

S. No.	Material and approximate Composition per cent	Melting point °C	Porosity per cent	Sp. gr.	Coefficient of expansion $deg.^{-1}.10^6$	Thermal conductivity $Wm^{-1} deg^{-1}$	Dielectric const.	Tensile strength MN/m^2	Compressive strength MN/m^3
1.	Concrete: hydrated cement ($CaO.SiO_2.\ Al_2O_3.H_2O$), Sand and ballast	—	4.20	2.4	10-14	1.8	—	2.5	25-40
2.	Building brick: 40-60 SiO_2 30-20 Al_2O_3	—	~20	1.7	5-6	0.7	—	5	25
3.	Alumina fire brick 10-40 SiO_2 50-90 Al_2O_3	—	~20	2.2	4-5	1.3	—	8	15
4.	Electrical porcelein (high voltage) 10 K_2O, 45 SiO_2, 45 Al_2O_3	—	<0.1	2.3	3	1.0	6.1	45	350
5.	Steatite porcelein: 60 SiO_2, 5 Al_2O_3, 30 MgO,	—	<0.05	2.65	8.3	3.3	6.1	70	600
6.	Alumina Single crystal: 99.9 Al_2O_3	2050	0	3.98	—	4,2	—	500-700	2000
7.	Electrical grade 95 Al_2O_3	—	<0.05	3.65	—	—	8.9	200	2000
8.	Silica (SiO_2): Quartz single crystal	1600	0	2.65	7.5(a) 13.7(c)	5.4(a) 9.2(c)	4.5	—	—
9.	Quartz polycrystalline	1600	0	2.65	16.9	7.1	4.5	—	—
10.	Glass (non-crystalline).	—	0	2.22	0.55	1.2	4.1	100-120	—

position. For example, a refractory used as a furnace lining may react with the contents of the furnace and change its composition at the surface. Hence, the chemical stability of ceramics is of great importance to thermal shock resistance. Important properties of some ceramics of interest are shown in Table 8.1

8.4. GLASSES

The word *glass* in its widest sense is used to describe a particular state of matter which is known as the glassy or vitreous state. This state is obtained when a liquid cools and becomes more viscous, until it is so viscous that it has the apparent physical properties of solid. Two essential features on which glass formation depends are: (a) there should be a temperature range in which the viscosity of the liquid increases very rapidly with decrease in temperature and (b) the liquidus temperature must lie in, or preferably below this range. If the viscosity of a liquid is already very high at the liquidus temperature, the rate of crystal growth will be negligible and the resultant super cooled liquid is *glass*. A large number of silicate materials are termed as *glass*. Thus *a glass may be defined as a hard, brittle and transparent noncrystalline solid material which is not attacked by organic substance, salts or acids with the exception of hydrofluoric acid.* The most distinguishing features of glass are as follows:

(a) Transparency making it most suitable for the use in windows and optical devices.

(b) Good corrosion resistance.

(c) Poor resistance to thermal shock.

(d) Good electrical resistivity.

(e) Its conductivity improves at high temperatures while the opposite is true for metals.

(f) Some special glasses having electrical conductivity are useful for a few special applications such as self-depositing and antifogging wind shields.

Glasses are made of naturally occurring inorganic oxides such as silica or sand. Besides this, chemical compounds which form glasses are oxides like B_2O_3, P_2O_5, etc. Others ingredients used are mixtures of these oxides or other oxides in different proportions. There is a great variety of glasses depending upon their composition.

8.4.1. Lime—Soda—Silica Glass

In these glasses silica is the main constituent (60-75 per cent) alongwith oxides of sodium and calcium as the two major modifying oxides. The addition of increasing amounts of Na_2O to SiO_2 lowers the melting and softening temperatures of the latter. Increasing addition of Na_2O to SiO_2 decreases the resistance to chemical attack and if enough Na_2O is used, the glass becomes water soluble known as water glass. By introducing lime, in addition to sodium oxide resistance to water, chemicals and abrasion is improved. However, excess lime causes the glass to crystallise on cooling and looses transparency. To improve the chemical resistance. a small amount of Al_2O_3 (1.2 per cent) and some MgO as a part of CaO are added. A typical composition of a common glass may be 70 per cent SiO_2, 15 per cent Na_2O, 9 per cent CaO, 3 per cent MgO and 2 per cent Al_2O_3. This type of glass is the most widely manufactured and accounts for well over 90 per cent of all glass in present day use. It is used in the manufacture of glass containers, flat glass, electric lamp bulbs and fluorescent tubing. It is also used for some optical purposes, where a high refractive index is not required.

8.4.2. Borosilicate Glass

In this boric anhydride (B_2O_3) is used in place of lime. This glass generally contains 75-81 per cent SiO_2, 10-13.5 per cent B_2O_3, 4.5-6 per cent Na_2O and 2-5 per cent Al_2O_3. Its two outstanding properties are high chemical resistance and low coefficient of expansion which make it most suitable for laboratory and medical ware, oven and table ware, and industrial glass ware. Borosilicate glass may contain a small quantity of fluorine which is used to lower the viscosity. Calcium phosphate may also be included in borosilicate composition to produce opalization during forming of the glass. Pyrex is an example of such glasses known for their low coefficient of expansion (about 40×10^{-7} cm/cm/°C).

8.4.3. Vitreous Silica

Vitreous silica is pure silica glass, and the highest quality product is used primarily for the manufacture of prisms and windows in optical instruments, particularly when a high degree of transmission in the ultraviolet and near infrared is required. Vitereous silica may be prepared by melting quartz at a temperature of about 1800°C, but this atways contains alumina as trace impurity which reduces the ultraviolet transmission of the glass. A very pure form of vitreous silica can be prepared using redistilled $SiCl_4$ as the raw material and this form of silica has a high ultraviolet transmission, but due to the presence of hydroxyl group shows a poor infrared transmission. Vitreous silica has an extremely high chemical resistance and a low thermal expansion, and it is therefore used for certain types of laboratory ware. However, due to the high melting point, poor workability and tendency to retain air bubbles, its use is limited.

8.4.4. 96 per cent Silica Glass

A less expensive alternative of vitreous silica is 96 per cent silica glass. In this case the article is performed from a borosilicate glass, and then heat treated so as to induce phase separation in the borosilicate. The sodium-rich phase is leached out by acid treatment, and the resulting porous silica-rich article is then heated to its softening temperature to consolidate into a 96 per cent silica glass article, similar in shape to the original, but slightly smaller. This glass, like vitreous silica, has a high chemical resistance and a low coefficient of expansion.

8.4.5. Neutral Glasses

This includes the glasses which are highly resistant to chemical attack and are used in the manufacture of ampoules and vials for injection solution, and syringes. Neutral glasses can be regarded as a specialised area of soda-lime glass, in which some of the alkali has been replaced by alumina, boron oxide, zinc oxide and other constituents.

8.4.6. Leaded Glasses

This group of glasses is used for the manufacture of high quality table ware, and also for some optical glass where a high refractive index is required. The so-called 'full lead crystal' is potash-lead silicate, with about 37 per cent PbO. However, it is fairly common practice to manufacture 'half lead' glasses with about 17-18 per cent PbO and with some of the potash replaced with soda. Leaded glasses containing as much as 92 per cent PbO, are used for special purposes such as protection against gamma radiation and in electronic tubes because of high surface resistance. These glasses are sometimes called *flint glasses*.

8.4.7. Phosphate Glasses

These contain P_2O_5 as a replacement for most or all of the SiO_2. Phosphate glasses are usefull if transmission of a wide range of wavelengths is important. Phosphate glass transmits 80 per cent of the entire ultraviolet spectrum, whereas, ordinary window glass transmits almost none of the short ultraviolet waves, and upto about 80 per cent of the long ultraviolet waves.

8.4.8 Raw Materials for Glass Making

In every glass of present day in commercial use silica is the main constituent for which sand is the chief raw material. A large number of other raw materials used fall under the following groups:

(*i*) **Modifires.** Since pure silica glass requires an extremely high temperature to melt and work, modifiers are necessary to reduce the melting and working temperatures. The common ones are the alkalies, the alkali earths, lead oxide, zinc oxide, boron oxide, etc.

(*ii*) **Melting and refining agents.** These are materials which are added in small quantities to the glass batch (mixed with raw materials) in order to promte refining, i.e., the removal of small gas bubbles from the glass. These include sodium sulphate, sodium nitrates, sodium chloride, arsenic oxide, calcium fluoride, carbon, etc.

(*iii*) **Colouring and decolouring agents**. These are materials which are added in small quantities either to produce a definite colour, or to neutralize an undesired colour which would otherwise be obtained when sand of less purity is used. Important colouring agents are Cr_2O_3 (green), CrO_3 (yellow-green), CoO (blue), CuO (red), Fe_2O_3 (brown), etc Decolouring agents are selenium, cerium oxide, neodymium oxide, etc.

(*iv*) **Opalizing agents**. These are the materials which allow the glass to be melted in the normal way, but which permits separation or crystals or droplets in the glass during, working and thus give an opalescent appearance to the finished glass. Fluoride and calcium phosphate are the two common agents added for this purpose.

8.4.9. Fabrication of Glass

Small scale production of glass is accomplished by bath melting pots or tanks. For large scale production, glass is made in regenerative furnaces. The raw materials (sand, Na_2CO_3 and lime) are charged at one end of the furnace and at the other end (exit) of the furnace there are devices for drawing the glass into sheet, tubing, filaments, etc. Some of these fabrication processes are similar, but not exactly like the methods used for metal processing. Blowing is another important method of shaping glass used for making bottles and incandescent lamp bulbs. Automatic machines remove the proper size of *gob* of molten glass and blow the desired shape in a split mould. Pressing of glass is accomplished by forcing a plunger into a gob of glass confined to a cast iron mould. Glass is also rolled and cast by the same methods as used for metals. Designs may be cut into the roll surfaces to produce a particular surface finish on the sheet. After fabrication, glass objects must be annealed or slowly cooled to prevent formation of residual stresses. Glass filaments are sometimes spun into thread which is then woven into cloth. The cloth is useful as a noncombustible textile and reinforcing material for laminated plastics. Unwoven filaments are used to make insulating butts and air filters. They are also used for reinforcement of plastic objects, such as moulded chairs.

8.4.10. Failure or Fracture of Glasses

Glasses are noncrystalline and isotropic. There is complete lack of orderly arrangements of units in the glass structure The lattice arrangement of glass is very much disorderly represented in three dimensions. In silica glass discrete units of $(SiO_4)^4$ are contained in tetrahedrally coordinated groups. These groups are connected with similar other units by common oxygen atoms, which keep the structure electrically balanced. Though Si-O distance is the same as that of crystalline material, the distortion is caused because of variable Si-O-Si angle.

The solid material having crystal lattice structure are capable of resisting deformation by some external forces and thus the deformations are within the elastic limits and permanent deformation or fracture occurs only when the externally applied forces are greater than the intermolecular binding forces. But glass does not have any crystal lattice structure and is brittle which is responsible for the failure of glass (fracture) without yield or deformation.

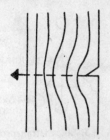

FIG. 8.1. Propagation of crack in a glass.

Fracture in glass is caused by small imperfections, flaws or irregularity, most of which occurs on the surface. Flaws like very fine cracks (invisible even under microscope) cause concentration of stress which will be intensified to many times greater than the nominal stress at that point under tension. Thus a crack proceeds and propagates quickly resulting into fracture (Fig. 8.1). This effect is significant under impact loading and the glass fractures almost without any plastic deformation. Glass will break under forces of less energy compared to the ductile materials having the same strength and deforming extensively before fracture (Fig. 8.2).

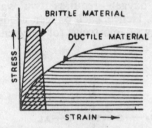

FIG. 8.2. Energy requirements to fracture ductile and brittle materials.

8.5. SILICATES AND THEIR STRUCTURES

The group of silicate minerals is perhaps most important as this group includes about 25 per cent of known minerals and nearly 40 per cent of the common minerals are silicates. Except a few, most of the igneous rock-forming minerals are silicates, constituting more than 90 per cent of the earth's crust. The soil from which we grow our food, is made up in large part of silicates. The materials used for building construction such as brick, stone, concrete, glass etc. are either silicates or mainly derived from silicates. This group consists of mainly eight mineral series, i.e. (i) olivines, (ii) pyroxenes, (iii) amphiboles, (iv) micas and clay minerals, (v) feldspar, (vi) quartz, (vii) aluminium silicates, and (viii) garnets.

8.5.1. Silicate Structures

The radius ratio of the silicon ion (0.42 Å) to that of the oxygen ion (1.42 Å) is 0.300 which indicates that 4-fold coordination will be stable state of silicon-oxygen groupings. The fundamental unit on which the structure of all silicates is based consists of four oxygen ions at the apics of a regular tetrahedran surrounding and co-ordinated by the four-valent silicon ions (Fig. 8.3). The structural element (chain, sheet, etc.) are joined together by bonds to cations lying between them, or in the case of framework, cations may be held in the spaces of the frame work. Within the tetrahedral groups the main element substituting of Si^{4-} is Al^{3+} and this substitution is limited in amount which rarely exceeds Al : Si=1:3.

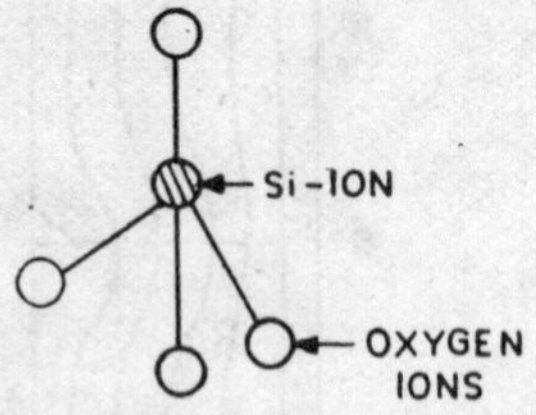

FIG. 8.3. Silica tetrahedron SiO_4^{4-}.

(*i*) **Tetrahedral structure**. Each of four oxygen ions receives one valency electron from silicon. But oxygen requires two valency electrons to be satisfied and stable. Hence, each oxygen needs one more valency electron. The deficiency of electrons for oxygen ions is met in two ways:

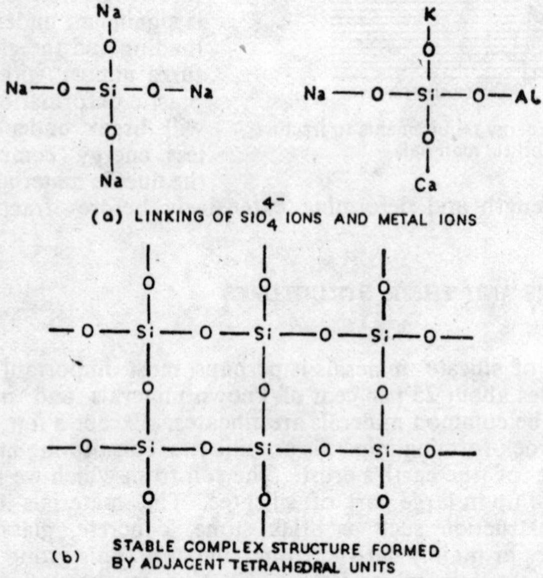

(a) LINKING OF SiO_4^{4-} IONS AND METAL IONS

(b) STABLE COMPLEX STRUCTURE FORMED BY ADJACENT TETRAHEDRAL UNITS

FIG. 8.4. Tetrahedral structure.

(*a*) By taking an electron from some other metal atom. In this case $(SiO_4)^{4-}$ ions and metal ions are linked as shown in Fig. 8.4(*a*).

(*b*) By linking the silicon of the first tetrahedral unit to a silicon of an adjacent second tetrahedral group as shown in Fig. 8.4(*b*). In this case an un-ending group with silicon ions and oxygen ions are formed. The structure in this case is more complicated. The silicon ions and the oxygen ions linkage

FIG. 8.5. Tetrahedral structure showing electrically satisfied silicon and oxygen in linkage.

as shown in Fig. 8.5 is electrically satisfied and this helps in the extension of silicate structure in the space and is identical with carbon to carbon linkage. In this the formula of the structure is represented by $(Si_2O_7)^{6-}$ and the Si : O ratio is 1:3.5.

Thus the type of the silicate structure depends on the way in which the unbalanced oxygen electrons are satisfied. All silicate structures are based on the tetrahedral $(SiO_4)^{4-}$ amionic group. These groups may be independent (island silicates) or linked together by sharing corner O^{2-} ions into couplets, rings, chains, layers, or frame works. The silicates are classified on the basis of the type of structural elements into which the tetrahedral groups are linked.

(*ii*) **Island structures.** This is also known as $(SiO_4)^{4-}$ silicate structure. The oxygen atoms at SiO_4 tetrahedral corners and in

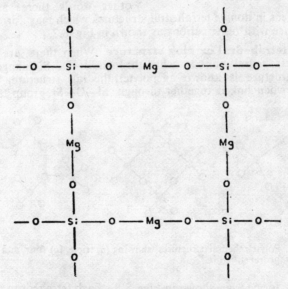

FIG. 8.6. Island structure of Mg_2SiO_4.

approximate hexagonal close packing. This structure is electrically neutral, i.e. the positive and negative charges are equal. The common minerals having island structures are beryllium silicate (Be_2SiO_4), magnesium silicate (forsterite), zircon ($ZrSiO_4$), silimanite [Al_2O (SiO_4)], etc. In case of magnesium silicate, $(SiO_4)^{4-}$ ion receives four electrons from adjacent four atoms of magnesium. Second electron of each magnesium atom is linked to the other silicate (SiO_4) unit. Thus magnesium electrons (Mg^{++}) act as link between $(SiO_4)^{4-}$ ions. This results in a strong structure as shown in Fig. 8.6. In this case SiO_4 units are separated by Mg-ions, hence known as "island structure."

(*iii*) **Double tetrahedral structures.** In this type of structures one of the oxygen is common member of two silica tetrahedral units.

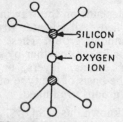

FIG. 8.7. Doub'e tetrahedral silicate $(Si_2O_7)^{6-}$.

This oxgen is fully satisfied electrically because it has received on valencey electron from each of the two silicon ions. Rest of the three oxygens attached to each silicon ion must acquire valency share from some external source. Chemical composition of the double tetrahedral structure is $(Si_2O_7)^{6-}$ ions. In other words there are six active oxygens in double tetrahedral structures which may form complex structure with other cations as shown in Fig. 8.7.

(*iv*) **Polytetrahedral or ring structure.** When there are three or more tetrahedral units attached through Si—O—Si linkages, the resulting structure is known as polytetrahedral structure. These tetrahedral when linked together through Si—O—Si group, a ring

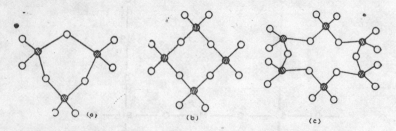

FIG. 8.8. Polytetrahedral structures showing (*a*) triple, (*b*) four, and (*c*) six tetrahedral structure.

structure is formed as shown in Fig. 8.8. Each tetrahedron of silicon $(SiO_4)^{4-}$ shares two oxygen ions giving rise to the chemical compostion of Si_3O_9, Si_4O_{12}, Si_6O_{18}, etc. and producting $(Si_3O_9)^{-6}$, $(Si_4O_{12})^{8-}$ and $(Si_5O_{18})^{12-}$ ions respectively. Thus 6, 8 and 12 active oxygen ions are available respectively for the formation of the complex structure with other external cations. In this way oxygen ions linking the tetrahedral units are obviously electrically satisfied.

In this way a large variety of tetrahedral units are obviously electrically satisfied. In this way a large variety of tetrahedral units may be formed such as four-unit, five-unit, six-unit, etc. Which in turn will form the most complicated silicate structures. In this Si and O ratio is 1:3. Examples are benitoite, $BaTiSi_3O_9$ (triple tetrahedral); chabazile, $Ca_2(Al_2Si_4O_{12})$. $6H_2O$ (four tetrahedral), and beryl, $Al_2 (Si_6O_{18})$ (six-tetrahedral).

(v) **Single chain structure**. In a silica tetrahedral (SiO_4) all the four oxygens are active from which one can be attached to the second tetrahedral. This way oxygen atom linking the two tetrahedral units becomes electrically fully satisfied. The third tetrahedral unit can be attached to the oxygen which is parallel to the chemically satisfied oxygen atom. It can be extended in both directions to a infinite length (Fig. 8.9) giving rise to the formation of a single chain structure of silica tetrahedron. The chemical composition can be repre-

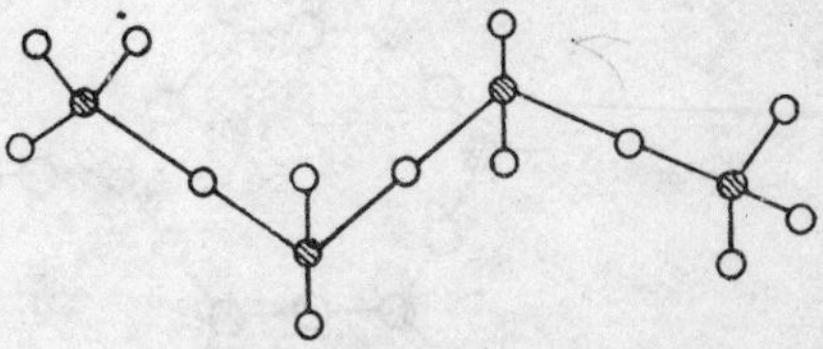

FIG. 8.9. Single chain structure of silica tetrahedron.

sented by $(SiO_3)^{2-}$ and Si and O ratio is 1:3. The example of this type of structure is *pyroxene* group, such as pectolite, $NaHCa_2(Si_3O_9)$.

(vi) **Double chain structure**. When two parallel and identical chains are polymerised by sharing oxygen to every alternate tetrahedron, double chain structure is formed as shown in Fig. 8.10. Formation of chain structure is identical to the polymerisation of organic materials. The difference between the two is the nature of forces holding the chain together. In organic material weak Vander Waal's forces keep the adjacent chains together, whereas in ceramic materials the chains are held together by ionic bonds.

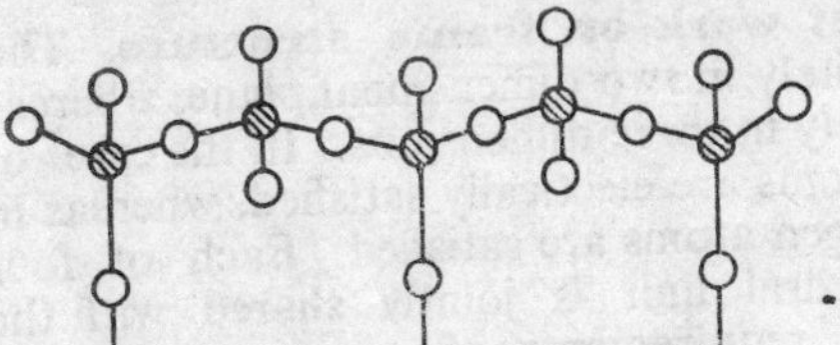

FIG. 8.10. Double chain structure silicates.

Since the ionic bonds between the chains are not strong enough, fracture or cleavage results parallel to chain. Amphibole group minerals $(W, X, Y)_{7-8}\{Si_8O_{22}\}(O, OH,F)_{12}$ exhibit this nature. The fibrous nature of asbestos is an example where low strength between the silicate chains exists. In this Si:O is 1:2.75 and it can be chemically represented by $(Si_4O_{11})^{6-}$.

(vii) **Sheet structure**. This structure mainly results due to infinite extension of the double chain structure in two dimensional plane rather than along a line. In these structures three oxygens of each tetrahedron are linked with the adjacent units. Thus all oxygen ions are electrically satisfied by silicon ions except one in each tetrahedral unit, which is free to link with external cations. This forms hexago-nal rings of silica units arranged in sheets. The structure has an indefinite extension as shown in Fig. 8.11. With a Si:O of 1:2.5. Chemical formula may be represented as $(Si_2O_5)^{2-}$. These are also called layer silicates. The examples of this group are mica, chlorite, talc, serpentine etc. Ceramic minerals like clays also possess sheet structure. The cleavage of mica, plasticity of clay and the lubricating characteristics of talc are all due to this type of structural arrange-ments.

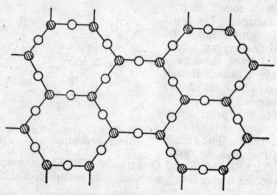

FIG. 8.11. Sheet structure silicates.

(viii) **Three dimensional net work or frame structure**. The sheet structure extends infinitely in two dimensional plane, whereas frame structure extends infinitely in three dimensions. In the case of former, only three oxygen atoms are electically satisfied, whereas in the latter one, all the four oxygen atoms are satisfied. Each of four oxygens of particular tetrahedral unit is jointly shared with the adjacent unit and the valency requirements of oxygen atoms are fully satisfied. This is called frame structure. The frame structure can not be easily illustrated on plane diagram. The ratio of Si and O is 1:2 and can be represented by SiO_2 or Si_nO_{2n}. The framework structures are generally hard, ordinary sand (quartz, tridymite and crystobalite) are the typical examples of frame work structure available in silica minerals. These are electrically balanced molecules. In addition to these, there are many more silicate minerals such as felspar in which aluminium replaces silicon and alkali or alkaline earth cations in the lattice and thus the deficiency of positive charge is balanced. Like aluminium, titanium also replaces silicon. Iron does the same in case of sheet structures.

(ix) **Vitreous structures**. It is an amophous material having three dimensional frame work structure containing covalent bonds and hence it is more rigid. For example, glass is a vitreous silicate.

8.5.2. Polymorphism

When a materials exists in many forms, i.e., different crystal structures, the phenomenon is called *polymorphism* or *allotropy*. Usually a preferred structure exists at any given pressure and temperature, the latter being the common variable. For example, carbon can exist either as diamond (diamond cubic structure) or as graphite. Conversion of graphite (hexagonal structure) to diamond is extremely difficult whereas the reverse is easy above 1000°C. Similarly iron exists as b.c.c. at room temperature (α-iron), as f.c.c. between 906°C and 1400°C (γ-iron), and again as b.c.c. between 1400°C and its melting point (δ-iron). In this example all the changes occur readily as the material is heated or cooled. Polymorphism is not only confined to crystals of elements, but also occurs in compounds. The best example is silica (SiO_2) which has many crystalline froms out of which quartz is most common. At room temperature, silica tetrahedral is stable having hexagonal pattern (quartz) and at 870°C the stable arrangement is broken (tridymite). Again at 1470°C it attains stable configuration arranged in cubic pattern (cristoballite) which exists upto the melting point (1710°C). Hence, silica occurs in three polymorphic or allotropic forms, i.e., quartz, tridymite and cristoballite. Each of these modifications is stable over a fixed range of temperature. The inter-relationship between these forms of silica is important from the manufacture as well as application view point.

The temperature range for stability of the three different forms may be represented as follows:

$$\underset{\text{Quartz}}{} \overset{870°C}{\rightleftharpoons} \underset{\text{Tridymite}}{} \overset{1470°C}{\rightleftharpoons} \text{Cristoballite} \quad \ldots(8.2)$$

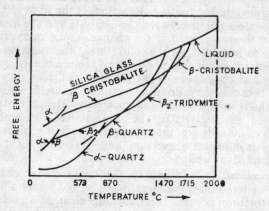

FIG. 8.12. Transformation of silica.

The transformation of quartz to tridymite and similarly tridymite to cristoballite is not so simple as shown above. Further modifications of these crystalline structures and their stability ranges are shown in Fig. 8.12. In these transformations of silica minerals, two distinct types of thermal changes are involved, i.e. (a) conversion and (b) inversion.

(a) **Conversion**. In this, quartz changes to tridymite and then to cristoballite and vice versa. This type of change involves structural rearrangement. For example, β-*quartz* which is hexagonal, changes at 870°C to β-tridymite (trigonal) and at 1470°C to β-*cristobollite* (cubic). These transformations are very slow and sluggish because of the presence of Si-O bond which is very strong. Hence pure quartz may exist in stable phase at room temperatures and at temperature greater than 870°C.

High temperature polymorphic forms like tridymite and cristobalite once formed, can be kept at room temperature indefinitely without reconverting into quartz. Reversion, however, to quartz would take place in an infinite length of time.

Pure quartz crystals are highly stable at temperatures even well above 870°C. After prolonged firing, however, it is converted to tridymite. The rate of conversion is accelerated by means of catalysts otherwise it might take a geological year. While some of the catalysts accelerate and promote the formation of tridymite, others help to increase the rate of formation of cristoballite. Catalysts used are alkali metals such as lithium, sodium, potassium, ferric oxide, calcium oxide, magnesium oxide and various other alkali oxides. Reaction occurs both in solid as well as liquid state.

In solid states the catalysts (promoters) form nucleated regions where quartz grains contact. This phenomenon spreads very rapidly till whole particle is decomposed. In liquid phase the catalysts get mobility and hence, their activities are greatly increased. Very small amounts of a catalyst are required to cause conversion when liquid state is formed during heating. Reaction, in the solid state, depends upon the contact points between the catalysts and the quartz grains. Hence, for the rapid speed of the change, more quantities of promoters are to be added. In the solid states, the reaction is fast only in the beginning of the firing and falls if the promoters are not added sufficiently and continuously. The alkali earth oxides are very efficient catalysts because they do not produce a liquid phase with silica either at the temperature of firing or service. Hence, these oxides are mostly used as catalysts for the production of high grade products. In India barium salts are used as catalysts in the silica industries. The catalysts influence conversion and determine the nature of the product formed as well.

(b) **Inversion**. In addition to the conventional changes, silica minerals undergo other changes when heated where a little orientation in structure occurs. This rearrangement in structure is called inversion. In this, reversible reaction occurs between the α and β varieties of the silica minerals. For example, reaction from α-quartz to β-quartz and vice versa which occurs exactly at particular temperatures. These reversible reactions are instanteneous and much faster than the conversion reactions. Hence, inversion temperature range is rather short as shown by the following reactions for quartz, tridymite and cristoballite.

$$\alpha\text{-quartz} \underset{}{\overset{573°C}{\rightleftharpoons}} \beta\text{-quartz} \qquad \dots (8.3)$$

$$\alpha_1\text{-tridymite} \underset{}{\overset{117°C}{\rightleftharpoons}} \beta_1\text{-tridymite} \qquad \dots (8.4)$$

$$\alpha_2\text{-tridymite} \underset{}{\overset{163°C}{\rightleftharpoons}} \beta_2\text{-tridymite} \qquad \dots (8.5)$$

$$\alpha\text{-Cristoballite} \underset{}{\overset{220\text{-}280°C}{\rightleftharpoons}} \beta\text{-Cristoballite} \qquad \dots (8.6)$$

α-quartz at 573°C is very much deformed and distorted. At temperatures obove 573°C it acquires stable β-quartz configuration as

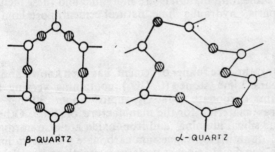

β-QUARTZ   α-QUARTZ

FIG. 8.13. α to β-Quartz inversion.

shown in Fig. 8.13. This change or inversion is mainly due to the straightning of bonds accross oxygen at the temperature of 573°C and above and the reaction is very rapid as the bonds are not broken. On cooling, again distorted form of α-quartz appears. This change from β to α-quartz at 573°C and below is accompanied by a volume decrease in the structure. Fig. 8.14 illustrates the thermal expansion of quartz from room temperature to 875°C.

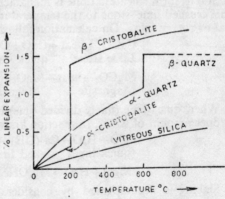

FIG. 8.14. Thermal expansion of silica phase.

Tridymite exists is two forms β₁ and β₂ in the metastable range, where inversion at 117°C and 163°C are to α_1 and α_2, respectively. Because *tridymite* itself exists in two metamorphic forms, the inversions are complex and still unpredicted. Volume change accompanied, however, is very small.

Cristoballite also undergoes changes at a temperature range of 220-280°C. In this case also, the bonds are straightened without any rupture and accompanied by an instantaneous increase in transparency. The inevrsion effect may be measured by the small thermal change which takes place during the progress of the reaction. While heating, the reaction is an endothermic and while cooling, it is an exothermic.

8.6. CEMENTING MATERIALS

These are the materials which are used for bonding solids together. Most of the cementing materials are inorganic and these include lime, plaster of paris, hydraulic lime, natural cement, port land cement and others.

8.6.1. Lime

Lime mortar, the fore runner of cement, has been known and used for over 5000 years. Lime stone ($CaCO_3$) containing verying amounts of magnesium carbonate ($MgCO_3$) upto about 30 per cent, is used as the raw material for the manufacture of lime. Other impurities such as silica, alumina and iron oxide are also normally present in small quantities. Magnesium carbonate persent in lime stone is considered beneficial, since it undergoes reactions parallel to those of $CaCO_3$ and result in lowering of the caleining temperatures. On the other hand, silica is harmful impurity since it reacts with the lime (CaO) to form silicates. Lime is manufactured by calcining (heating) the crushed lime stone to the temperature of about 1100°C in vertical or rotary kilns. On calcination following reactions take place:

$$CaCO_3 + heat \rightarrow CaO + CO_2 \uparrow \qquad \ldots (8.7)$$
Lime stone   quick lime

$$MgCO_3 + heat \rightarrow MgO + CO_2 \uparrow \qquad \ldots (8.8)$$
Magnesite   Magnesia

When quick lime (finely divided lime) is hydrated by mixing it with proper amount of water, a reaction known as slaking occurs:

$$CaO + H_2O \rightarrow Ca(OH)_2 + heat \qquad \ldots (8.9)$$
(quick lime)   slaked lime

$$MgO + H_2O \rightarrow Mg(OH)_2 + heat \qquad \ldots (8.10)$$

Slaking is accompanied by considerable evolution of heat and increase in volume. When slaking is carried out under proper controls, the slaked product is a fine white powder. From this powder, lumps of $x\ CaO.y\ SiO_2$ and unslaked MgO are removed which otherwise will cause cracks in lime mortar after setting. Hardening of lime is accomplished by reaction of $Ca(OH)_2$ with CO_2 from air which is accelerated by the excess water present. Thus a liquid phase, rather than gas-solid phase reaction is involved.

$$Ca(OH)_2 + CO_2 \xrightarrow{H_2O} CaCO_3 + H_2O \qquad \ldots (8.11)$$

$CaCO_3$ is less soluble than $Ca(OH)_2$ and hence precipitates out from solution in crystalline form. The interlocking of $CaCO_3$ crystals converts the plastic mass into a solid.

Uses of lime. Lime is mainly used in the form of slaked lime as an ingredient of mortar or plaster.

8.6.2. Gypsum and Gypsum Products

The raw material used for the gypsum products is a stoney mineral known as gypsum ($CaSO_4$. $2H_2O$). Some impurities such as SiO_2, Al_2O_3, $CaCO_3$, etc. are normally present in gypsum but these are not often considered harmful in the quantities they are normally present. Gypsum products tend to be white if pure and get somewhat darkened by the presence of sufficient impurities. In order to get various products, i e. half hydrate and anhydrite, calcination of gypsum is carried out at different temperatures. The crushed gypsum is heated in kettles or in rotary kiln equipped with stirring mechanism to promote uniform heating of the contents and also to prevent local overheating of the kettle. The dehydration of gypsum is a two-stage process:

$$CaSO_4.\ 2H_2O \xrightarrow{110\text{-}130°C} CaSO_4.\tfrac{1}{2}H_2O + 1\tfrac{1}{2}H_2O \qquad \ldots (8.12)$$
dihydrate $\qquad\qquad\qquad$ half-hydrate

$$CaSO_4.\ \tfrac{1}{2}H_2O \xrightarrow{175\text{-}205°C} CaSO_4 + \tfrac{1}{2}H_2O \qquad \ldots (8.13)$$
half-hydrate $\qquad\qquad$ anhydrite

The half-hydrate is quite stable and is packaged in bags for use as an ingredient of plaster. The anhydrite tends to absorb water rapidly and gets converted to the half-hydrate. If the anhydrite is overheated during calcining, it tends to become inert and loses its ability to harden.

Hardening of gypsum. Gypsum is a peculiar substance in that the hydrate is less soluble in water than the half-hydrate. Thus, if the half-hydrate is mixed with water it slowly reacts with precipitate needles of di-hydrate:

$$1\tfrac{1}{2}H_2O + CaSO_4.\tfrac{1}{2}H_2O \rightarrow CaSO_4.\ 2H_2O \qquad \ldots (8.14)$$

The formation of an interlocking mass of dihydrate crystals is responsible for the hardening of gypsum. This is also known as hydraulic cement as it hardens slowly by reaction with water.

There are a number of factors which affect the rate of initial stiffening or setting of gypsum. For example, use of warm water (i.e. raising the temperature of plastic mass) sets its plaster, and finely ground gypsum dissolves faster in water and thereby increases the rate of reaction with water. However, in case of gypsum the problem is not of accelerating the setting rate, but it is rather to retard the rate. This is achieved by use of animal glues which keep the mixture plastic for about one hour. Other organic substances are also used as retarding agents. Without retarders, setting occurs in about 10 minutes. The setting and hardening of gypsum are accompanied by an increase in volume and evolution of heat.

Properties of gypsum. The strength of gypsum depends upon several factors such as amount of water used during mixing, the amount of anhydrite present before mixing, kind and quantity of fillers and foreign substances present. Strength increases with decreasing amounts of mixing water as long as enough water is used to give a plastic mix. Increasing amount of anhydrite results in greater strength. Since higher calcining temperatures produce a higher proportion of anhydrite, they result in improvement in strength, unless they are so high that they produce inert or dead burnt gypsum. The strength of gypsum usually varies between 70 and 150 kgs/cm^2, although higher strengths are possible. Gypsum is a good fire-resistant having good insulating properties and thus it retards fire damage to wooden and steel framing. When exposed to fire, the insulating properties of gypsum ore improved by loss of water of hydration and an accompanying increase in the porosity of the mass.

Uses of gypsum. Gypsum is used for wall boards, moulds, decorating architectural details, interior tile, and medical application (casts for broken bones and dental use). Gypsum mixed with equal or one-half equal parts of lime is used for finish plaster. Lime on setting undergoes a contraction while gypsum expands. The net result is a plaster free from cracks.

8.6.3. Portland Cement

Portland cements are by far the most important of the inorganic materials. When mixed with water it has a plastic flow and after some hours it becomes solid, hard mass with varying strength. This product derives its name from its resemblance to stone quarried in portland Bill on the South Coast of England. Portland cements are mainly calcium silicates and calcium aluminates, a typical composition being 65 per cent CaO, 20 per cent SiO_2, 5 per cent Al_2O_3 and 10 per cent balance (including Fe_2O_3). This is a synthetic material unlike lime and gypsum, which is made by careful and controlled calcining of mixtures of clay-like and lime bearing materials. The clay-like materials furnish SiO_2 and the calcined mass consists principally silicates of calcium. Since portland cement sets and hardens by reaction with water, it is considered a hydraulic cement. It is most important and the best of the hydraulic silicate cements. The other silicate cements are natural products. Because the composition of natural ones varies, they do not have properties as reliable as those of portland cement.

Manufacture of portland cement. The calcareous materials such as lime stone, dredged marine shells and urgillaceous materials such as clay, slate, shale or blast furnace slags, etc. are mixed, ground and calcined together in a rotary kiln at about 1500°C. A molten phase is formed by the alumina and ferric oxide in which the lime and silica can dissolve and react together to give die- and tri-calcium silicates, which then crystallise out. The fused particles coming from the kiln are known as clinker. The clinker is cooled by a counter-current flow of air in a rotary kiln type cooler. After cooling, the slinker is mixed with small amounts of gypsum and water, ground to an extremely fine particle size and stored. Gypsum is added to control setting of the cement. A small amount of water is used to hydrate any free lime present before the cement is ground, thereby improving the soundness of the cement. The reaction products quantitatively are as follows:

Tricalcium silicate, $3CaO. SiO_2$ 45 per cent
Dicalcium silicate, $2CaO. SiO_2$ 30 per cent
Tricalcium aluminate $3CaO. Al_2O_3$ 10 per cent
Tetracalcium alumino ferrite
          $4CaO. Al_2O_3. Fe_2O_3$ 10 per cent
Balance   5 per cent.

The proportion of these compounds, called the mineralogical composition, is more important than the oxide composition in determining the properties of the cement such as the rate of hardening and heat evolution, or the resistance to attack by sulphate bearing water.

Setting and hardening of portland cement. The hydration reactions which occur on mixing cement particles and water are very complex. About 2 parts by weight of cement to one of water are necessary to complete hydration and achieve full strength. When mixed with water, it has a plastic flow and after some hours it becomes solid, hard mass with varying strength. Setting and hardening are accompanied by hydration and to some extent hydrolysis of the various compounds. The reactions involved are similar to those involved in the setting and hardening of gypsum. The reactions can be written as follows:

$$3(3CaO.SiO_2)+6H_2O \rightarrow 3CaO.2SiO_2.3H_2O+3Ca(OH)_2 \quad \ldots (8.15)$$
$$2(2CaO.SiO_2)+4H_2O \rightarrow 3CaO.2SiO_2.3H_2O+Ca(OH)_2 \quad \ldots (8.16)$$
$$3CaO.Al_2O_3+12H_2O+Ca(OH)_2 \rightarrow 2CaO.Al_2O_3.Ca(OH)_2.12H_2O \quad \ldots (8.17)$$
$$3CaO.Al_2O_3+30H_2O+3(CaSO_4.2H_2O) \rightarrow 3CaO.Al_2O_3.$$
$$3CaSO_4.36H_2O \quad \ldots (8.18)$$
$$4CaO.Al_2O_3.Fe_2O_3+10H_2O+2Ca(OH)_2 \rightarrow 6CaO.Al_2O_3.$$
$$Fe_2O_3.12H_2O \quad \ldots (8.19)$$

The hydration reactions are exothermic. The volume of cement increases with hydration. In the large structures of concrete the heat evolved is somehow removed and allowances for expansion are provided. Hydrated cements dissociate on heating by destroying the bond which held the mass together. This shows that the portland cement has temperature limitations as it changes its phase. The hydrated calcium silicate dissocates at about 40°C giving back calcium silicate and water which does not act as a cement. So the concrete looses its strength. Only in the case of hydrated calcium aluminate the reversal of the reaction is very slow and the dissociation occurs at about 90°C higher than that of the hydrated calcium silicate. Hence cements for high temperature applications are predominantly composed of calicum aluminate.

Factors affecting the rate of setting and hardening. Unless a retarder is added, portland cement takes an initial set too quickly for most applications. Gypsum is used as the retardant and is added at the mill before final grinding of the product. It has been found that 2 per cent gypsum provides the most effective retarding action. The initial set of portland cement should be between 45 minutes and 10 hours.

When the small particles of cement are mixed with water they react to form a layer of hydrate and gel. In order to continue the reaction, water must diffuse or migrate through the everthickening coating. Thus, the hardening of concrete is dependent upon both physical (diffusion) and chemical (hydration) processes which are speeded by a rise in temperature. In fact, cement mixed with water above 75°C will set permanently, known as flash setting. Conversely a drop in temperature slows the reaction. The degree of fineness of the cement also affects the speed of reaction. The finer the cement the greater the surface exposed to the mixing water and hence faster will be the hardening. It is for this reason that cement is ground so carefully after fusion. The presence of calcium chloride has been found to increase the speed of hardening but it does not greatly change the time of set. Calcium chloride is added on the job when the cement is mixed into concrete.

8.7. CONCRETE

Concrete includes concrete made with portland cement as well as concrete made with asphaltic cements. Portland cement concrete consists of a mass of aggregates held together by a hard binder of portland cement and water. In asphaltic concrete, aggregates are held together by an asphaltic cementing material. Portland cement concrete is more versatile than bituminous which is used mainly for road surfaces.

8.7.1. Cement Concrete

A hard substance known as cement concrete is formed after mixing cement, sand and stone chips with water. It sets and hardness due to addition of water. Cement acts as a binder for sand and coarse aggregate (stone chips), whereas, the sand and chips are the fillers which do not react with water or cement. For good cement concrete, it is essential that particle sizes of aggregate should be such that void ratio is minimum.

Cement concrete is very strong in compression but it is extremely weak in tension. Due to this reason, plain concrete can only be used when the structure is in pure compression, examples are floors, roads, etc. But steel is equally strong in compression and tension. Hence, combination of cement concrete and steel is an ideal one because in combination, the materials will resist compression and tension both when combined together. This combination of steel and cement concrete is called reinforced cement concrete (RCC). It possesses the following advantages:

(a) It is fire resistant, strong and durable and not attacked by termites.

(b) Monolithic structures can be built by RCC and hence their rigidity is more as compared to other forms of constructions.

(c) Water does not penetrate into it so readily and for all practical purposes it is impermeable.

(d) Materials used in such construction are easily available in nature.

(e) Different types of shapes can be made as it is easier to do the casting of RCC.

(f) It is comparatively cheaper.

QUESTIONS

1. Differentiate between the terms ceramic and clay.

2. What are the different ceramic products? Name the various raw materials used in manufacturing of ceramic products.

3. Compare and contrast the crystalline and amorphous structures. What are the advantages of crystalline and amarphous structures?

4. What are the various silicate structures? Discuss with examples.

5. Discuss island, framework, chain and sheet structures.

6. Discuss the principle and theory of glass fracture.

7. Discuss the different types of rock deposits in earth crust.

8. Which stones are used for masonry construction? Discuss their specific applications.

9. What are refractory materials? Discuss briefly the various types of refractories giving their applications.

10. Enumerate the various properties of refractories.

11. Discuss briefly the various steps involved in shaping of clay.

12. Outline the properties of building bricks and their types.

13. What are the important properties of ceramics? Discuss in reference to their specific applications.

14. What are the various types of glasses? Discuss their properties and applications.

15. Outline the general procedure for glass manufacture and fabrication.

16. Discuss the polymorphism phenomenon in silicates.

17. What are the various cementing materials? Indicate their uses and properties.

18. What is portland cement? Give its manufacturing procedure.

19. Discuss the various reactions involved in setting and hardening of portland cement.

20. What are the factors affecting the rate of setting and hardening?

9

SEMICONDUCTORS AND FERRITES

A semiconductor is a material which is partially insulating and partially conducting having a specific resistance in the range of about 10^{-2} to 10^6 Ohms-cm. All semiconductors are found to have less resistance at higher temperatures. They contain small amount of intentionally added some impurities. The most common semiconductors, i.e., silicon and germanium have the covalently bonded diamond cubic structure. Each atom is joined to each of its four nearest neighbours by sharing an electron pair. Thus, each atom has the equivalent of a closed valency cell and the binding of the electrons to the atom is very strong. The binding is responsible for the wide forbidden energy gap i.e. 5.0 ev in diamond. Coming down the group IV column in the periodic table, there is same effect but bond strength decreases. Silicon has a gap of 1.1 ev and germanium about 0.75 ev.

Out of the two, germanium is a typical semiconductor. At room temperature it has a specific resistance of about 60 ohms-cm., but when droped with 0.0001 pct. of arsenic, its resistance falls drastically to about 0.1 microhm-cm.

9.1. CHARACTERISTICS OF SEMICONDUCTORS

In general, a semiconductor must possess the following characteristics:

(*i*) A forbidden energy gap between the valence bond and the conduction bond of about 1.0 electron volt, e.g. silicon has a gap of 1.1 ev and germanium about 0.75 ev.

(*ii*) Sensitivity of its resistance to minute amount of impurities.

(*iii*) Decreasing resistance with increasing temperature.

A material showing decreased conductivity with rising temperature is classed as a conductor whereas a material showing increased conductivity with rising temperature is considered a semiconductor. This criterion distinguishes conductors and semiconductors when the two materials have comparable levels of electrical conductivity.

9.2. CLASSIFICATION OF SEMICONDUCTORS

Semiconductors can be classified in the following two groups:

9.2.1. Intrinsic Semiconductors

In an intrinsic semi conductor, the valence band of electron energies is nearly or completely filled and is separated from the empty conduction band by a relatively small energy gap Eg. If the quantity Eg/kT is almost equal to unity (where k is Boltzman's constant & T is the absolute temperature), the material can work as an intrinsic semiconductor. Further intrinsic semiconductivity can be explained by considering the diamond cubic structure of silicon and germanium, which has been shown in Fig. 9.1 by a two-dimensional network. Here the atoms are located at the nodes of the net, and the shared electron pair is represented by a double link. At $0°K$ atoms are at rest and all electrons are firmly held by the covalent bonds giving a perfect insulator. When the valence electron is thermally activated and removed from the covalent bond to become a free conduction electron, it produces a defect, i.e. a vacancy or a hole, in the electronic energy band distribution as shown by the single link at AB in Fig. 9.1. The ejected electron, X is available for conduction and drifts away on application of an electric field. At some later time, the missing link is restored by capture of an electron from a neighbouring bond. The hole thus shifts to a neighbouring bond and from there to another bond and so on. Such a hole plays the role of a positive charge carrier and can transport the charge as effectively as the freed electron. Thus, both the electron and the hole contribute to conduction and are considered to be imperfections of the covalent structure. The structure becomes intrinsically imperfect through production of this defective bond.

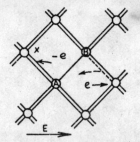

FIG. 9.1. An illustration of intrinsic type semiconductor.

9.2.2. Extrinsic Semiconductor

Extrinsic semicoductors are generally dilute substitutional alloys in which the valence characteristics of solute atoms are different than that of solvent material. Depending upon the type of impurity atoms introduced by substitution into the lattice of the host material, the alloy can conduct either by a conductance electron or hole mechanism. For silicon and germanium, these impurities are provided in two ways:

(a) Elements from group V of periodic table such as phosphorus, arsenic and antimony. These are called n-type (negative) impurities or donors.

(b) Elements from group III of the periodic table such as aluminium, gallium and indium. These are called p-type (positive) impurities or acceptors.

Silicon and germanium are having four valence electrons and they crystallise in a diamond cubic lattice. When an element of group III such as aluminium, is substitutionally introduced into the silicon lattice, a mismatch in the electronic bonding structure results due to the deficiency of the aluminium atom in bonding orbitals relative to the silicon host. It is shown in Fig. 9.2 by the absence of a black cross adjacent to aluminium atom. Thus it has one defective bond, or a hole, which is available for conduction as a positive charge by accepting an electron from a neighbouring bond and the hole can move throughout the crystal as a positive charge carrier. In such an alloy, the mechanism of charge transport is due to holes in the electronic bond structure, and this type of alloy is called a *p*-type (with positive charge carriers) extrinsic semiconductor. The process of adding minute amount of appropriate alloying element to create an extrinsic semiconductor is called 'doping a crystal' and the element added is called the 'dopant'.

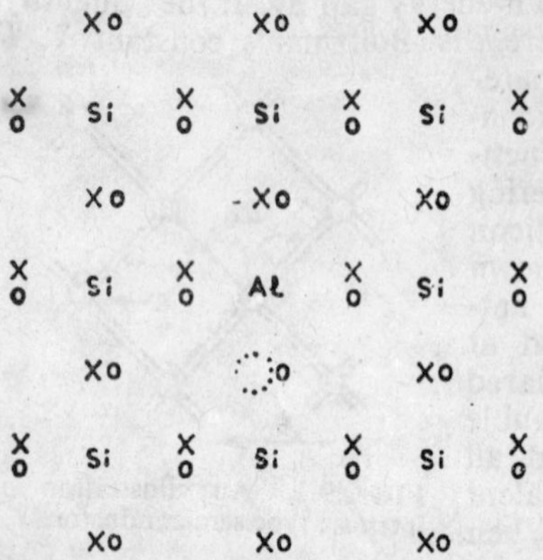

FIG. 9.2. An illustration of extrinsic type semiconductor.

An atom from group V such as phosphorus has five valence electrons, i.e. one more than silicon or germanium. It needs only four to share an electron pair with each of the four nearest neighbours of silicon and germanium in the diamond structure. Thus. it has an extra electron which it can donate to the semiconductor. Although this electron (donated) is still associated with parent phosphorus atom, it is loosely bound and requires little additional energy to be removed from its parent nucleus and made into free conductance electron. In terms of an energy bond diagram (Fig. 9.3) this means that the extra electron occupies an energy level in the forbidden region that is just slightly lower than the boundary of the conduction band. Adding a small amount of energy (much less than Eg) to this electron promotes it into conduction band. Such an energy level is called a donor level, and the atoms of group V which provide these additional eletrons are called donor atoms. Because the conduction mechanism is due to the extra electrons introduced into the structure, such materials are called *n*-type (with negative charge carriers) extrinsic semiconductors.

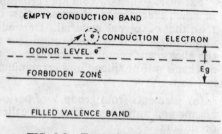

FIG. 9.3. Energy bond diagram.

The concentrations of dopant added to create extrinsic conductance are generally very small (1 part in 10^5-10^7) as too large a concentration of dopant will destroy the semiconductive property by converting the material to a conductor. In the process of manufacturing semiconductor grade silicon and germanium, extreme care has to be taken to obtain ultrapure materials with relatively perfect crystal structures before tiny amounts (in ppm) of an appropriate dopant are added.

In addition to the elemental semiconductors silicon and germanium, numerous compounds such as gallium arsenite (GaAs) and lead sulphide (PbS) also exhibit semiconducting properties. The same concept applies regarding donar or acceptor, except that elements from different group of the periodic table must be used. In the case of group III-V compounds such as GaAs, substitution of group II elements for the group III member results in the production of a p-type semiconductor, whereas substitution of a group VI element for the group V member results in an n-type semiconductor.

9.3. PREPARATION OF TRANSISTOR SEMICONDUCTOR METERIAL

Transistor semiconductor materials such as germanium and silicon must be prepared to standards of almost absolute purity. After purification by an efficient vacuum melting method known as zone-refining, the doping materials required to produce n-type or a p-type transistor, are added in amounts of a few parts per billion. Unless such purity standards are met, the characteristics of the transistor cannot be controlled within proper limits.

9.4. PHOTOCONDUCTIVITY

The photoconductive effect results when a semiconductor is irradiated with a considerable high photon energy to cause an appreciable reduction in the electrical resistance. A semiconductor is distinguished by a relatively small energy gap between the valence bond and the conduction bond. The absorbed photon energy lifts an electron across this gap to the conduction condition. There is a large number of photoconductive materials, but more commonly used are selenium, silicon, cadmium sulphide, lead telluride, lead sulphide and thallium sulphide. The photoconductive material is usually a thin film deposited on a substrate material which are generally used as detectors or switches to record the presence of visible light, ultraviolet or X-radiation. Cadmium sulphide is preferred for X-ray detection.

9.5. RESISTIVITY OF SEMICONDUCTORS

The corresponding resistivities due to conduction by electron and hole respectively can be shown separately as

$$\rho_e = \frac{m_e}{e^2 n_e t_e} \qquad \qquad \ldots (9.1)$$

and $\qquad \rho_h = \dfrac{m_e}{e^2 n_h t_h}$ $\qquad \qquad$ ... (9.2)

where m_e and m_h are the 'variable's electron mass and the 'mass' of hole, t_e and t_h are mean free times, and, N_e and n_h are the numbers of conducting electrons and the number of holes per unit volume, respectively.

The total resistivity 'ρ' is given by

$$\dfrac{1}{\rho} = \dfrac{1}{\rho_e} + \dfrac{1}{\rho_h} \qquad \qquad ... (9.3)$$

and conductivity $\sigma = \sigma_e + \sigma_h = e^2 \left(\dfrac{n_e \, t_e}{m_e} + \dfrac{n_h \, t_h}{m_h} \right)$ $\qquad$ ... (9.4)

The ratios t_e/m_e and t_h/m_h depend on details of crystal structures and only moderately on temperatures. On the other hand, n_e and n_h increase exponentially with increasing temperature (a property common to all semiconductors). This gives a corresponding decrease in resistivity. This contrasts sharply with normal conductors in which there is essentially a linear increase in resistivity with temperature.

9.6. DEPENDENCE OF SEMICONDUCTIVITY ON TEMPERATURE

For conversion of covalent electron to conducting electron and a hole can be written similar to dissociation reaction:

$$\text{Covalent electron} \rightleftharpoons \text{Conducting electron} + \text{hole} \qquad ... (9.5)$$

Like chemical dissociation the process shifts more or less to right, depending on temperature and the strength of bond. At any given temperature, however, there is a constant ratio of charge carriers to covalent electrons. Dissociation is thus governed by the same law of mass action which governs normal chemical reactions. Thus $n_e \, n_h$ is constant, but this constant changes with temperature and strength of covalent bond. This is applicable to both intrinsic and extrinsic semiconductors. In an n-type semiconductor, however, emphasis is primarily on n_e while in a p-type semiconductor, emphasis is mainly on n_h.

9.7. FERRITES

Broadly ferrite may be defined as nonmetallic materials exhibiting ferromagnetic properties. These are cubic spinels having structure similar to that of magnetite. It is their molecular constitution which is responsible for their magnetic properties. Ferrites are generally a mixture of iron oxide and oxides of rare earth metals. The specific crystal structure of these materials, known as spinel structure, is a close packd arrangement of oxygen ions with the metallic ions located in the interstices. These materials having extremely high electrical resistivity, are particularly useful when low eddy current losses are a desirable feature. In addition, these spinels have a considerable lower density than solid metallic materials, making them especially attractive in modern, low weight applications. These spinel materials can be made in any required composition due to the possibility of easy grinding into powder and further processing them by powder metallurgy techniques.

With the combined properties of a magnetic material and electric insulator, these ferrites are a compound of trivalent iron oxide with one or more bivalent metallic oxide having the chemical formula $MO.Fe_2O_3$ or MFe_2O_4 (M is a bivalent metal ion such as Mn^{2+}, Fe^{2+}, Co^+, Ni^+, Cu^{2+}, Mg^{2+}, Cd^{2+}, or Zn^{2+}). Most of the ferrites are stoichiometrically balanced consisting of one mole of bivalent oxide and one mole of ferric oxide. However some ferrites deviate appreciably from 1:1 ratio. In a simple ferrite, only one type of metal ion exists as M, examples are nickel-ferrite, zinc-ferrite, copper-ferrite, cobalt-ferrite, etc. The mixed ferrites contain two or more kinds of metal ions, examples are copper-zinc ferrite, manganese-zinc ferrite, nickel-zinc ferrite etc.

9.7.1. Manufacture of Ferrites

Fig. 9.4 given on p. 274 Shows a typical flowsheet for polycrystalline ferrite preparation. The technique is comprised of several steps, i.e., (i) preparation of oxides, (ii) mixing, (iii) presintering, (iv) grinding and mixing of presintered product, (v) shaping, (vi) sintering, and (vii) finishing.

(i) **Preparation of oxides**. The starting materials are usually high purity oxides, carbonates, nitrates or hydroxide of the concerned metal. Non-oxide materials are converted into oxides by low temperature calcination. Sometimes a small amount of a constituent such as calcium, carbon etc. is added to obtain the modified properties of the ferrites.

(ii) **Milling and mixing**. The oxides are milled dry or wet. In case of wet-milling slurry is drawn off and the water is removed by filter press and the formed cake is dried in ovens at 110°C, whereas in the dry method, the powder mix is lightly pressed into blocks which facilitate the subsequent firing in the kilns.

(iii) **Presintering**. Presintering is carried out in a furnace at temperatures 900-1060°C for a period of 3-15 hours in order to bring about the initial chemical reaction between the constituents and to achieve a homogeneous product. During this process the spinel crystal structure of ferrite is formed.

(iv) **Crushing and grinding of presintered product**. The presintered powder lumps are then crushed to form a granulated material and then ball milled to get the required particle size.

(v) **Shaping**. The binders and lubricants are added to the presintered product. Choice of binders and lubricants depends on many factors such as shaping method, required length of the ferrite, avoidance of unwanted residue etc. The most common binders are

ammonium alginate, acrylates and polyvinyl alcohal and the lubricants employed are zinc or ammonium-stearate, wax and wax-emul-

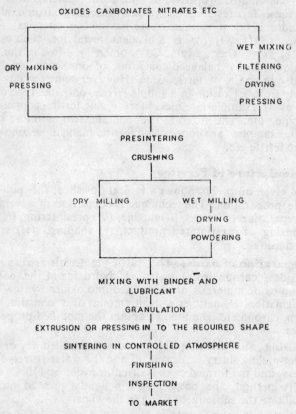

FIG. 9.4. Simplified flowsheet for preparation of polycrystalline
ferrite.

sions. A small amount of water is also added for obtaining a uniform
and consistent product.

After the addition of a suitable binder and lubricant, the powder
is compacted into desired shape by die pressing or extruded in the
form of rods or tubes. Sometimes slurry casting method is also
adopted especially for the production of oriented barium ferrite
components when the material is pumped in the slurry form into the
die and the particles are aligned by application of magnetic field
before and during the pressing operation.

(vi) **Sintering**. This is the most important step conducted in the
manufacture of ferrites to achieve the required magnetic and dielectric properties in a ferrite. The pressed or extruded products are

fired in a furnace at about 1200-1450°C in a gas atmosphere containing oxygen, nitrogen or air. The temperature employed depends upon various factors such as chemical composition of material, binder used, properties of ferrite desired, grain size and shape of starting materials, etc. After firing, the ferrites are cooled in a controlled atmosphere.

The sintered polycrystalline ferrite is not fully dense material but contains sufficient pores. The amount, size, shape and distribution of the pores depend on the several factors such as forming techniuue, firing temperature, sintering atmosphere, time of sintering, etc. which affect the physical properties of the ferrites. The size, shape and orientation of the grains of sintered ferrites greatly influence its magnetic properties. For example, high permeability ferrites are produced if the grains are uniform in size and nearly spherical in shape.

(*vii*) **Finishing**. Surface grinding is invariably essential in order to achieve the dimensional accuracy for having a controlled air gap between the mating surfaces required for a specific magnetic permeability.

9.7.2. Application of Ferrites

(*a*) Single crystals of ferrites are used in research for studying the fundamental properties.

(*b*) Manganese-zinc ferrite, nickel-zinc ferrite, magnesium-manganese ferrite and copper-zinc ferrite known as soft magnetic materials, are employed as transformer and conductor core, and magnetic antenna in radio broadcast receivers.

(*c*) Cobalt, barium and strontium ferrites known as hard or permanent magnetic materials are used in loudspeaker magnets, lifting magnets and magnetic chucks, motor and generators, pole pieces of motor car alternator generators, dynamic reproducers, magnetic lenses for focussing electron beams, etc.

(*d*) Magnesium-manganese, copper-manganese and lithium-nickel ferrites are employed in magnetic amplifiers, variable inductors, computer storage element, memory and switching applications in digital computers and data processing circuit, and many other such applications.

(*e*) Manganese ferrites showing low dielectric loss at microwave frequencies are widely used in microwave devices.

(*f*) Ferrites are also used at radio-wave frequency.

(*g*) Ferrites also find an extensive use in various other fields such as ferrite filters, ferrite radiaters, travelling wave tube alternator, ferrite dielectrical coupler, etc.

QUESTIONS

1. What are semiconductors and what is the basis of their classification?

2. What is an intrinsic semiconductor? Give its properties and function.

3. What is an extrinsic semiconductor? Describe in brief its working and application.

4. What are the factors influencing the resistivity of semiconductors? What is photoconductivity?

5. What are ferrites? Give their applications.

6. Give a flowsheet showing the various steps involved in the manufacture of ferrites.

7. Write short notes on the following:

    (a) Semiconductor.

    (b) Ferrite.

    (c) Intrinsic semiconductor.

    (d) Extrinsic semiconductor.

10

COMPOSITE MATERIALS

A combination of two or more materials which are used in combination to rectify a weakness in one material by a strength in another can be called a composite. According to this, structural stuff and the paint, as well as pearlite (alternate platelets of ferrite and cementite) can also be regarded as composites. However according to a recently developed concept composite is not only a combination of two materials but the combination has its own distinctive properties.

In terms of properties such as strength, heat resistance and other desired characteristics, the composite is superior than either component alone and the properties obtained of composite are unattainable in the composite constituents.

Wood and bone are well known composites found in nature. Wood is composite of strong cellulose fibers and cementing material known as lignin, whereas bone is composite of strong but soft callogen (a protein) and a hard but brittle apatite (a mineral).

Man made composites not only imitate but also seek to improve nature. For example, fiber glass having a wide variety of applications, consists of glass fibers in polymers. The bimetallic strip used in devices such as thermostat is another example of the modern composites. This can be made from a thin strip of brass and a similar piece of iron. If the two pieces are separate and heated simultaneously, the brass would expand more than iron. If the two are welded together and the composite heated, the brass with its greater expansion forces the iron to bend. At the same time the iron forces the brass to bend with it. The resulting deflection can be used to indicate temperature or to operate an on-off switch.

Other examples are tungsten carbide tools is which tungsten carbide particles are cemented together with a small amount of cobalt and reinforced concrete beam (steel for tension resistance and concrete for compression resistance). From these examples two points can be concluded for composites:

(*i*) Either material alone would not be useful in a specific use and the combination has a new different property, and

(*ii*) The behaviour of the composite (the combined action) is of great importance in the utilization of the composites.

10.1. GENERAL CLASSIFICATION OF COMPOSITES

Composites can be classified in three groups:
- (*i*) Particle composites,
- (*ii*) Layered composites, and
- (*iii*) Fiber-reinforced composites.

10.1.1. Particle Composites

In this, particles of varying shape and size of one material are dispersed in matrix of a second material. The particles may be added to liquid matrix material which later solidifies; they may be grown in place by a reaction such as age-hardening, or they may be pressed together and then interdiffused via the powder process. The most important engineering aspect is to extend the range of strength and other properties of inexpensive materials by suitable additions of other materials. In such composites, both rhe matrix and the particles share the load-bearing function.

The effective strengthening of such composites depends very much on the interparticle spacings. The interfacial bonding between the particles and the matrix may be important but certainly not as critical to composite strength as in fibrous composites. Tungsten carbide and tungsten-thoria have long been used as cutting tools and lamp filaments, respectively.

10.1.2. Layered Composites

In many familiar applications, layered composites are used extensively. Plywood, a very commonly used composite is a laminated composite of thin layers of wood in which successive layers have different orientations of the grain or fibre. The stainless steel cooling vessel with a copper clad bottom is another example, where stainless steel provides corrosion resistance while the copper provides better heat distribution over the base of the vessel. In a small heat exchanger, where weight, corrosion resistance, and thermal conductivity are critical considerations, permanent bonding of stainless steel to both sides of a copper-case (a three layered composite) and forming it into a helical coil geometry will provide a satisfactory answer.

10.1.3. Fibre-Reinforced Materials

Fibre-reinforced materials are those in which three components are involved. Filament (providing mechanical strength); a polymer matrix (en-capsulating the filaments); and a bonding agent (tying fibre filaments to polymer).

The most commonly used fibres are glass fibres but it need not be limited to glass, and the fibres of metal, ceramic and other materials are used to provide much wider ranges of properties than glass can. The fibres can be used in the form of continuous lengths, staple fiibres or whiskers.

Though a wide variety of cross-section of fibre is possible, circular cross-section is most common because of the ease of production. For large vessels to contain gas or liquid at high pressure, continuous glass filaments are wound in a mandrel after passing through a liquid polymer bath. The winding pattern can be chosen to place more fibres along the directions of greatest stress with or without stretching. This technique is altogether different from normal metallurgical techniques used for melting strong alloys and thus has the great advantage of not needing high temperature or high pressures for working.

Fibre-reinforced materials can be made quite anisotropic through directional control of the strong fibres in the relatively weak matrix. This makes it possible to make components where strength control is required in different directions. This implies tehniques for producing the most efficient structural sections.

Fibre glass reinforced plastics are extensively used in ships and ground installation as well as air-craft. Use of fibre glass reinforced plastics resulted savings in both weight as well as cost. For example in Boeing 727 jet, air-liner, the substitution of metals by composites resulted in a 33 pct. reduction in weight.

The application of composite materials to the automobiles industry started about 2 decades ago to make the car body from fibre glass reinforced polyester. Nearly at the same time reinforced plastics were applied in hydrospace vehicles on a large scale. Due to their good insulation characteristics, many composites find their applications in electrical industries, for example fibre glass laminates are used for printed circuit boards.

The development of advanced composite materials began only in the past decade with the successful production of a number of high strength fibres. The success in producing continuous graphite filaments on commercial scale was also achieved. The success achieved in the developments of boron composites, metal matrix composites, and in carbon-carbon composites has recognised the great potential of composite materials.

The applications of fibre-reinforced composites covers an extremely broad area ranging from the small household materials to aeroplane. The impact of fibre-reinforced composite materials is of great importance to all industries, particularly in view of the limited possible improvements in metallic materials. The fibrous composites will be competitive with most other structural materials.

10.2. THE MAJOR FUNCTIONS OF THE INDIVIDUAL PHASES IN FIBROUS COMPOSITES

There are three phases in each composite material i.e. fibres, matrix and the fibre-matrix interface, each has its own function which is discussed as follows:

10.2.1. Fibres

The fibres in a composite materials are often purposely aligned with the direction of loadings. Externally-applied forces are transferred to and distributed among the fibres. The transferring and distribution of loading are achieved through the matrix material and take place at the fibre-matrix interface. The fibres are responsible for the stiffness of the composite and they also lower the density of the composite where metal matrix is used. Although fibres are generally more brittle than the matrix, the breaking of fibres at localized regions does not trigger catastrophic failure of the composites because the cracks originating in the fibres are arrested by ductile matrix. Likewise cracks extending in the matrix cannot find a continuous path when they encounter the harder fibre material.

10.2.2. Matrix

It provides the toughness to the composite. It also binds the fibres together and protects them from hostile environment.

10.2.3. The Fibre-Matrix Interface

This plays a very important role in the behaviour of composite materials. The nature of the interface determines the wetting and bonding between the constituent phases. This, in turn, controls the effectiveness of load-transference and the strength of the composites. The mechanical coupling of a fibre and a matrix at an interface may result in additional stress fields locally, and may further complicate the mechanical behaviour of the components. The imperfect bonding between the fibre and matrix can also enhance the ductility of the composite, because cracks cariginally propagating normal to the fibres may split a weakly bonded interface. Consequently, the crack front is blunted and cracks extending in the direction of loading eventually become inactive.

10.3. MATRIX MATERIALS

Plastics are widely used as matrix material in composites. Plastic resins used as matrix materials for fibre-reinforced products are thermosetting and thermoplastic (discussed in Chapter 7). For example, polyster resin, epoxy resin, high temperature resistant polymer (phenolics, silicone etc.) are common as matrix materials. Other matrix materials such as metal and ceramics are also used for specific purposes.

10.4. REINFORCEMENT MATERIALS

The basic function of fibres in composite materials is to carry the load along the direction of reinforcement. In addition to strength, fibres also enhance the stiffness of a composites According to American Society for Testing of Materials (ASTM), the term 'fibre' can be used for any material in an elongated form such that it has a minimum length to a maximum average transverse dimension 10:1, a maximum cross-sectional area of 5.1×10^{-4} cm^2, and a maximum transverse dimension of 0.0254 cm. Continuous fibres in composites are usually called filaments. The term 'wire' is usually for metallic filaments. When a fibre has a rectangular shape with the ratio of width-to-thickness at least 4:1, it is called a ribbon.

Fibrous reinforcement materials can be catagorised according to their structure as following:

10.4.1. Amorphous Materials

Amorphous materials are generally characterized by the lack of a long-range order. Glass and fused silica fibres are typical of this class. Glass fibres used in composite materials are generally manufactured as continuous filaments. In this process first the raw glass is melted in a furnace and then fibres are drawn from the molten glass at high speed. Commercially produced filaments have diameters ranging from 2.4×10^{-4} to 1.9×10^{-3} cm.

These fibres, after receiving a protective coating are collected in the form of bundles, known as strands. The treatment of the glass fibres is given to have their good adhesion with matrix. When a group of parallel strands are gathered in the form of a ribbon, and wound onto a cylindrical tube, it is called a continuous roving. Sometimes strands are assembled by twisting them together known as yarns. Both glass fibre strands and yarns can be used to form woven rovings and fabrics, respectively.

The major advantages of using glass fibres as reinforcement materials is their lower cost compared to any other kind of fibres currently available. They can be easily fabricated in the form of continuous filaments. However, the low softing point of glass fibres restricts their uses, to resins and low melting point matrices. Since the strength of glass fibres is affected by the existence of any flaws on their surfaces, great care has to be taken in handling them.

High silica content fibres can be made by treating common glass fibres with a hot aci l which dissolves the impurities and fibres with a high silica content will be obtained. High silica content fibres used in composite materials have purities ranging from 99 to 99.4 pct. SiO$_2$. They are available in the form in which common glass fibres are available. Quartz fibres are produced from high purity natural quartz crystals and their typical SiO$_2$, content is 99.95 pct. Filaments drawn from quartz crystals are extremely thin which are usually combined into strands and other textile forms.

High silica and quartz content fibres show excellent thermal stability and thus can be used at temperatures upto 1650°C. These fibres are used in heat shields for re-entry vehicles, as well as other thermal blast shields. The price of quartz fibres is appreciably higher than that of high silica content fibres, due to the great difference in the cost of the raw materials.

10.4.2. Whiskers

Whiskers are characterised by their fibrous structures which have almost no crystalline defects. They possess high strength and high elastic modulus and are available in a size range of several mm in length and several microns in thickness or diameter. Is is known from dislocation theory that near ideal strength is the result of perfect distribution of interatomic forces which are achievable by perfection in crystal as the small crystals can be made more perfect, whiskers (small crystals) are grown under completely controlled conditions. In ordinary cases due to the uncontrollable growth of crystals during solidification irregularities are introduced in the form of vacant atom sites as well as irregularities in atomic distances. The irregularities reduce their strengths. Table 10.1 represents the comparative strengths of some materials in the form of small whiskers and bulk material.

TABLE 10.1. *Strength of Whiskers in Fibre Form and Strength in Bulk*

Name of the Material	Strength of Whisker in fibre form kg/cm²	Strength in bulk form kgs/cm²
Graphite	2,50,000	150
Iron	1,50,000	2,000
Tungsten Wire	42,000	17,000
Piano Wire	27,000	3,200
Fibre Glass	15,000	500
Nylon	6,000	1,000
Aluminium	5,000	3,000

Numerous materials including, metals, oxides, carbides halides, and organic compounds have been prepared in the form of whiskers.

Whiskers of Fe, Cu, Ag, Pd, Mn, Hg, Zn, Cd, Sn and Cr are in use.

Factors affecting the strength of whiskers. The size and temperature are the two main factors which affect the strength of whiskers. T.S. of alumina increases from 7,700 kgs/cm² at 400 microns diameter to more than 2,30,000 kgs/cm² at 10 microns diameter but however, the relation is not linear whereas increase in temperature tends to produce significant reduction in whisker strength.

Special characteristics of whiskers. Whiskers are hair-like single crystals in appearance normally having single dislocation running along the central axis. If tensile stress is applied along this axis, the dislocation is unable to slip. As no other dislocations are available. the crystal cannot yield until the dislocation starts at the point K (Fig. 10.1). The stress than falls to that necessary to move the dislocations and again reproduce rapidly so that plastic flow starts. Fig. 10.1 shows the comparison between tensile properties of a copper whisker and as ordinary polycrystalline copper. From the figure it is clear that whiskers have several fold strength. However, the production cost of whiskers is many-many times more than the production cost of metal in bulk.

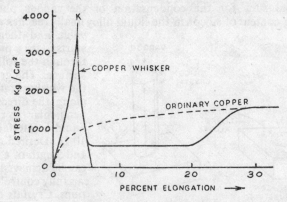

FIG. 10.1. Tensile properties of copper whisker and ordinary copper.

Production of whiskers. Whiskers in general can be grown by three main techniques i.e.,

(*i*) an evaporation-condensation process,
(*ii*) vapour-liquid-solid mechanism, and
(*iii*) chemical reduction.

Evaporation-condensation process. In this process metals are heated to a temperature higher than their melting points. A temperature gradient is maintained between the source of evaporation and condensation in the growth chamber. The temperature at the substrate for vapour condensation is kept below the m.p. of the metal. The supersaturation and consequently the condensation of vapours at low temperature enable whiskers to grow. Metallic whiskers such as Ni, Cu, Fe, Al, Ag, Ge, etc. have been grown by this method in various sizes. The evaporation condensation process is not suitable for the growth of oxide whiskers in view of their high m.p. and low vapour pressures.

Vapour-liquid-solid-mechanism. An addition of small amount of impurity promotes the growth of filamentary crystals. Impurities such as Au, Ni, Cu and Mg all have this effect and the growth rate is much faster in length than in thickness. There are other impurities which do not promote filamentary growth and, hence films or nodular deposits are obtained. This process is of particular importance for growing silicon crystals.

For the controlled growth of silicon whiskers by this mechanism, single crystal silicon wafers are used as substrates. An impurity such as gold is added to the substrate. The temperature of substrate is then raised to the range of 600-800°C which is below the m.p. of both gold and silicon. In this temperature range a liquid alloy of gold and silicon is formed. A mixture of H_2 and $SiCl_4$ gases is introduced into the deposition chamber. Silicon vapour is generated upon the reduction of $SiCl_4$. The surface of the liquid alloy layer provides preferential sites for the condensation of the vapour phase. The increasing content of silicon in the liquid alloy finally reaches a critical value and then silicon starts to precipitate through the solid liquid surface. The growth of the whiskers takes place along the direction perpendicular to the solid-liquid interface (Fig. 10.2). Desired diameter and length of a whisker can be achieved through carefully controlled conditions. Crystals of aluminium, boron, germanium, MgO, NiO, selenium and silicon could be grown by this mechanism. Whiskers grown by the vapour-liquid-solid mechanism can be produced in large quantity.

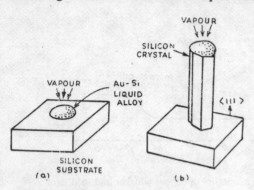

FIG. 10.2. Vapour liquid-solid mechanism for the growth of the silicon crystal.

Chemical reduction. Whiskers have also been produced by chemical reduction. H_2 reduction of halides of Cu, Fe, Ni and Co is widely used. The process of vapour-phase reaction has been used to produce aluminium oxide and silicon nitride whiskers.

10.4.3. Polycrystalline Materials

The fibrous structures in polycrystalline form consist of randomly oriented grains. The common ceramic fibres in this category include alumina, mullite, lithia-alumina spinel etc. Important polycrystalline metallic ones include W, Be and stainless steel. Carbon filaments are also polycrystalline in structure and usually have a certain degree of crystallinity in the form of graphite.

Among these fibres, the metallic filaments are widely used in composite materials due to the possibility of (*i*) their easy production on large scale, and (*ii*) capability of bonding with plastics as well as metals. Metal filaments can be produced by convertional wire drawing, electrochemical plating or melt drawing. The melt drawing process is suitable for making micron and sub-micron diameter wires. In this process glass filled with molten metal is drawn to fine diameter. Since the surfaces of the filaments are well protected, wires prepared by the melt process have strengths which are much greater than those produced by conventional wire drawing. The method of vapour-deposition, widely used in whisker preparation, can also be used to produce metal filaments.

Metallic wires are characterised by their high elastic modulii and ductility. Among them Mg and W are most outstanding metallic wires which have been used to reinforce ceramics, resins, and metal matrix materials. The strength of polycrystalline materials in general is greatly affected by their grain sizes. The effects of recrystallization and grain growth tend to reduce their strengths at high temperatures.

Carbon filaments have gained increasing importance in the composite technology. This is due to their unique properties such as low density, chemical inertness, and great strength at elevated temperatures. The graphite whiskers have extremely high T.S. and modulus of elasticity. The fabrication of the graphite filaments involves a precursor conversion process in which textile fibres usually rayon and polyacrylonitrile (PAN)-based fibres are used as precursor materials. polyvinyl alcohol, phenolics and pitches also have been used as precursors.

The organic fibres are first pyrolysed by heating at low temperature. Carbonization of the fibres is then followed at temps. above 1000°C. In the case of PAN based fibres, the tension is applied on the precursor, when it undergoes hydrolysis in a protective atmosphere. In rayon based fiberes, the stretching is applied during graphitization. The carbon formed at low temperature exhibits a random amorphous structure in which the basal planes are not stacked in the regular sequence of a HCP crystal and the interlayer spacing is larger than 3.354Å. This type of carbon structure, also known as turbostratic, can be transformed into the regular graphitic structure by heat treatment of the carbon graphitization at elevated temperatures in the range of 2000-3000°C. Carbon fibres produced after graphitization contain graphite crystallites. PAN-based fibres are round and are available in untwisted strands. Rayon based fibres are crenelated and are furnished in yarns. Carbon fibres produced by precursor conversion have achieved a tensile strength (TS) of 7×10^6 kg/cm^2.

10.4.4. Multiphase Materials

Fibres in this category consists of two or more phases having one or more phases in crystalline form. Fibres made of materials such as boron, boron carbide, silicon carbide, and borides can take the form of multiphase materials. Boron fibres are of particular interest in the modern composite technology due to their superior specific strength. In other properties the boron fibres can be compared to glass fibres. It is not feasible to produce boron fibres by conventional fabrication means because (i) it is hard and brittle and (ii) its m.p. is high (2050°C). Boron fibres are produced by chemical vapour plating in which boron vapour can be obtained by either hydrogen reduction of halide systems or thermal decomposition of boron hydrides. Boron vapours generated in both the cases are deposited on a substrate of materials such as tungsten possessing high m.p. and thermal stability at high temperatures.

In addition to boron, filaments including silicon carbide, boron carbide, titanium carbide, titanium diboride, carbon etc. can be produced by the vapour-plating method. These filaments also show better stability at high temperature than boron filaments.

Various considerations in selecting the reinforcing materials, are specific strength, specific modulii, density, performance at elevated temperature, and finally their cost.

10.5. CLASSIFICATION OF COMPOSITE MATERIALS DEPENDING UPON THE MATRIX USED

10.5.1. Resin Matrix Composite Materials

Glass fibres are the most widely used reinforcing materials in resin based composites. The highest glass content (upon 90 pct.) in resin-matrix composites is achieved by filament winding. The composite materials with filament winding are superior in strength compared to others. Fibre glass reinforced plastics, although superior in specific strength and dielectric properties, are poor in specific stiffness. However, the development of boron filaments and their incorporation into epoxy resin bring about a bright future for their application in primary aircraft structure. The strength of boron-epoxy composites is comparable to that of glass fibre composites, while their specific stiffness is far better than glass fibre composites. Resin matrices also have been reinforced with strong whiskers. When the resin matrix is reinforced with silicon-nitride whiskers in random orientation, significant improvements in both tensile modulus and strength were observed.

Resin matrix composites can be fabricated by the methods such as "hand-lay-up," spray up, bag moulding, filament winding, continuous production technique and closed moulding methods.

Hand-lay-up. This is the simplest method of making fibre reinforced plastics, in which a layer of random fibre mat or woven fabric is first laid on the reinforcing materials. This process is repeated until the desired thickness of composite is obtained. Air trapped in the resin is squeezed out by a roller. The resin which is catalyzed, is then allowed to cure at room temperature. Polyester and epoxy are the two most common resins used in hand-lay-up fabrications. Sometimes for specific purposes such as reducing inflamability, decoration, providing extra weight etc, organic or inorganic fillers such as wood flour, clay, saw dust, sand stones, etc. are added to the resin. The moulds in hand-lay-up are generally made of wax, clay, wood, metal, paper or plastic sheets. Some releasing agents such as polyvinyl alcohol, silicons, or mineral oils are often used for facilitating the easy removal of the final product from the mould. This method is very suitable for making a limited production of models and prototypes. It also has been used to fabricate complex products which are not practical to make with matched dies, as well as extremely large parts such as boat hulls.

COMPOSITE MATERIALS   287

Spray-up. In this method, fibres are first cut into desired length by a copper. A mixture of fibre, resin and catalyst is sprayed onto a mould. A roller is then used to smooth the surface and remove entrapped air.

Bag-molding. Bag-molding is used to improve quality of hand-lay-up products by further removing the entrapped air. The three basic bag-molding methods are vacuum bag, autoclave and pressure bag.

Vacuum bag method. The lay-up of resin and reinforcing materials is first covered with a perforated parting film and a layer of jute bleeder material. The combination allows the bleeding of air and excess resin. Then the lay-up is covered with a flexible film diaphragm, such as cellophane or nylon, which is sealed to the mold. The vacuum is then drawn upon the whole system. The bagging process should immediately follow the lay-up in order to avoid the hardening of resins. The entire bagged system can be cured in an oven or an autoclave system.

Autoclave curing. In this large metal pressure vessel is used and is pressurized with a gas (N_2) in the range of 4 to 8 kg/cm . The autoclave system is heated and the hot gas is circulated to provide a uniform temperature within the vessel. The vacuum system continues to function during the cure cycle in order to remove additional air and volatiles emitted during polymerization of the matrix system. Finally the laminate (component) is removed from the autoclave for debagging.

Pressure-bag-system. This provides an economical alternative to the autoclave system when a heated platen press or comparable equipment is available. The pressure bag may be pressurized with air and is confined by the platens of the press. The pressure bag system does not, however, possess the general flexibility of the autoclave system.

Filament winding. This employs continuous filaments which are wound onto a mandrel in predetermined orientations. Since it is possible to align the reinforcements along the direction of high stress, the strength of filaments can be utilized in an efficient manner. Filaments winding is commonly used in aerospace industry to fabricate rocket motor cases and radars as well as in commercial applications such as storage tanks, pipes, and pressure vessels. The fibre glass is the most important one used in filament winding. Various plastic resins such as polyesters, epoxies, and phenolics can be used in filament winding depending upon temperature range of working.

For fabrication either wet winding or dry winding can be employed. In wet winding, the fibres are impregnated with resin just before winding, whereas in dry winding the filaments are preimpregnated for winding. There are two different patterns of winding, i.e., planer and helical. In planer winding, the mandrel is stationary and the fibre feed arm rotates about a longitudinal axis for one complete revolution. The fibres in each layer lie adjacent to but not crossing our one another. In helical winding, unlike planer winding, the mandrel rotates while the feed carriage shuttles back and forth. As a result, the filaments are wound in a helical form which is characterized by the filament cross over on the mandrel. The product of winding is then allowed to cure with or without the application of heat and pressure. For objects with open ended shapes (cylindrical pipes) the mandrel can be forced out easily. For closed pressure vessels, the mandrel cannot be removed infact. In these cases the mandrels are usually made of water-soluble hard salt or low m.p. metals, they are removed by solution or melting.

Continuous production techniques. These are truely automated methods used in the fibre composite industry. In one method glass fibres impregnated with the thermoset resin are drawn continuously through a die to obtain the desired shape of the end product. The curing is achieved by using an oven, or through external heating of the die. Glass content as high as 60-80 per cent by weight can be achieved in this process.

Another typical continuous production method is for making laminated sheets where chopped glass fibres, impregnated with polyester resin, are sand-witched between two cellophane webs. The resulting products are corrugated and flat sheets which are used as translucent building panels. Other products made by continuous processes are filament-wound pipes, rigid laminated strips for sporting goods, and other similar products.

Closed moulding methods. Matched die moulding, pre-mix-moulding, and injection moulding all fall under this category. They are employed when detail is important and when a two-sided finish is desired. Two piece male and female moulds are used in these methods.

Matched die moulding is usually employed in the production of structural parts of complex contours with close tolerance. Reinforcing materials in the form of glass mats, chopped glass, preforms, or fabrics are used. Plastic resins are than applied onto the reinforcements, and curing is achieved through heating and pressing the moulds.

Premix moulding differs from matched die moulding in that it employs a ready-for-use moulding compound which is a mixture of chopped glass fibres, resin, catalyst and filler. The main attraction of this method is the comparatively low cost and the ease with which it can be moulded. It is particularly suitable for moulding objects with variable wall thickness and sharp contour changes. Because of the good electrical properties as will as resistance to corrosion, heat and flame, reinforced moulding material are used in a variety of applications to replace wood, metal and ceramics. Common applications are in circuit panels for telephones, air conditioning partitions, shower floors etc.

The injection moulding process also utilizes a moulding compound which is injected into the moulding cavity of the mould. But unlike premix-moulding, the compound used in injection moulding consists of thermoplastics. Typical resins used include nylon, polyethylene, polypropylene, polycarbonates, polystyrene and polyvinyl chloride. Thermoplastics reinforced with glass have shown marked increase in strength and rigidity as well as decrease in thermal expansion. The reinforced thermoplastics are finding their extensive use in appliances, electronics and household goods.

10.5.2. Matrix Composite Materials

The technology of metal-matrix composite materials has emerged very fast in recent years. Compared to glass-fibre-reinforced plastics, metal-matrix composites are superior for their performance at elevated temperatures. The strength and elastic modulii of metal matrices are higher than those of resin matrices over a wide range of temperature. Metal-matrix composites show much higher ductility and thus stress concentrations induced by cracked fibres can be relaxed through the plastic deformation of the matrix. As a result, there is less chance of a brittle failure of the composite. The majority of the load applied to a metal matrix composite is carried by the reinforcing fibres. Since the metal matrices are strong in shear strength, and in general, well bonded to the fibres, short fibres can be used effectively for the purpose of strengthing. An obvious disadvantage of this type of composites is their relatively high density. There are several methods for fabricating metal-matrix composites used for specific requirements. Important processes are powder metallurgy techniques, liquid-metal infiltration, diffusion bonding, electroforming, vapour deposition, rolling, and extrusion.

Powder metallurgy techniques. The technique of powder metallurgy has been discussed in Chapter 11. The product, resulting from this process is uniform in composition In this process, powders of ceramics or metals are first prepared and then fed into a mould of desired shape. Pressure is then applied to further compact the powder. In order to facilitated the bonding among powder particles the compacted product is often heated to a temperature which is below its melting point but high enough to develop significant solid state diffusion. The use of heat to bond solid particles is known as sintering or firing.

Metallic materials such as Cu, Ni, Al, Co, and steel are often used in the powder process as matrix materials. The metal matrices in the form of powders are first mixed with whiskers or chopped fibres. The combination is then consolidated by pressing, sintering, hot extrusion, or rolling in order to enhance the density and strength of composites.

Liquid metal infilation. Metals having low m.p. such as Al, Mg, Ag, and Cu can be used as matrix materials in this process. Fibres collimated in a mould are infiltrated with liquid metal. By this process it is possible to cast composite structures such as rods and beams by passing a bundle of filaments through a liquid-metal bath in a continuous manner. Structures solidified in this manner have uniform corss-sections with uniaxial reinforcement and need little additional work. However, the application of the liquid-metal infiltration is limited by the available choice of matrix and reinforcing materials. Further the degradation of many fibres at high temperatures rule out their use.

Diffusion bonding. In this process the matrix metals are used in the form of foils or tape. In order to fully develop the bonding strength, foils as well as fibres are first thoroughly cleaned and then laid on the metal sheets in predetermined spacing and orientation. Alternate layers of metal foils and reinforcing fibres can be arranged for the desired contents of reinforcements. The lay-up is encased in a metal can which is sealed and evacuated. The whole assembly is subsequently heated and pressed to facilitate the development of diffusion bonding. Filament of stainless steel, boron, and silicon carbide have been used with matrices such as Al and Ti alloys.

Electroforming. Electroforming has the advantage of combining the fibre and matrix materials at low temperatures and thus degradation of reinforcing materials can be avoided. The major apparatuses for electro-forming consist of plating bath and a mandrel which serves as the cathode in the deposition process. A continuous filament is wound on to the mandrel while the metal matrix material is being deposites. Monolayer tapes formed by this process can be further consolidated into composite structure members by diffusion bonding. Filaments of boron, silicon carbide and tungsten have been successively incorporated into a nickel matrix by electroforming. Other matrix metals as well as alumina whiskers, have also been employed in thin method of fabrication.

Vapour deposition. The process of vapour deposition is carried out by decomposing a compound of the metal matrix material and its subsequent deposition on the reinforcing materials. A main advantage of this technique is that the chemical decomposition process can be accomplished at the relatively low temperature and the degradation of fibres can be minimized. However, the slow and costly process of vapour deposition is its major disadvantage. Metals such as Al and Ni have been used for deposition.

Rolling. Both hot and cold rolling can be employed to incorporate filaments and metal strips into continuous tapes The fibres and metal strips are fed through roller under applied pressure. The rollers are heated to a high temperature in the case of hot-rolling. Both pressure and temperature serve to accelerate diffusion bonding. The sand-witched construction of continuous tapes by the rolling process is restricted to a few layers in thickness However, tapes fabricated in this manner can be further consolidated by diffusion bonding.

Extrusion. It is similar to extrusion of metal powders. The wire consisting of steel core surrounded by an aluminium alloy sheath is produced by simultaneous feeding of the reinforcing filaments and extruding of the matrix metal. Composite wires formed in this manner can be further rolled into tapes and plates through diffusion bonding. There are other methods of extrusion in which fibres are first aligned in matrix powders, and this assembly is pressed into the form of bars. A single preform, or several of them sealed in a cane, are extruded to the desired dimension.

Other methods. Methods such as plasma spray, pneumatic impaction and the simultaneous growth of the reinforcing and matrix materials from a melt also have been used for producing metal-matrix composites. The method of plasma srpay is suitable for low m.p. metals. It employs a plasma torch which sprays matrix materials in the form of liquid droplets onto a rotating mandrel covered with aligned fibres. The composite formed is then removed from the mandrel and hot pressed to eliminate voids. As an example, aluminium has been successfully sprayed on silicon-carbide-coated boron fibre. Composite tapes formed in this manner can be further consolidated into structural parts by diffusion bonding. Pneumatic impaction has been used to consolidate the mixture of metal powders and reinforcing materials by applying high pressure impact.

10.5.3. Carbon-fibre Reinforced Composites

The major attractions of the composites are high degree of stiffness and strength, low density, and good fatigue strength and damping capacity. Two types i.e. carbon-epoxy composites and carbon matrics are important:

Carbon-epoxy composites. The composites can be fabricated in an aluminium vacuum-injection type matched die. The carbon composites usually suffer from low compressive and inter-laminar shear strengths. Generally graphite fibre-reinforced epoxy is available in the form of prepared tapes which can be cured and consolidated into laminates by using autoclave or press moulding.

Carbon-carbon composites. Composite materials with carbon fibres and reinforcing carbon matrices are being developed very rapidly. The application of carbon-carbon composites have been made in air-craft structures, re-entry vehicle heat shields, rocket engine nozzles and turbine blades. Other applications such as disc-brakes, hot pressing dies, hot seales, and bearing materials are important. The excellent high temperature performance of the composites for their applications is due to their low density, improved strength at elevated temperature, thermal shock-resistance, and chemical inertness. Two basic methods have been used to incorporate carbon matrices with carbon fibres, the chemical vapour deposition (CVD) process and the carbonized organic technique.

Chemical vapour deposition process. In this, the carbon matrix is formed by decomposing a hydro-carbon gas and the subsequent deposition of carbon on a fibrous substrate. Hydro-carbon gas mixed with an inert gas is introduced into the deposition chamber. An induction coil is used to heat the gas and fibrous substrate to a uniform temperature. Infiltration of the carbon into the fibres is achieved at 100°C and at pressure less than 50 torr. The properties of the pyrolytic carbon matrix formed in this manner are affected by the deposition temperature, pressure, gas composition, and flow rate. A relatively uniform deposition with high density can be achieved by this method.

Carbonized organic technique. In this the fibres are impregnated with an organic material and subsequently are converted to carbon in an inert atmosphere by carbonization at about 1200°C. Phenolics, epoxy resins and coaltar pitches, having carbon yields 40-70 weight per cent have been used as organic precursors. The combined matrix material such as coaltar pitch can be further graphitized upon heat treatment because of its platelet-like structures. On the other hand, the cross linked structures of phenolic and epoxy prevented them from being graphitized. The glass-like carbon so formed has lower tensile strength and Young's modulus than that formed by the chemical vapour deposition method.

QUESTIONS

1. What are composite materials and how are they classified?

2. What are fibre-reinforced materials? Why are they preferred for many specific applications? Give their limitations.

3. What are the various phases in fibrous composites? Give a brief account of their functions.

4. What are whiskers and filaments? What are their special characteristics?

5. Describe briefly the different methods for the production of whiskers.

6. Classify the composite materials based on matrix.

7. Describe the different methods used for fabricating the resin-matrix composite materials.

8. Give the advantages and limitations of metal-matrix composite materials. Mention in brief the various techniques employed for their production.

9. What are the various techniques employed for making carbon-fibre reinforced composites? Give their applications and limitations.

11

POWDER METALLURGY

Powder metallurgy may be defined as the art and science of manufacturing fine metal powders and their processing to obtain finished or semi-finished objects with or without the inclusion of non-metallic constituents. Thus the branch of powder metallurgy essentially includes the following operations:

(*i*) Preparation and mixing of required metal powders.

(*ii*) Compacting the powders to the desired shape, causing the particles to form a compacted mass strong enough to withstand ordinary handling.

(*iii*) Subsequent heating or sintering of compacted objects at elevated temperature in a furnace under non-oxidising atmosphere or vacuum with or without fusion of low-melting constituent (used for eliminating voids) in order to develop the metallic objects of satisfactory shape, strength and density.

11.1. ADVANTAGES AND LIMITATIONS OF POWDER METALLURGY

11.1.1. Advantages

Powder metallurgy technique is becoming increasingly popular due to its manifold advantages outlined below:

(*i*) Metal shapes can be produced to exact dimensions at high rates.

(*ii*) The process is economical compared to the other fabrication processes such as forging, casting (precision and die casting), machining etc.

(*iii*) The process provides an excellent quality control due to less number of rejects and less expenditure.

(*iv*) Numerous costly machining operations and scrap losses are eliminated in addition to the tooling costs and raw material inventory.

(*v*) High melting point metals and their carbides (Mo, W, Ta etc.) can be easily processed by powder metallurgy techniques.

(*vi*) Porous, objects such as filters, oil impregnated bearings can be made conveniently by this process due to the possibility of precise porosity control in the compacts.

(*vii*) Mixtures of metals and nonmetals or two immiscible metals can be easily fabricated. Examples are copper-graphite brushes for electric motors, and metal-ceramic combinations (cermets) for use in high temperature applications.

(*viii*) Common casting defects such as gas pockets, blow holes, inclusions etc. are completely absent.

(*ix*) Control of grain size and uniform structure can be obtained.

(*x*) The process possesses an excellent reproducibility and thus no further machining is required

(*xi*) Design aspects are comparatively simple.

(*xii*) Requirement of highly skilled and qualified personnel is not a restriction for the process.

11.1.2. Limitations

A large number of advantages of powder metallurgy technique makes its adoption versatile. However, some limitations as given below are also associated:

(*i*) Production of high purity powders of required specifications is comparatively difficult as well as expensive.

(*ii*) Production of small number of objects is not economical due to heavy expenses involved in suitable tooling and equipment and high cost of powders.

(*iii*) Production of various alloy powders such as stainless steel, bronze, brass etc. of required composition is difficult and expensive.

(*iv*) Porosity in the parts may result in oxidation at the surface as well as throughout the whole body.

(*v*) Heavy investment may be needed for manufacturing large parts by powder metallurgy technique.

(*vi*) Absence of plastic flow in powders under pressure limits the shape and size of the articles to be produced. Therefore, shapes with weak or thin sections, sharp angles and corners are avoided.

(*vii*) The strength, ductility and density of powder metallurgy objects are considerably lower than for corresponding wrought or cast parts. Density is usually less than 90 per cent compared to the density of cast metal, whereas ductility may be sometimes as low as only one-tenth of the conventional metal.

11.2. FACTORS AFFECTING THE QUALITY OF THE POWDER METALLURGY PARTS

The quality and properties of powder metallurgy products are dependent mainly on four factors, i.e., (1) percentage of voids or porosity, (2) distribution of voids, (3) strength of the bond between particles, and (4) temperature of sintering.

11.2.1 Percentage of Voids

For better strength percentage of voids should be less which can be controlled by having a range of particle sizes. Porosity is also influenced by the pressure used during compacting. Increase in pressure results in decrease of porosity.

11.2.2. Distribution of Voids

The distribution of voids is mainly dependent on various factors such as size and shape of the object, method of pressing and a type of lubricant used in mixture of powders. It is observed that the dry powders do not transmit pressure uniformly in all directions and therefore under-cut sections tend to have lower density. This problem can be overcome by use of multiple punches. Compressing from bath top and bottom ends of the compact also results in more uniform distribution of pressure and porosity. Further, lubricant may be used to improve uniformity of pressure and porosity throughout the object.

11.2 3. Strength of Bond between Particles

The strength of the bond between particles is dependent upon the area of contact, which in turn is affected by some of the variables affecting porosity. Bond strength is also influenced by cleaner surfaces of particles. Oxide layers are very common sources for difficult bonding and thus metal powders should be free from oxide layer and other dirt on the surfaces.

11.2.4. Sintering Temperature

The temperature used for sintering also affects the porosity of objects. Higher temperatures usually result in higher density. However, expansion of trapped gases causes a decrease in density of certain sintering temperatures. High porosity required in some parts can be obtained by mixing volatile solids with the powder particles before pressing, whereas very low porosities can be obtained by a second pressing after sintering or by impregnation with a molten alloy.

11.3. APPLICATIONS OF POWDER METALLURGY

Powder metallurgy technique is indispensable in a number of instances. For example, processing of refractory metals (W, To, Mo etc.) and cemented carbide is practicable only by powder metallurgy technique. These materials can not be processed by any other conventional method, since it is extremely difficult to have furnace refractories which can withstand their high melting temperatures as well as chemical attack at these temperatures. Further, manufacture of components of two or more insoluble metals or containing metallic as well as nonmetallic components is not possible by any other technique. For example the objects of W-Cu, graphite-bronze, W-Ag, Cu-Pb, Cu-Carbon, Fe-Pb etc. are produced by liquid-phase sintering i.e. sintering above the melting point of one metal but below the melting point of the other metal.

Powder metallurgy technique is unique for producing the parts possessing controlled porosity. Filters and self-lubricating bearings are common examples of this category.

At present use of powder metallurgy techniques is well established and perfected in various fields. The important applications of powder metallurgy in various fields are discussed below:

11.3.1. Refractory Metals

Powder metallurgy techniques are widely used in manufacturing the components of refractory metals such as tungsten, molybdenum and tantalum are used for electric light bulbs, flourscent lamps, radio valves, oscillator valves, mercury arc rectifiers and X-ray tubes in the form of filament, cathode, anode, screen and control grids.

11.3.2. Refractory Carbides

These are mainly used in the construction of various machines such as lathes, wire drawing mills, shearing machines, mining machines and other similar machines. The various parts of machines made of refractory carbides include dies, blocks, jaws, cutting-tools, stamping and blanking tools, squeezing razer blades, stone hammers, chisels etc.

11.3.3. Automatic Applications

In the developed countries, automobile industry utilizes powder metallurgy techniques extensively for various components. Various parts made by powder metallurgy include porous bearings, starters, screen wipers, vehicle dynamos, clutches, brakes etc. Self-lubricating bearings find their extensive use in motor cars, trucks, buses, tractors, gasolene and diesel engines, and in aircraft. Sintered oil-pump gear and shock absorber parts are widely used in passenger cars and trucks. Other automative applications include electrical contacts, crank shaft drive, piston rings, door mechanisms, connecting rods, and brake linings.

11.3.4. Aerospace Applications

Use of powder metallurgy has gained great importance in rocket, missile, satellites and space vehicles. Tungsten parts having uniform distribution of porosity are employed in plasma jet engines and ion engines operated at about 1850°C. Silver-infiltrated tungsten is used in nozzles for rockets and missiles. Sintered bronze bearings, prealloyed bushings, filters, ferrite cores etc., are used in various space satellites and vehicles. Beryllium is used in gyroscope and heat shields of propulsion unit of missiles. Metal powders such as beryllium, aluminium, magnesium, and zirconium are used as solid fuels in rockets and missiles.

11.3.5. Atomic Energy Applications

Composite materials made by powder metallurgy techniques are employed in various fuel elements and control rod systems. Dispersion strengthened materials are used in atomic reactors and rockets, magneto-hydro dynamo generators, high temperature gas turbines and computers. Uranium oxide distributed throughout the stainless steel matrix is used as fuel. Beryllium, zirconium and hafnium metal powders are used for making control rods and radiation reflectors. Other materials used for various purposes are uranium carbide, thorium, beryllium, zirconium and their alloys.

11.3.6. Applications in Defence

Powder metallurgy techniques employed in defence include the different parts of rockets and missiles, cartridge cases, frangible bullets in ammunition, rotating bands for high velocity projectiles, tracers, higher explosives etc.

11.3.7. Miscellaneous Applications

Metal filters find their wide application in chemical, pharmaceutical and automotive industries. Porous electrodes are used in various batteries to supply electricity. Electrical contacts are used in relays, timers, switch gears, arcing contacts, electrical brushes etc. Powdered metal cases are employed in radio and television because of increased circuit stability. Ferrites are used in the production of transformers and magnetic yoke for deflection system in television receiver and the magnetic antenna in radars or platform in radio receivers. Other fields of application include projectors and cameras (pinions and gears), clocks (pinion, wheel and roller), sheets, strips and tubular products for variety of applications, type writer (cams, gears and panels), ball point pens (sintered tungsten carbide as ball), sewing machine (bearings), etc.

An interesting application of powder metallurgy is in the production of surgical implants and prosthesis designed to replace or repair parts of the bony skeleton of the human body.

11.4. PRODUCTION OF METAL POWDERS

Different techniques can be adopted for producing metal powders depending upon the nature of metal and characteristics of the powders. The process used for production of powders can be broadly classified into two groups i.e. mechanical processes and physico-chemical processes. Though there is a large number of processes under each group, the important ones in the two groups are as follows:

(i) **Mechanical processes:**
(a) Milling or grinding.
(b) Atomization.

(*ii*) **Physico·chemical:**
  (*a*) Thermal decomposition.
  (*b*) Reduction of compounds.
  (*c*) Gaseous reduction of solutions.
  (*d*) Electrolysis.
  (*e*) Precipitation from aqueous solutions.

11.4.1. Milling or Grinding

It is the most versatile process used for producing powders of required sizes. It involves the application of impact forces on the material to be ground and the milling action is carried out by the use of different equipments such as ball mill, rod mill, disk mill, impact mill, eddy mill, vortex mill etc. However, the important ones are ball mill, eddy mill and vortex mill.

(*i*) **Ball mill.** The material to be ground is filled in the ball mill along with a large number of hard wear resistant solid balls which affect the breaking of particles by falling of balls on the material. The ball mills used are of two types i.e. rotary mill and vibratory mill. The latter one is more efficient due to carbined effect of vibration and rotary motion.

(*ii*) **Eddy mill.** In this mill the grinding is affected through impact of metal particles against each other. The eddy mill consists of two fans mounted at the opposite ends of an entirely enclosed casing. The fans rotate in opposite direction producing opposing gas streams with high velocity. These opposing gas streams carry the powder particles and pulverization is caused by their collision. Oxidation and spontaneous combustion (due to heat evolved during grinding) of the powders are avoided by water cooling of the mill and introduction of inert gas in the chamber. The powders produced by this mill are characterised by disc like shape of the particles which is suitable for the manufacture of sintered products.

(*iii*) **Vortex mill.** In this type of mill the particles are fractured by mutual collision. This type of mill consists of two or more high speed propellers rotating with in a relatively small mill.

(*iv*) **Micronizer.** It is also based on the similar principle as eddy mill. In this high velocity jets (7-35 kgs/cm^2) of air or superheated steam are injected in a particular direction into the grinding chamber.

Milling or grinding process has the following advantages:
  (*i*) Powders are obtained in the controlled size.
  (*ii*) Mill operation is very simple.
  (*iii*) Involves the use of cheap raw materials such as machine wastes etc.
  (*iv*) This is suitable on large as well as small scale operation.
  (*v*) This is particularly suitable for brittle materials such as carbide metal mixture and cermets.

Disadvantages of Milling Process:

(i) Work hardening is caused during milling.

(ii) There is a possibility of excessive oxidation of final powder.

(iii) Particle welding and agglomeration may take place.

(iv) This can be used for only brittle or embrittled materials.

(v) Quality of powders is comparatively poor.

(vi) Production rate is slow.

Application of the Milling Process

Milling or grinding process can be used effectively in the following cases:

(i) Iron from electrolytic cathodes used for mechanical parts (high density) and electronic core powders.

(ii) Manganese used for welding rod coatings.

(iii) Nickel used for filters, welding rods, sintered nickel parts etc.

11.4.2. Atomization

Principally atomization consists of mechanical disintegration of a molten metal stream into fine particles by means of a jet of compressed air, inert gases or water. There are various methods of atomization but the important ones are (i) D.P.G. Spinning disc method, (ii) Mannesmann R.Z. Process, (iii) Centrifugal process, and (iv) Rotating electrode process or rotory atomizer.

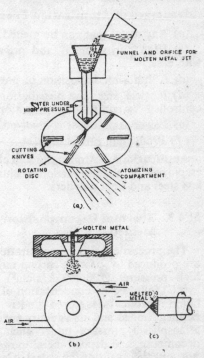

(i) **D.P.G. Spinning disc method.** Fig. 11.1 (a) shows the schematic representation of this process. The molten metal is first poured into a heated tundish and passes through a small hole in the centre of its base in the form of a thin stream falling on a number of knives fixed on disc which rotates at high speed (1500-3500 rpm). The metal stream coming out from the orifice strikes the high velocity water jet fixed below the tundish and as a result powder is produced which is collected on a filter bed placed at the base of the atomizing chamber. The wet powder is dried and sieved for separating out various grades.

FIG. 11.1. Aluminium powder production by atomization: (a) Disc atomizer, (b) Mannesmann process for atomization, and (c) Rotating atomizer.

(*ii*) **Mannesmann process.** In this process, a stream of high carbon liquid iron or molten cast iron containing about 3.5 per cent carbon was atomized by passing it through a high pressure jet [Fig. 11.1 (b)].

(*iii*) **Centrifugal process.** This method is based on the disintegration of a stream of molten metal by centrifugal force.

(*iv*) **Rotating electrode process or rotary atomization.** In this process, the front end of a rotary electrode is heated (by electric plasma heating), allowed to melt and than liquid droplets are thrown off by centrifugal action and finally collected in a helium filled chamber [Fig. 11.1 (c)]. The final product is homogeneous and free from contamination compared with inert gas atomization.

There are many modifications of the above processes used for different special metals and alloys. Qualities of powders such as degree of fineness and particle size distribution can be controlled by varying metal head in furnace, metal temperature, gas pressure, nozzle dimension, speed of rotation, etc.

Advantages of Atomization Process:

(*a*) Any metal that can be melted, can be made into powder.

(*b*) High purity metal and pre-alloyed powders can be produced with ease.

(*c*) A uniform composition of powder is achieved.

(*d*) Particle size, size distribution, shape and structure etc. can be controlled by control of atomization parameters.

(*e*) Lower capital cost is involved.

(*f*) Production rate is high.

Applications. Atomization technique has been successfully employed for the production of aluminium, copper, lead, zinc, stainless steel and steel powders.

11.4.3. Thermal Decomposition or Gaseous Pyrolysis Method

The process consists of preparation of liquid metal carbonyls which are produced by passing carbon monoxide gas over impure metals at high pressure (100-200 kgs/cm^2) and suitable temperature (200-270°C) followed by condensation of resulting gaseous carbonyl. The liquid carbonyl is stored under pressure. The liquid carbonyl is then boiled and its vapours are introduced into a heated vessel at atmospheric pressure under such conditions that carbonyl vapours decompose and deposit metal powders within the heated space and not on the walls of the vessel. Carbon monoxide thus generated is recycled for continuous processing. Thermal decomposition of carbonyls can also be obtained by atomization with centrifugal atomizers. The reversible reaction involved in the process can be represented as

$$M(CO)\times \underset{200°C \text{ and } 200 \text{ kgs/cm}^2}{\overset{400°C \text{ and } 1 \text{ atm.}}{\rightleftharpoons}} M+XCO \quad \dots \quad (11.1)$$

Control of proper decomposition temperature is very important because low temperature will result in slow and incomplete decomposition while higher temperature (above 400°C), would lead to oxidation of metals in carbon monoxide atmosphere. Metal powders in various forms can be obtained by varying the working conditions. This process offers the following advantages:

(i) Resulting powders are of spherical shape and fine size.

(ii) Powders obtained are quite pure (99.5 per cent) containing only small amounts of carbon, oxygen and nitrogen.

(iii) Sinterability of the powders produced by carbonyl process is excellent.

Disadvantages:

(i) Process is limited to those metals which can form carbonyls under suitable conditions.

(ii) Capital cost as well as operation cost are high.

(iii) Highly skilled people are required to control the process due to sofistication of the process.

Application. This process can be used to manufacture the powder of iron, nickel, tungsten and their mixtures required for various purposes.

11.4.4. Reduction Method

Reduction of various compounds such as oxides, halides, sulphides, hydrides etc. by the use of suitable reducing agents in the form of solid, liquid or gas under suitable conditions results in the production of respective metals in the form of powders. Reduction of oxides with hydrogen or carbon is perhaps the oldest method of producing metal powders. However, other compounds such as formates and oxalates may also be used as starting compounds for reduction. This process generally results in extremely fine powders with irregular shape and considerable porosity. Various reducing agents serving the purpose are hydrogen, dissociated ammonia, carbon monoxide, coal gas, enriched blast furnace gas, natural gas, partially combusted hydrocarbons, alkali metal vapours, carbon and other reactive metals. However, the choice of the reducing agent is dependent on the convenience and economy of operation. Among these, carbon is the cheapest reducing agent, but its use presents the difficulty for control of carbon content in the final powder. Hydrogen, dissociated ammonia and other gases rich in hydrogen can be used conveniently but their higher cost is a limitation. When the carbon and other reducing gases are unable to reduce the compounds satisfactorily and economically, metallic reducing agents are used for reduction of various oxides involving exothermic thermit reaction. Examples of metallothermic reduction are (*i*) production of chromium powder by the reduction of chromium oxide (Cr_2O_3) with magnesium, (*ii*) zirconium powder by reduction of zirconium oxide (ZrO_2) with calcium or magnesium in inert gas atmosphere, and (*iii*) thorium metal by the calcium reduction of thorium oxide (ThO_2) in an inert gas atmosphere.

Hydrides may also be used where very active nascent hydrogen is needed for the reduction of more stable oxides. For example, CaH_2 acts as an extremely powerful reducing agent as it dissociates into nascent hydrogen and matallic calcium at temperatures 800-600°C and both are powerful reducing agents. The chemical reaction for the hydride process can be expressed by the equation

$$MXOY + YCaH_2 = XM + YCa + YH_2O \qquad \ldots (11.2)$$

An eutectic alloy of copper and titanium in the form of powder is produced by this technique. Copper oxide and titanium hydride powders are mixed in proper proportion and heated under hydrogen or vacuum at slightly higher temperature than the melting point of eutectic alloy. The reaction product is held for a sufficient time in order to have complete diffusion between copper and titanium. Pulverization of cooled molten eutectic alloy results into powder. Required properties of the powders can be obtained by proper control of various factors such as (*i*) purity, particle size and shape of the raw materials, (*ii*) temperature and time of reduction, (*iii*) type of reducing agent, and (*iv*) the flow rate and pressure of gas in case of gaseous reductant.

For the reduction of anhydrous chlorides of titanium, zirconium, hafnium or vanadium, sodium, magnesium and calcium are employed to get spongy matals which are subsequently ground.

Reduction process offers following advantages and disadvantages:

Advantages:

(*i*) Particle size of powders can be easily controlled as the oxides can be easily comminuted to the desired degree of fineness due to their brittleness.

(*ii*) Powders obtained show good compactibility.

(*iii*) A wide range of shape, size and porosity can be obtained.

(*iv*) Carbon reduction of various oxides is of particular interest as it is the cheapest one.

Disadvantages:

(*i*) High purity oxides are required.

(*ii*) Carbon reduction is limited mainly to iron.

(*iii*) Process is applicable to only easily reducible oxides.

(*iv*) In case of gaseous reduction and halide reduction, high cost of production is involved.

Applications

(*i*) Iron by carbon reduction.

(*ii*) Nickel, cobalt, copper, tungsten, molybdenum by gaseous reduction.

(*iii*) Titanium, zirconium, hofnium, uranium etc. by reduction of their halides by metals.

11.4.5. Electrolytic Method

Metal powders can be conveniently produced by electrodeposition from an aqueous solution as well as fused salts using soluble or insoluble anodes. Though this process has been successful for producing a large number of metal powders but commercially it has been adopted for copper, beryllium, iron, tin, nickel, cadmium, antimony, silver, and lead powders. By electrodeposition, metal powders can be deposited in following three ways:

(*a*) Deposition as a hard and brittle deposit which is subsequently ground to powders of required size.

(*b*) Deposition as a soft and spongy substance which is loosely adherent with flufy texture and this can be easily pulverised by light rubbing, and

(*c*) Direct deposition as powder from the electrolyte which drops to the bottom of the cell.

The conditions favouring the production of powders on a cathode which can be easily removed and pulverised are: (*i*) high current density, (*ii*) low metal ion concentration, (*iii*) high acidity, (*iv*) addition of colloids, (*v*) low temperature, (*vi*) high viscosity and (*vii*) circulation of electrolyte to minimize the convection. By controlling these conditions, powders of the desired characteristics can be produced.

The metal powders deposited by electrolytic processes are of crystalline and dendritic structure with a low apparent density and flow rate. These powders are more suitable for pressing due to the tendency for individual particles to readily interlock. In the case of powders, obtained from hard and brittle deposits, the shape and particle size will depend on the mechanical methods employed for subsequent comminution. In general, angular or needle shape powders are produced. Electrodeposition of some metals of interest by aqueous bath is discussed below:

Iron. Iron powder is commercially produced by the electrolysis of chloride or sulphate bath. Addition of ammonium chloride is beneficial as it increases the conductivity and reduces oxidation of product. Preference to chloride bath is due to the possibility of sulphur precipitation in the deposit and anode passivity.

Copper. In this case the electrolyte employed is a mixture of copper sulphate and sulphuric acid. The copper concentration in the electrolyte has a considerable effect on cathode current efficiency, apparent density and particle size of the powder. Anode is used of crude copper resulting spongy deposit of copper which is removed and pulverized.

Alloys. The preparation of alloy powders is also possible by employing an electrolyte consisting of two or more metal salts. In this way electrolytic bronze and brass powders are being produced commercially.

Fused salt electrolysis. If electrolysis is performed in fused condition at a temperature below the melting point of the metal, the deposition of metal will take place in the form of small crystals with dendritic shape. Though a large number of metal powders can be prepared by this process but it is mainly employed for the production of zirconium, titanium, tantalum, uranium and thorium. The main technical difficulty associated with the process is the removal of entrained or adherent fused salt. Fused salt electrolysis offers several advantages as well as disadvantages mentioned below:

Advantages:

(*i*) The process is comparable in economics even with the methods employed for cheaper metals.

(*ii*) Powders of remarkable characteristics are produced with high degree of purity, excellent compactibility and good sinterability.

(*iii*) A wide range of powders can be produced by change in bath composition.

(*iv*) Control of the process is easy.

Disadvantages:

(*i*) The process is mainly confined to special purpose powders or particular metals.

(*ii*) It is unsuitable for the production of alloy powders.

(*iii*) It is a slow process.

(*iv*) Low production rate and high operating costs result in overall higher cost of powders.

(*v*) The deposited powders are prone to oxidation and thus thorough washing and drying or annealing is required which is mainly responsible for its higher cost.

11.4.6. Gaseous Reduction of Aqueous Solution

Metal powders particularly of nickel, cobalt and copper can be precipitated on commercial scale by the reduction of aqueous solutions or slurries of metal salts with hydrogen at high temperature (130-210°C) and high pressure (30-65 kgs/cm^2). The reduction reaction involved in the process can be represented as

$$M^{++} + H_2 \rightarrow M^\circ + 2H^+ \qquad \qquad \ldots (11.3)$$

Resulting metal powders are washed to remove the last traces of salts and then dried in hydrogen. For copper the drying temperature is sufficiently high, whereas for nickel and cobalt, moderate temperature is required.

Advantages:

(*i*) Ores can be directly used for the production of powders owing to the possibility of purification during leaching.

(*ii*) Powders of fine size are produced.

(*iii*) Purity of powders produced is high i.e. 99.2-99.8 per cent.

Disadvantages:

(*i*) It is applicable to only few metals such as nickel, copper and cobalt.

(*ii*) Process control is difficult due to the involvement of high pressure and high temperature.

(*iii*) On small scale, the process is uneconomical.

11.4.7. Cementation Process

Copper and nickel powders can be produced by cementation reaction from their solution, i.e., adding less noble metal scrap (Fe, Zn, Al) to the solution of metal salts. The cementation reactions involved may be represented as following:

$$M^{++}+Fe \rightarrow Fe^{++}+M \qquad \qquad \ldots (11.4)$$
$$M^{++}+Zn \rightarrow Zn^{++}+M \qquad \qquad \ldots (11.5)$$
$$3M^{++}+2Al \rightarrow 2Al^{+++}+3M \qquad \qquad \ldots (11.6)$$

The particle size of powders is dependent on the temperature of solution, concentration of solution, and type of scrap. In this process metals used for reduction (cementation should be very pure as all the impurities associated in the scrap will join the cemented powder. The powder so produced is quite prone to oxidation and thus thorough washing and drying under vacuum or hydrogen is necessary.

Advantages:

(*i*) It is the simplest process in operation.

(*ii*) Capital investment is very low.

(*iii*) Very fine powders can be obtained.

Disadvantages:

(*i*) Costly pure metals are required for cementation.

(*ii*) Repeated washings are required to remove the entrapped solution.

(*iii*) If excess of cementation metals are added, the powders will be contaminated and thus very controlled amounts are to be added.

(*iv*) Cementation process presents problems for disposal of resulting salt solution of reducing metals.

(*v*) If the process is based on recovery of reducing metals and their recycling, heavy investments will be neededs.

11.4.8. Production of Alloy Powders

It is the common practice to use either blended elemental powder mixture or prealloyed powders. In general premixes are easy to compact and effect less tool wear but they need longer times than prealloyed powders. Among the ferrous alloy powders, stainless steel, high speed steel, iron-nickel, iron-manganese, iron-molybdenum and iron-nickel-molybdenum are common whereas among the non-ferrous metal alloy powders, bronzes, brass, aluminium bronze, copper-nickel and nickel-silver are common. Several methods can be employed for making these alloy powders, such as atomization, combined thermal decomposition of carbonyls, combined precipitation of metals in electrolysis and spray drying, etc.

Simultaneous thermal decomposition of several carbonylic metals, or unstable organic compounds result in the production of alloy powders. Examples are iron-nickel powders with nickel content in the range of 10-80 per cent and iron-nickel-molybdenum powders with a molybdenum content upto 1.5 per cent and with varying nickel contents.

Complex alloy powders such as iron-nickel, iron-manganese, iron-molybdenum, iron-nickel-molybdenum, brass, bronze etc. are produced by electrolytic deposition method by using (i) a mixture of electrolytes containing two or more metal salts, (ii) using cast alloy of required composition as the anodes or (iii) composite anodes of the appropriate metal and alloy component.

11.5. CONDITIONING OF METAL POWDERS

The metal powders produced as such may not possess required characteristics for subsequent processing. To get the powders of uniform characteristics and chemical properties some preliminary treatment called conditioning may be necessary. These treatments include mechanical, thermal or chemical treatments or alloying of the powders (mixing). For examples, impure, wet or defective powders may require washing, drying or softening by annealing in a reducing atmosphere. Size distribution and shape may be varied by sieving, mixing or milling. There are three major steps involved in conditioning of metal powders:

1. Preliminary heat treatment.
2. Pulverization and screening.
3. Blending or mixing.

11.5.1. Preliminary Heat Treatment

Before blending the metallic powders, preliminary heat treatment is carried out in a reducing atmosphere or under vacuum which considerably affects the structure and the other properties of metal powders. It eliminates work hardening, reduces the impurity content (due to reduction of oxide film content and combustion of carbon) and alters the apparent density. Heat treatment at higher temperatures result in increase of apparent density of powders whereas low temperature heat treatment decreases the density. These changes caused by preliminary heat treatment greatly improve the compacting characteristics of the metal powders.

11.5.2. Pulverization and Screening

Preliminary heat-treatment or annealing process generally results in the sintering of powder particles which form a spongy mass which necessitates pulverization of the powder and screening prior to its further use. This disintergation of powder agglomerates is done very carefully in order to avoid the work hardening of the powder.

11.5.3. Blending or Mixing

Blending is an operation of inter-mingling of different powders of same composition or various grades of the same powder, while mixing is confined to the thorough intermingling of powders of more than one material. However, both the terms are commonly used for any of the process. Blending or mixing is of particular importance in the preparation of alloys from elemental powders required for the production of dispersion strengthened alloys, porous bearings, sintered friction material, electrical and magnetic materials etc. Some additives such as binders or lubricants may be added to facilitate pressing and to achieve the desired green strength and porosity in the final components.

The main objective of mixing is to obtain uniform distribution of powder with respect to density, particle size, and shape in order to get consistent performance during pressing and sintering. Blending should be carried out for just the required time as excessive blending may cause partial segregation and work hardening. The operation may be conducted in air, under protective atmosphere or under suitable liquid to avoid partial or complete oxidation as well as segregation.

11.5.4. Various Equipments Used for Blending of Different Powders

Laboratory ball mills rod mills are suitable for mixing hard materials such as carbides and cermets but not for deformable powders. Double cone mixers and Y-cone mixers can be used for any type of powders. Air-mix machine (consisting vertical cylinder body with conical bottom) is particularly suitable for mixing powders of low density.

Mixing may be carried out dry or wet depending upon the medium in which the milling is performed. Wet milling is preferred when more fine and uniform mixture of powder particles is required. Alcohal, benzene, distilled water, glycerene or acetone can be used as liquid medium in sufficient amounts so as to make the powder in the form of a thin paste. On completion of the mixing process, the liquid is driven off by drying operation. The mixed or blended powders are normally screened after the mixing operation in order to eliminate any unwanted foreign substances or balled up aggregates of powder and lubricant. Immediately after this the powders are transferred to press hopper and stored under air, vacuum or liquid in scaled containers.

11.6. COMPACTION OF POWDERS

Compaction is a process by which the metal powders are pressed into compacts of desired shape with adequate strength to withstand ejection from the tools and subsequent handling upto the completion of sintering without any breaking or damage. There are three stages or changes taking place during compaction:

(i) In the first stage particles are brought close together without any deformation, caused by the particle movement and rearrangement.

(ii) During second stage plastic deformation and cold working take place because the pressure applied is greater than the bulk yield stress of the material. However, the plastic flow is homogenous instead of local.

(iii) The third stage is confined to bulk compression and involves fracture or fragmentation of brittle powders.

For compaction of metal powders various techniques can be employed. However only few of them are employed commercially which can be classified in following three groups:

1. Pressureless shaping techniques.
2. Cold pressure shaping techniques.
3. Hot pressure shaping techniques.

11.6.1. Pressureless Shaping Techniques

In this technique, required shape is given to a powder mass prior to sintering without the use of any external pressure and this type of process is termed as loose sintering. In this process the metal powder is filled and vibrated mechanically into the mould and heated to the sintering temperature. This is the simplest method involving low cost of equipment as well as operation. However, this process can be used only for making high porosity (50-90 per cent) products and can not be used for the production of complex shaped parts because of many reasons, namely, (a) difficulty in removing the object from the mould after sintering, (b) flow characteristics of the powder, and (c) considerable amount of shrinkage during sintering. By selecting suitable powders, sintering temperature and time, it may be possible to produce parts of high density, but dimensional accuracy is a common defect. Materials used for mould and die are generally carbide, graphite, stainless steel or cast iron.

Applications. (i) Large ingots (upto 2 tons) of carbonyl iron and nickel powders are produced which are further treated by rolling or forging.

(ii) Highly porous filters from various powders such as, bronze, stainless steel, monel, tungsten etc. are easily formed by this technique.

(*iii*) Extremely porous sheets of nickel required for electrodes and beryllium bars are conveniently produced by this technique.

11.6.2. Cold Pressure Shaping Techniques

The cold pressure shaping techniques are most widely used for processing metal powders. There is a large number of techniques falling under this group. Important techniques are: (*i*) cold die compaction, (*ii*) isostatic pressing, (*iii*) powder rolling, (*vi*) cyclic compacting, (*v*) centrifugal compaction, (*vi*) powder extrusion, (*vii*) explosive forming, (*viii*) high energy rate forming, and (*ix*) vibratory compacting.

Cold die compaction. This is a simple technique and is considered to be the 'conventional technique'. In this process a die cavity is uniformly filled with metal powder which gives a certain packing density. By applying pressure the required density is achieved. After compaction the pressed part is ejected by the movement of the die

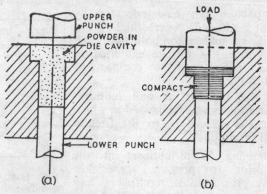

FIG. 11.2. Simplified diagram for die compaction.

and punch. A simplified arrangement for die compaction system is shown in Fig. 11.2. The density and strength of unsintered compact are referred as green density and green strength, respectively.

A most commonly used relationship between applied pressure and density given by Shapire, Kolthoff and Konopicky, is represented as

$$l_n \frac{1}{1-D} = KP + C \qquad \qquad \dots (11.7)$$

where D = relative density, P = applied pressure,

K = compaction constant and C is another constant.

A plot for density as a function of applied pressure is shown in Fig. 11.3.

Friction between various components such as between moving punches and die wall, between adjacent particles, internal friction within the powder particles during deformation and friction between powder particles and the die-wall etc. cause a considerable loss of compaction energy which in turn affects the density and density distribution within the compact, strength of the compact, ejection a fter pressing, and the wear of die.

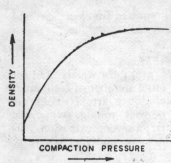

FIG. 11.3. Typical pressure-density curves for die compacting.

When pressure is applied from one side only, maximum density exists in the top layer just below the movable punch and nearest the die-wall whereas minimum in the bottom layer nearest the die wall. Density variation is also observed in the horizontal plane. This density variation can be improved by the following three methods:

(i) Compaction can be performed by pressing at both ends where high green density will be built up on both ends and the minimum density will be exhibited in the centre section of the compact as illustrated in Fig. 11.4.

(ii) By the use of die-wall lubricant density variation can be minimized in which pressure loss is reduced due to the friction between die and punch.

(iii) Admixing of solid lubricant into the powder prior to pressing appreciably reduces the pressure loss resulting in less density variation within the compact as well as less die wear.

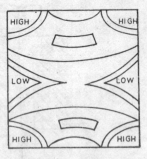

FIG. 11.4. Basic green density distribution for double end die compaction.

Components required for die compacting. The basic components of the equipment required for compacting metal powders in metal dies are:

(i) A mechanical or hydraulic device for required pressure.

(ii) A die of suitable material having a cavity of required shape and dimensions.

(iii) Feeding mechanism for filling the loss powder in the die cavity.

(iv) Upper and lower punches of required strength and design to permit the application of pressure and to assist the enjection and removal of the pressed part from the die.

(v) Metal cores for the formation of internal section of the compact, and (*vi*) Proper control to maintain the rate and magnitude of applied pressure, the degree of movement and speed of punches, ejection of the pressed part, etc.

Types of die-compaction techniques. (*a*) *Single action compaction.* This technique is illustrated in Fig. 11.5. The die and lower punches are kept stationary during the application of pressure through the upper punch. After compression of the powder, the lower punch is raised in order to eject the part from the die cavity while the die still remains stationary. The part may also be ejected by keeping the lower punch stationary and lowering the die from

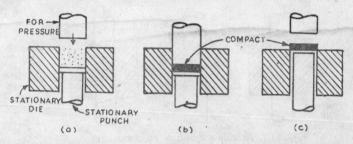

FIG. 11.5. Single action compaction: (*a*) powder filled, (*b*) compression, and (*c*) ejection.

the part. This technique is used for the manufacture of only flat, thin parts such as washers, discs, thin rings etc. This process involves the use of simple tools and can be operated by any type of mechanical or hydraulic presses. However, it is undesirable for the production of articles having considerable height due to non-uniform distribution of density.

(*b*) *Double-action compaction.* In this technique, powder is pressed simultaneously by both the top and bottom punches in opposite

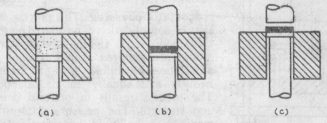

FIG. 11.6. Double action compacting system: (*a*) powder filled, (*b*) compressing, and (*c*) ejection.

directions (Fig. 11.6). The ejection of the part is carried out by the upward movement of the lower punch, keeping the die table stationary.

(*c*) *Double-action floating die compaction.* In this technique the bottom punch is kept stationary and the die is supported in the position by springs. In the beginning, compaction takes place by the descent of the punch into the die without causing any movement of the die. Afterwards, the frictional forces between the powder and die wall become so much that these frictional forces exceed the supporting forces of die resulting in the downward movement of the die with the further descent of upper punch and the powder is compacted. The relative movement between the lower punch and the die cause the application of pressure from the lower punch. The net result is the same as in case of double-action compaction. After releasing the pressure the part is ejected either by moving the lower punch upward or by moving the die further down from the part.

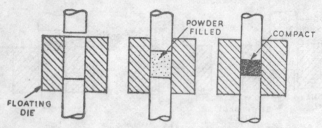

FIG. 11.7. Double action floating compaction.

Fig. 11.7. illustrates this technique. It is mainly used to manufacture thicker sections requiring compacting from both directions.

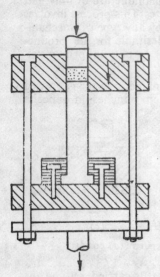

FIG. 11 8. Double action withdrawal die compaction technique.

(d) *Double-action withdrawal compaction.* In this method double action compaction is achieved by pulling the die mechanically downwards at a controlled rates and the object is ejected by the continuation of the downward movement of the die. This technique is shown in Fig 11.8. It can be used to produce all the thin or thick parts needing pressing from two directions.

Isostatic pressing. This process consists of consolidation of powdered material contained in a tightly sealed flexible mould into required shapes through the application of uniform pressure simultaneously and equally in all directions. The process results in uniform density and strength. The pressure transmitting media may be liquid (hydrostatic pressing) or gases, powders, rubber or plastic (isostatic pressing). Fig. 11.9 represents a typical case of isostatic compaction. The metal powder is loaded in a suitable flexible envelope (mould) which is tightly sealed against leakage. These envelopes may be made from natural rubber, synthetic rubber, PVC, thin metal foils etc. The mould containing powder is placed in high strength pressure vessel filled with oil or water which is pressurised

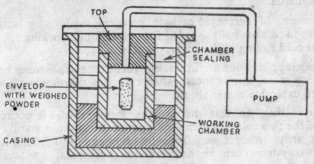

FIG. 11.9. Isostatic pressing.

to the required pressure. The pressed part is taken out from the pressure chamber after releasing the pressure and opening the mould. Isostatic method offers the following advantages:

(a) Irrespective of the size of objects, even strength and density distribution within the compact is obtained owing to the absence of die-wall friction and reduced interparticle friction.

(b) The process is capable of producing complex shapes.

(c) High compact densities can be achieved without pores, air pockets, internal cracks etc. Internal stresses are less pronounced.

(d) Internal stresses are less pronounced.

(e) The process is economical for producing large sized compacts as well as less number of components.

(f) Articles having any ratio of height to diameter can be produced without any inconvenience.

(g) The use of rubber plastic envelopes makes the equipment flexible and also reduces the cost of die.

(h) Powder lubricant is not needed.

(i) The pressure needed for a particular green density is lower than that required for die compaction.

(j) Dimensional shrinkage on sintering is quite uniform and the sintered articles show better ductility.

Disadvantages of Isostatic Compaction:

(a) Only certain simple surfaces can be obtained accurately.

(b) Packing of powders to uniform density before compaction is difficult as a result of which it is difficult to obtain accurate dimensions and good surface finish.

(c) Due to batch type process, production rate is low.

Applications of Isostatic Compaction. (a) Processing of refractory metal powder such as tungsten, molybdenum, niobium etc. to stocks required for further processing to sheet, wire etc. or electrodes for consumable vacuum arc melting are made by this technique.

(b) Rocket-motor parts made of refractory metal are also produced by this technique.

(c) Processing of cemented carbide powders is done by isostatic compaction to make balls needed for ball milling, working rolls of high speed cold rolling mills, boring bars etc.

(d) Other applications are in nuclear fuel elements, furnace boats, crucible, insulators, cermet tools, exhaust nozzles, thermocouple wire, compressed explosive materials etc.

Powder rolling. In this process the metal powder is poured at one end of the two rolls revolving in opposite direction in wardly and the rolled strip emerges out from the other end. For rolling metal powders two systems can be adopted i.e. horizontal and vertical

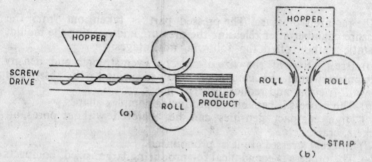

FIG. 11.10. Powder Rolling: (a) horizontal arrangement, and (b) vertical arrangement.

system. In horizontal system, the rolls are set directly above each other so that the strip emerges horizontally as shown in Fig. 11.10 (a), whereas in vertical system the rolls are set side by side so that the strip emerges vertically downward as shown in Fig. 11.10 (b). In case of horizontal arrangement, powder is poured onto a carrier and this method is more convenient from the view point of strip handling. In vertical arrangement, the powder is directly poured in the channel between the rotating rolls upto the required height on the roll surface. When the rolls turn, the powder is drawn into the gap between the rolls and is pressed into a strip. This method has the advantage of gravity feeding.

The rolling operation may be periodic or continuous. The former utilizes a certain batch of powder producing a finite length of strip. The latter is accomplished by the continuous feeding of the powder producing the strip of infinite length. The strip so produced is usually sintered in continuous furnaces at a suitable sintering temperature for a very short time. Further rolling of the sintered strip is usually needed to improve the properties to the required level.

Continuous rolling combined with continuous sintering, make the process capable of continuous production of strip. The characteristics of the finished strip are influenced by the factors such as surface finish of the rolls, roll gap, roll speed, rate of powder feed to the rolls, shape, size and size distribution of particles, and sintering temperature.

Cyclic compacting. This is a convenient and versatile technique involving low capital cost of plant for compacting powders into bar, sheet or strip of higher density in desired length sections. A schematic diagram is shown in Fig.

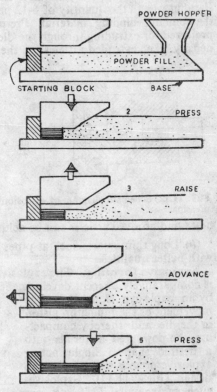

11.11. In step 1, the punch is raised and powder is charged into the channel formed by die walls. A starting block is required to keep the loose powder fill during the application of pressure. In step 2, the punch is lowered into the channel and the flat surface of the punch. In step 3, punch is raised after the pressure stroke. In step 4, leftward movement of powder by a prescribed distance is given which should be less than the length of the finished area of the punch so that fully compacted powder remains under the 'finishing area'. Step 5, is similar to step 2 except that the punch will now press the powder filled slightly to the right of the previous stroke. Cyclic repetition of steps 3, 4 and 5 will produce a continuous bar. The various steps of the method can be automated and production rates

FIG. 11.11. Operational sequence in cyclic compaction.

could be greatly increased. The compact of unlimited length so produced can be directly sintered and subjected to rolling for finishing. However the rate of production is slow due to the reciprocative nature of the punch.

Applications. Bar, plate, sheet and strip of common metals and alloys such as copper, iron, molybdenum, tantalum, brass, steel, nickel, magnetic alloys and iron-silicon alloys upto 5 cm width and 2.5 cm thickness can be conveniently produced.

Centrifugal compaction. The technique utilizes the centrifugal forces caused by the high speed of rotation of the die during compression. The centrifugal force acts on every individual powder particle contained in the die, compacting the powder particles. A specialized use of this process is in the manufacture of tubular products.

Powder extrusion. The process consists of forcing the mixture of powder and binder at high pressure through the appropriate die. The binding material performs two fold function: (a) binds the powder particles, and (b) minimises the friction against the die wall. Paraffin wax in the quantity of 6-12 per cent by weight is used as the common binding material. Pre-pressed mixtures are generally preferred for extruding through the die in order to attain the desired density. The extruded articles are then sintered to get the proper density and strength. A schematic diagram of powder extrusion pressing is shown in Fig. 11.12. The mixture of powder and binding material is kept in a container and the plunger is pushed towards the die by a hydraulic press.

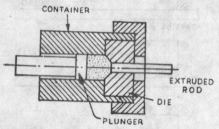

FIG. 11.12. Schematic diagram of extrusion pressing.

Applications. (a) Consolidation of carbide, dispersion strengthened materials, tubes and grooved articles can be achieved easily.

(b) Long thin objects such as pipes can be produced economically with better qualities.

Explosive forming. The explosive compacting of metal powders is comparatively a recent development, where the pressure generated by an explosive is used for the movement of the punch or piston in the die and thereby compacting the powdered materials into a desired shape. Single acting explosive press is the simplest in design (Fig. 11.13). Explosives such as dynamite, TNT etc. are used in practice.

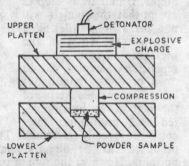

FIG. 11.13. Single acting explosive press.

Advantages:

(a) Compacts of very high and uniform green density (94-99 per cent of theoretical) can be obtained.

(b) Expensive hydraulic equipments are not required.

(c) Much higher pressures can be generated.

(*d*) Components made by explosive technique require less sintering compared to cold compacted parts to attain high density.

Disadvantages:

(*a*) Costly explosives are required.

(*b*) Process control is more difficult than conventional one.

Applications. (*a*) Compacts of metals, refractory materials, ceramics and cermets requiring high pressures can be made by this technique.

(*b*) Cylindrical compacts of uniform density can be easily produced.

(*c*) Large size metal plates and tubes can be economically produced.

High energy rate forming. In this process the machine employed consists of a device for storing energy in the form of compressed gas (usually nitrogen or products of combustion of petrol-air) and suddenly release of pressure accelerating the ram to high speed. It has the advantages like low running cost, high cycling rate and availability of machine in a wide range of energy capacities.

Vibratory compacting. This involves the application of vibration during compacting of a powder with in a rigid die. Both high-frequency low amplitude and low frequency high amplitude vibrations have been applied successfully. This process needs lower pressure resulting into reduction of dies cost and pressing equipment costs. Internal stresses of the compacts are also less due to uniformity of pressure. This process is useful for the production of large and complex parts of carbides, ceramics as well as ductile metal powders.

11.6.3. Hot Pressure Shaping Techniques

This group includes the various processes such as (*i*) hot pressing, (*ii*) hot extrusion, (*iii*) hot rolling, (*iv*) powder or sinter forging, (*v*) hot isostatic compaction, (*vi*) hot coining, and (*vii*) spark sintering.

Hot pressing. A schematic diagram of hot pressing is shown in

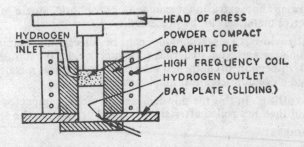

FIG. 11.14. Schematic diagram for hot pressing.

Fig. 11.14. In this process graphite die is used under protective atmosphere. Heating is done by water-cooled high frequency coil. The powder is placed in a die and pressure is applied simultaneously with heat. In other words, the two basic steps such as compacting and sintering are combined in one process.

Advantages:

(a) Without the use of lubricant or binders powder metallurgy parts having the properties nearing to solid metal can be produced.

(b) Large size parts can be conveniently and economically produced.

(c) The design is simplified as practically no allowances for sintering and shrinkage are necessary.

(d) Compacting pressures needed are low.

(e) The temperature required is low and more easily attainable than that required for conventional sintering.

(f) This technique is employed to process the powders such as carbides and cermets which are difficult to process by cold pressing.

Disadvantages:

(a) Production rate is comparatively low.

(b) Life of die is less.

(c) Considerable difficulties are involved during processing and ejection of the parts under protective atmosphere.

Applications. This technique of hot pressing is suitable for making metal bonded diamond tools, mining bits and wheels, metallic oxides (uranium oxide as nuclear fuel Mo/Al_2O_3 cermets), carbides (silicon and tungsten), borides, nitrides, silicides as tools, tips, disks, dies and shaped pieces, and large parts weighing upto 1000 kgs.

Hot extrusion. The powders are first cold compacted in a mild steel or stainless steel container and then extruded at the appropriate temperature to yield a completely dense material with better mechanical properties, and controlled grain size and grain orientation.

Advantages:

By using hot extrusion technique, pyrophoric, toxic and even radioactive materials can be processed.

Applications. This technique can be successfully employed for processing cermets, fuel materials (uranium oxide in stainless steel matrix), dispersion strengthened materials, refractory metals, beryllium and chromium etc. into simpler shapes.

Hot rolling. In this the powder is first cold compacted into a strip and then hot rolled after sintering and preheating the strip.

Advantages:

(a) Better properties than those of the cold rolled products are obtained.

(b) The metals like molybdenum and tungsten which are difficult to cold roll, can be easily processed.

Disadvantages:

(a) Equipment required is complex.

(b) Working under protective atmosphere is difficult as well as costly.

Applications: (a) Aluminium alloys can be processed from atomized coarse powders.

(b) Zinc sheet from coarse zinc powder can be made successfully.

(c) Molybdenum and tungsten sheets can be made easily by hot rolling technique.

Powder or sinter forging. Performed compacts made by any conventional process are heated to hot working temperature in a protective atmosphere and then immediately transferred to closed die for forging operation. After forging is completed, the component is withdrawn from the die and is cooled in protective atmosphere to minimize oxidation.

Advantages:

(a) Process is capable of producing densification upto 100 per cent and closed dimensional tolerances.

(b) Process requires lower sintering temperature to obtain the metallurgical sound structure.

Disadvantages:

Major problem associated with the process is die life particularly with complicated parts.

Applications. This is mainly used for production of fuel elements used in nuclear reactors.

Hot isostatic compaction. The process consists in enclosing the powder in a pressure-tight metal container of appropriate geometry which is subjected to isostatic pressure with simultaneous application of heat. The desired densification is obtained by maintaining this condition for sufficient time.

Advantages:

(a) This technique avoids pressure, temperature and size limitations of hot pressing because refractory tool materials are not involved.

(b) The problems of contamination owing to tool material—powder reactions are also avoided.

(c) High degree of accuracy and shape can be achieved.

(d) Isotropic microstructure in complex shapes can be produced.

Disadvantages:

Process is complex and operating cost is high.

Applications. This technique is suitable for consolidation of refractory metals, high melting point compounds, super alloys, beryllium, high speed steel, cermets and ceramic materials.

Hot coining. It is used to produce highly dense parts with very close dimensional tolerances and better mechanical properties. After compacting and sintering the part is reheated and compacted immediately in the impact press. Although this method is expensive because of the necessity of additional compacting and heating equipment, this is particularly useful for cermet materials.

Spark sintering. This involves direct electrical heating of metallic powders in a graphite die for a very short time under pressure or rubber mould with isostatic pressing. This process gives rapid production and high densities of components. However, the process is less common due to complexity. This technique is employed for rapid production of beryllium, titanium and nickel parts.

11.7. SINTERING

Sintering may be defined in general as the heating of loose or compacted aggregate of metal powders below the melting point of the base metal with or without the application of external pressure in order to transform into a more dense material by interparticle bonding. Thus, it may be considered as progressive transition taking place without melting, from the state of agglomeration of metallic particles to a massive state which should be free from porosity and possess desired physical and mechanical properties. Sintering results in the strong bonding between particles causing required strength, dentification and dimensional control. Sintering is usually carried out at a temperature in the range of 0.7-0.9 of the absolute melting point of metal powder in a single component powder system or the melting point of the base metal in multicomponent powder system. Sintering process in general is associated with the processes such as removal of absorbed matters, movement of atoms by diffusion, recrystallization and grain growth, formation of grain boundary and closing of viods present in the green compacts, etc.

In addition to interparticle bonding, sintering process is followed by various changes such as dimensional changes, chemical changes, electrical property changes, phase changes, relief of internal stresses, and al'oying. In general, density mechanical strength, ductility, electrical and thermal conductivities are favoured by increased amount of sintering. To obtain the desired properties of components, sintering is carried out at a constant temperature and time is varied.

11.7.1. Sintering Stages

With respect to time three stages occur in successive phases, i.e. (i) adhesion without shrinkage, (ii) dentification and grain growth, and (iii) final stage with closed pore spaces.

Adhesion without shrinkage. Initial heating of the compacts results in the stage of initial bonding and neck growth which may continue for some time and overlap the other stages. This affects a greater extent of bonding within the sinter mass.

Densification and grain growth. During the second stage of sintering marked densification takes place resulting in maximum shrinkage due to the formation of a network of pores followed by grain growth. During this stage some isolated and closed pores also result due to the absorption of small pores into big ones.

(*iii*) **Elimination of the last isolated and rounded pores**. During the third stage the spherodization of isolated pores increases rapidly resulting into decrease of porosity. This phenomenon takes place more quickly in the vicinity of the grain boundary. Finally further densification proceeds at a correspondingly low rate.

11.7.2. Liquid Phase Sintering

This process is characterised by persistance of liquid phase during the entire sintering period. This type of sintering is possible in case of multi-component system (having widely different melting points) at a suitable temperature. In general liquid phase sintering consists of following three stages:

(*i*) Melting of low melting constituent and flow of liquid formed with the rearrangement of the solid particles.

(*ii*) Rapid dissolution of fine particles of solid constituent and its reprecipitation on the larger particles.

(*iii*) Coalescence of solid particles with slow densification.

Advantages:

(*a*) A density very close to theoretical one can be easily obtained.

(*b*) The rate of diffusion through the liquid phase is greatly increased resulting into better alloying.

(*c*) Product is obtained having more desirable metallurgical structure and excellent mechanical properties.

Applications. Iron-copper, tungsten-copper, and tungsten-silver contact materials, sintered tungsten carbide with cobalt, bronze formed porous copper-tin-graphite bearings, etc. can be conveniently material, by liquid phase sintering.

11.7.3. Infiltration

This process consists of two steps, i.e. (*i*) preparation of a porous body of high melting point metal power, and (*ii*) subsequent filling the pores of porous body with a molten metal (infiltrant) having lower melting point. In practice infiltration is achieved either by immersing the process metal body in the molten infiltrant metral or by placing the porous component in contact with the solid infiltrant metal in the form of powder, powder compact or sheet on top of the porous body. The whole assembly is heated in a sintering furnace at a suitable temperature (between the melting points of two metals). The method is used mainly to prepare two phase structure. There are two stages occurring in filtration:

(i) Infiltration proper which involves filling of the pores of the porous body with the molten metal by capillary action.

(ii) In the second stage, structural changes occur during the soaking period, i.e., period in which the system is placed at the temperature of infiltration after filling all pore volume.

Advantages:

(a) Increased strength and high density are possible due to the formation of a solid solution of porous body and infiltrant.

(b) The infiltrated parts are suitable for pressure tight applications due to the absence of inter-connected porosity.

Essential requirements in selecting a suitable infiltrant:

(a) Melting point of infiltrant should be considerably lower than that of base metal.

(b) It should not form high melting compound with the base metal.

(c) A good wetting of the base metal by the liquid (infiltrant) is essential.

(d) The metal should have only limited solubility in the infiltrant metal or vice-versa.

Applications. This technique is successfully used for producing the objects of tungsten-copper, tungsten-silver, molybdenum-copper, copper infiltrated iron and steel products, cobalt infiltrated tungsten carbide, etc.

11.7.4. Sintering Practice

The essential equipment required for sintering is a furnace provided with close control and regulation of temperature, heating time, heating rate and sintering atmosphere. The choice of a type of furnace depends on the basis of its specific application. In general, the factors controlling the choice of furnace are:

(a) Working temperature range,

(b) Largest size of component to be sintered,

(c) Required atmosphere during sintering,

(d) Desired output, and

(e) Production, operating and maintenance costs for a given production.

11.7.5. Furnace Construction

A simplified diagram of sintering furnace is shown in Fig. 11.15. The furnace essentially consists of the following sections:

(i) A burn off chamber.

(*ii*) A high temperature zone, and

(*iii*) A cooling and discharging zone.

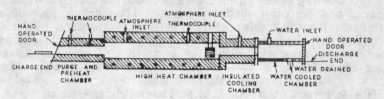

FIG. 11.15. Simplified longitudinal section of a sintering furnace showing principle parts.

(*i*) **A burn-off zone**. In this zone removal of air or lubricant vapours takes place. This is a very important part of the sintering furnace which is capable of working upto 850-900°C. The green compacts are subjected to slow heating. All the lubricants used in the compacting operation should be completely volatilized and expelled by the out flowing furnace atmosphere before the compacts are introduced in the high temperature zone of the sintering furnace.

(*ii*) **High temperature zone**. Here the compacts are subjected to actual sintering. High temperature zones are longer compared to the burn-off zone to allow the compacts to remain for enough time at required temperature in order to obtain the desired density and strength in powder metallurgy parts. The sintering time used in practice varies between wide limits which is dependent on the purity and nature of metals, sintering temperature, furnace atmosphere and intended application. However, the output of a sintering furnace is inversely proportional to the sintering time

TABLE 11.1. *Sintering Temperature and Time* (in High Temperature Zone) for Some Important Materials.*

Material	Temperature °C	Time, minutes
Copper	840-900	12-45
Brass	840-900	10-45
Bronze	760-870	10-20
Iron, Iron-Carbon etc.	1010-1150	8-45
Nickel	1010-1150	30-60
Stainless steel	1090-1290	30-60
Alnico magnets	1200-1300	120-150
Ferrites	1200-1450	10-600
Tungsten carbide	1430-1480	10-30
Molybdenum	2050	120 approx.
Tungsten	2340	480 approx.
Tantalum	2400	480 approx.

*Power Metallurgy Equipment Manual Part II Sintering Furnaces and Atmospheres, MPIF, New York, 1968, p. 65.

and thus it may be advantageous to use higher temperature and shorter duration.

(*iii*) **Cooling zone**. This section is provided to cool the sintered parts and prevent oxidation from air. The cooling zone of a sintering furnace consists of two parts i.e. (*a*) a short insulated cooling zone, and (*b*) comparatively long water jackated cooling zone. The former one allows the parts to cool from high sintering temperature to a low temperature at a slower rate in order to avoid thermal stresses. In the latter zone, cooling is affected below 150°C to prevent oxidation of the part upon striking the air.

Table 11.1 as on p. 323 shows the typical sintering temperature and time (in high temperature zone) for some materials of interest.

11.7.5. Types of Furnaces

Sintering furnace can be classified as following depending upon the heating system used and type of operation:

(*i*) **Fuel fired furnaces**. This type of furnace is normally used for working at low temperatures. In this heating is relatively cheaper since the products of combustion also provide the protective atmosphere. Two types of furnace i.e. (*a*) direct muffle type, and (*b*) radiant type, are in common practice. In the former type, muffles are supported along its entire length by high temperature refractory bricks and a reducing atmosphere is introduced when the muffle becomes red hot. This atmosphere is maintained even after the sintering operation is over until the muffle reaches a black heat range. This type of furnace can be used satisfactorily for low production rate with maintenance of extremely high purity atmosphere throughout the sintering operation.

Horizontally and vertically radiant tube furnaces require low maintenance upto 1000°C by using nickel-chromium alloy tubes and upto 1100°C by employing super alloys or ceramic coated tubes.

Semi-muffle type furnaces are employed to burn off the volatile matter of lubricants in the compacts before the sintering operation. This furnace is used only upto 400°C to avoid oxidation

(*ii*) **Electrically heated furnaces**. These provide extremely controlled temperature conditions. Three basic types of electric heating elements are used in electric sintering furnaces:

(*a*) Base metal alloy heating element of nickel chromium alloy or kanthal which can be used for 1000-1150°C depending upon the element used.

(*b*) Non-metallic heating element such as silicon carbide which can be used in the temperature range of 1000-1350°C and graphite (upto 2000°C).

(*c*) Molybdenum heating elements in hydrogen atmosphere which can be worked upto 1700°C. Molybdenum furnaces are particularly suited for sintering high melting materials such as stainless steel, refractory metals, cermets and tungsten carbide.

(*iii*) **Continuous furnaces**. Most widely used sintering furnaces are of continuous type in which components move continously through the various zones of the furnace. The main characteristics of the continuous furnace are:

(*a*) These are more expensive but are preferred over batch furnace for sintering large number of parts resulting overall low cost of sintering per piece.

(*b*) The components obtained from continuous furnance are more consistent in quality compared to batch furnaces.

In general continuous furnaces are suitable for a sintering time of 15 to 120 minutes but become uneconomical for lorger sintering times.

(*iv*) **Batch type sintering furnace**. In this type of furnace, the parts remain stationary. This is preferred where high purity or critically controlled sintering atmospheres, extremely high temperatures, large compact size and small number of parts are involved. Muffle or nonmuffle batch furnaces having gas-tight inter-locks for charging and discharging the load.

11.7.6. Sintering Atmospheres

The choice of a suitable furnace atmosphere is of utmost importance in all sintering processes. Type of atmosphere used is governed by the characteristics of the materials as well as by the desired properties in the sintered product. Changes in furnace atmosphere take place as a result of various reactions occurring at sintering temperature, for example, reaction of atmosphere constituents amongst each other (water gas), reaction between atmosphere and material to be sintered (reduction of oxide or decomburisation) and the reaction between atmosphere and refractories. This change in atmosphere may greatly affect the properties of the compacts and thus controlled atmosphere is necessary during sintering to avoid rejects and give consistent product.

Functions of Sintering Atmospheres

(*a*) It must prevent oxidation on the metal surface at the sintering temperature, otherwise it would interfere with the sintering process.

(*b*) It must avoid decarburisation and nitriding conditions.

(*c*) It must have the tendency to reduce surface films such as oxides on powder particles, if they are present and remove absorbed gases.

(*d*) It must not contaminate the metal powder compact at the sintering temperature.

Types of atmospheres. The common furnace atmospheres used in sintering are:

(*i*) Reducing atmosphere.

(*ii*) Neutral atmosphere.

(*iii*) Oxidising atmosphere.

(*i*) *Reducing atmosphere*. The most widely employed sintering atmospheres are reducing ones which may be further divided into three categories:

(*a*) Dry hydrogen or dissociated ammonia atmosphere.

(*b*) Exothermic atmosphere having low or medium carbon potential, and

(*c*) Endothermic atmosphere enriched with hydro-carbon gas to produce a carburising atmosphere.

(*ii*) *Neutral or inert atmosphere*. This group includes the use of vacuum, helium, argon gas and nitrogen gas. Use of vacuum, helium and argon gas is quite costly and may be employed on a small scale in very special cases.

(*iii*) *Oxidising atmosphere*. In a very few and special cases, air, steam, CO_2 or completely burnt hydrocarbon gases with premixed air may be used as the oxidising sintering atmosphere.

TABLE 11.2. *Controlled Atmospheres for Some Important Materials*.

Material	Atmosphere
Iron, Nickel, Copper, Brass, Bronze	Hydrogen, Argon, Exothermic gas. Endo-thermic gas, Vacuum, Cracked Ammonia.
Cobalt, Tungsten Carbide	Hydrogen, Vacuum.
Tungsten	Hydrogen, Argon, Cracked. Ammonia, Vacuum.
Stainless Steel	Hydrogen, Vacuum.
Molybdenum	Hydrogen.
Alnico Magnets	Hydrogen, Vacuum, Cracked Ammonia.
Aluminium, Chromium, Vanadium.	Vacuum.
Tantalum	Vacuum, Argon, Helium.
Gold, Platinum, Silver	Air.

Table 11.2 lists some appropriate controlled atmospheres required for a number of common materials.

11.8. PRODUCTION OF BEARINGS BY POWDER METALLURGY TECHNIQUES

An extensive use of powder metallurgy techniques is in the field of bearing materials which contain a pore volume of 17-30 per cent. Practically every automobile, refrigerator, air conditioner and washing machine contains sintered bearings. A great variety of bearings incorporating metal powders are used for different purposes. Examples are steel backed materials with a porous or nonporous sintered lining, unbacked porous sintered metallic parts impregnated with oil, sintered polytetra fluoroethylene parts, etc.

The great scope of the bearing materials has been realised due to the ease with which two phase materials (metal-metal, metal-plastic, metal-nonmetallic etc.) can be processed at low cost with controlled and better mechanical properties. Bearing materials in general should possess the following characteristics:

(a) Bearing materials should be able to sustain low or high rubbing speeds, light or heavy static as well as impact loads.

(b) These materials should show minimum tendency for welding in service.

(c) Materials used for bearing should have considerable mechanical strengths above the operating temperatures.

(d) Materials should have low superficial shear strength to cause lower friction loss of local metal to metal contacts.

(e) Materials should possess sufficient superficial heat conductivity to ensure rapid heat dissipation over the bearing housing through the shaft by conduction, and

(f) There should be low wear rate of both bearing and journal.

11.8.1. Steel Backed Materials with a Nonporous Sintered Lining

Lining materials can be broadly classified in three groups, i.e., (i) lead or tin based white metal (babbit), (ii) copper-based alloys, (iii) aluminium-based alloys. Copper-based alloys (Cu-Pb and Pb-bronze) or aluminium-based materials (Al-Sn) are normally preferred over white metal because it does possess sufficient strength to carry the load for most of the modern applications. These can be manufactured by spreading the powder on copper-plated steel strip to ensure a good bond and then passing the powdered strip in a reducing atmosphere (nitrogen/hydrogen) through a sintering furnace held at a temperature of 800-850°C where the sintering of powder particles takes place. This 'first sinter' strip is then passed through a rolling mill, resintered and finally an operation of size rolling is performed. These bearings find their extensive use in main and small end bushes in low duty compressors, gear box bushes, motor cycle bearings, etc.

11.8.2. Steel Backed Materials with a Porous-Plastic Impregnated Lining

This group mainly consists of the following two types of bearing materials:

(a) Impregnated with a mixture of polytetra fluoroethylene (PTFE) and lead which are employed as a dry bearing material due to extremely high degree of wear resistance of PTFE/Lead/Bronze surface.

(b) Impregnated in thermoplastic acetol copolymer which are particularly suitable for operation with a minimum lubrication.

The former type of bearing materials are made by sintering a layer of tin-bronze (about 0.25 mm thick) to copper-plated steel strip and than PTFE/lead mixture in the form of a thick paste is roll impregnated into this layer in such a way that a very thin layer of PTFE/ lead remains above the broze. Resintering is carried out above 327°C, a transition temperature of PTFE and finally the strip is worked by size rolls. Since a small proportion of bronze is to be exposed in the bearing surface during the running of such bearings, a thin PTFE/ lead layer is removed in order to expose a small proportion of bronze on the bearing surface which is required during the duty of bearing. The bearing materials of the latter group are manufactured by impregnating the bronze in acetol copolymer in such a way that a 0.25 mm thick machinable layer remains above the bronze.

11.8.3. Oil-Impregnated Porous Bearings (Self-Lubricating)

These materials should possess the capability of working under self-lubricating conditions with the lubricant present in the pores of the bearing. These may be operated under the conditions of dry friction. Porous bearings should possess the following properties:

(a) These should have adequate porosity to retain the maximum possible amount of oil while in use.

(b) Major proportion of porosity should be distributed throughout the material in the form of myriads of interconnecting channels and reservoirs.

(c) Materials must be capable to sustain stresses during working.

(d) Bearings should be produced to close dimensional accuracy.

Advantages of self lubricating bearings:

(a) No lubricant is required during working.

(b) These are resistant to corrosion.

(c) Machining of materials is simple and easy.

(d) Bearings are cheaper compared to those produced by casting and machining method.

Applications. (a) Where regular supply of lubricant is not accessible.

(b) These are preferred where the dirt contamination from the surrounding atmosphere may cause trouble in running the machinery such as conveyors, railways, farm machinery, automobile etc.

(c) Where the contamination of product with lubricant is undesirable, e.g. food and textile industries, household machines, photography and cinema, printing etc.

(d) Where there are frequent stops and starts such as telegraphic and wireless, pumps and fans etc.

Production of self-lubricating bearings. Porous bearings are made of bronze with or without the addition of graphite or other dry lubricant. Although, iron, brass or aluminium alloys may be employed, bronze holds a predominent position in this field. These may be impregnated with oil or marketed in dry condition itself. The basic steps in the production of a porous bearing includes (i) mixing, (ii) cold compaction, (iii) sintering, (iv) repressing and (v) impregnation.

For producing porous bearings, first the metal powders of high purity in the required proportion and a small percentage of fine natural graphite are blended to render the desired alloy composition. The mixed power are then compacted in a hydraulic or mechanical presses at pressure of 1500-5000 kgs/cm^2 to form green compacts of desired shape and uniform density. Compacted products are sintered in a reducing atmosphere at a temperature of about 800°C (for 90:10 bronze). Sintered products are then repressed to a fixed length in order to remove distortion, impart higher densities, get required degree of dimentional accuracy and a smooth surface finish. This step is essential not only for an optimum fit on the moving shaft but an accurate fit into the bearing housing is also essential. In case of smaller pore size, sizing operation may result in the closure of pores and thus careful machining may be required. The repressed compacts are finally impregnated with oil. The techniques employed may be immersion, vacuum or compressed air. In immersion technique the specimen is held in oil at 80-90°C for at least 30 minutes. This technique is a time consuming and due to higher temperature involved the oxidation of oil and high rate of oil loss from the pores is caused. In case of vacuum impregnation, evacuation of a chamber in which the specimen is kept removes most of the air and moisture from within the pores. After proper evacuation, oil is allowed to enter the vacuum chamber and the pressure is increased to atmospheric to force the oil into the pores. In some cases compressed air at pressures upto 7 kgs/cm^2 may also be employed for the same purpose. Vacuum or pressure techniques require considerably less time than immersion technique.

11.8.4. Dry Lubricated Bearings

The dry lubricated bearings contain a considerable amount of solid lubricants of low coefficients of friction and without sacrificing much of their strength. Mainly two solid lubricants are commonly employed in practice, namely, graphite and PTFE. These bearings operate completely dry and are mostly used when a liquid lubricant can not be tolerated. Examples are food processing, pharmaceutical and dextile industries.

(i) **Graphite bearings**. Manufacture of such bearings comprises the blending of metal powder and natural graphite, compacting in mechanical or hydraulic press, sintering and finally recompacting at higher temperature. Bronze, iron, nickel and bronze-based materials are commonly used as matrix materials for this type of bearings. In order to have sufficient strength along with maximum possible amount of graphite, fairly less porosity is the general requirement. Such condition can best be obtained by hot pressing, forging or extrusion technique in which graphite films formed during mixing will be broken up and fresh metal-to-metal contacts will be resulted.

These bearings are mainly used for hot water circulating pump, pumps handling styrens for chemical industry, looms for the textile industry etc.

(ii) **PTFE bearings**. PTFE is a special plastic having an extremely low coefficient of friction, low apparent specific gravity (0.51-0.57), high chemical stability at temperature range of -200 to $+300°C$ even in the presence of most corrosive agents. This is available as a powder which can be compacted and sintered or directly hot pressed/hot extruded/hot rolled into large-piece components. The compacting pressure is generally in between 150-200 kgs/cm^2 in air for about 90 minutes. Their use, however, is restricted to below 200°C. In general two types of PTFE/metal bearing materials are used in practice, (a) having continuous skeleton of metal, and (b) metal powder dispersed in PTFE matrix. The former type is more important for which two methods of manufacturing can be used, i.e., either hot pressing or aqueous impregnation. Hot pressing consists of placing a PTFE sheet on the porous metal, and forcing it into the pores under the simultaneous action of heat as well as pressure. In case of equeous impregnation, skeleton metal is put in a suspension of PTFE and water, and the subsequent sintering is employed. This technique is used for the manufacture of cylinderical bearings, thrust washers, steel-backed bearing materials of semicontinuous length etc.

11.9. PROCESSING OF CEMENTED CARBIDES

The production of cemented carbides has advanced to such an extent that this is now considered to be the most important branch of powder metallurgy. Due to the retention of extreme hardness along with considerable amount of toughness, these materials are commonly referred as 'hard carbides'. In general tungsten carbide-cobalt compositions are most widely used, but for certain applications such as machining tougHer materials, forming long and coiled chips etc., carbides of titanium, tantalum, molybdenum or niobium have also been used partly or wholly in place of tungsten carbide and cobalt is replaced by nickel, chromium, cobalt-chromium or cobalt-nickel-chromium alloys. The performance of these multicarbide compositions as tool materials is outstanding for the high speed machining of steel and other materials giving rise to long, coiled and tenacious chips.

11.9.1 Production of Cemented Carbides

Manufacture of sintered cemented carbide products consists of following steps:

- (*i*) Preparation of raw materials,
- (*ii*) Milling and mixing,
- (*iii*) Cold pressing,
- (*iv*) Presintering,
- (*v*) Shaping,
- (*vi*) Final sintering, and
- (*vii*) Final machining.

(*i*) **Preparation of raw materials**. Carbide powders are produced by the direct reaction of the carbon with metal or metal oxide. In the case of using metal and carbon, close control of composition is easily attained while in the case of using oxides, accurate control of final carbon content is difficult due to the combination of reduction and carburisation reaction in a single operation and thus often crushing and recarburisation may be required. The carbides of tungsten and molybdenum are produced in practice by the direct metal-carbon reaction while that of titanium and tantalum are produced by the reaction of oxide with carbon. The technique for production of carbide powders by metal-carbon reaction is comparatively expensive.

Production of tungsten and molybdenum carbides. Respective metal powder with appropriate amount of carbon black (6.9-7.2 percent) is blended in rotating mixers. Use of a slight excess of carbon over the theoretically required amount avoids the chance of undercarburisation. Carburisation of tungsten or molybdenum and carbon mixture (loose or precompacted) is carried out in boats at a temperature of 1200-1800°C in hydrogen atmosphere depending upon the metal and the particle size required. For fine particle size lower temperature is employed. Carbon deficiency in the tungsten carbide powder causes the formation of brittle carbide phases such as n-phase (Co_3WC), phase ($Co_3W_6C_7$) and K-phase ($Co_3W_{10}C_4$) during sintering. If the carbon content is below about 6.1 per cent, carburisation operation should be repeated to achieve the desired carbon content.

Preparation of other carbides. The oxide of the metal is blended in dry or wet condition with carbon black and subsequently dried. The mixture is then compacted and carburised in the temperature range of 1500-2300°C which depends upon the size required and metal involved. Generally carbon tube or high frequency vacuum furnaces are employed in practice.

(*ii*) **Milling and mixing**. The sintered and agglomerated carbide lumps obtained by carburisation are crushed by crusher (gyratory, jaw or rolls, stud mills, and hammer mills). The crushed carbides are further pulverised in eddy or ball mills. For the production of cemented carbide with maximum hardness and minimum porosity, very fine (1-2 μ) and uniform distribution of carbides or carbide solution with cobalt is required. Fine and uniform, distribution is usually obtained by ball milling (dry or wet) together of the constituents. Wet milling is invariably employed using a wide variety of liquids such as distilled water, acetone, alcohol, benzene, gasoline etc. The milling operation is followed by removal of liquid agent used during milling by means of vacuum or centrifugal filtration. After drying in boats, it is finally heat treated in reducing atmosphere to remove oxygen picked up during milling. After reduction treatment, the resulting mixture is sieved to remove undesired things such as cobalt agglomerate, cobalt flakes and other impurities. Before compacting, a lubricant such a paraffin wax dissolved in gasoline, stearic acid etc. is added to facilitate the pressing process and to avoid the formation of defects and cracks in the compacts. The lubricants are added in such quantities that residual lubricant is retained after volatilization of the solvent.

(*iii*) **Cold pressing**. Carbide-metal powder mixture along with the required quantity of lubricants is compacted in hydraulic presses in the shape of blanks or plates. Dies and punches are invariably lined with carbide due to the abrasive nature of the powders. Split dies are suitable for the compaction of large ingots requiring a pressure as high as 2000 kgs/cm^2. Isostatic pressing may be used to produce large carbide balls, bushes and hollow sections with more uniform density. Other techniques such as extrusion and hot pressing are also used.

(*iv*) **Presintering of compacts.** Presintering is carried out in hydrogen atmosphere in the temperature range of 900-1150°C depending upon the cobalt content and carbide grade. Before the operation of presintering, a heat-treatment at about 400°C is preferred in order to completely eliminate the lubricant by volatilization without causing any physical or chemical changes within the compacts. Both heat treatment and presintering can be carried out in a continuous push type or vacuum furnace. Presintering does not form any liquid phase and only solid-phase sintering of binder metal occurs resulting practically no shrinkage. These presintered compacts become capable to withstand for further handling, machining or slicing operations.

(*v*) **Final shaping**. Presintered materials are cut into desired sizes and subsequently machined with special cemented carbide tools and finally ground to the desired shape with metal bonded diamond or silicon carbide wheels.

(*vi*) **Final sintering**. Final sintering is carried out in the temperature range of 1350-1550°C which results into the final physical state of materials. Sintering temperature depends upon the composition and grain size of the carbide material but it is usually kept below the melting point of cobalt (1492°C). During this sintering operation about 20 per cent linear contraction occurs and thus this is taken care during making of presintered products. During sintering cobalt dissolves tungsten carbide in the solid state with the decrease in its melting point and finally a liquid phase consisting of 52 per cent cobalt and 48 per cent tungsten carbide (WC) is formed. For a given cobalt content sintering temperature can be known. For example, for 6 per cent cobalt content a temperature of 1400°C is desirable.

Sintering operation is carried out under hydrogen atmosphere or vacuum for 30 minutes to 120 minutes for obtaining high quality product. The furnaces usually employed for sintering are molybdenum resistor, carbon tube or high frequency vacuum furnaces.

Cemented carbide objects may also be produced by infiltration of porous carbide skeleton which is carried out either by immersing the rigid skeleton in the liquid cobalt metal or by placing cobalt or cobalt-tungsten carbide alloy on the top of the skeleton and then heating in a reducing atmosphere. The process is advantageously used for the manufacture of carbide materials with large content of binder.

(*vii*) **Final shaping.** Machining, grinding and polishing are used for finishing of fully sintered materials to required tolerances which are otherwise very difficult to obtain by either sintering or hot pressing. Practically all cemented carbide tools are ground in two steps:

(*a*) The rough grinding is usually performed with silicon carbide grinding wheel.

(*b*) Final shaping is done with a metal bonded diamond wheel. In some special cases of high precision, full diamond tools may be used.

Applications of cemented carbides. Cemented carbides are mainly used as cutting tools required for metal cutting and machining of abrasive materials. In a small proportion these are also used as wear resistant materials.

QUESTIONS

1. Define powder metallurgy. What are its merits and limitations over other methods of making metal objects?

2 What are the various factors affecting the quality and properties of powder metallurgy parts? How are they controlled?

3. Explain why the powder metallurgy method is indispensable to the manufacture of some components.

4. Give the various applications of powder metallurgy and explain the reasons for their use.

5 Discuss the various methods of production of metal powders. Indicate the major applications, merits and demerits of each.

6. Critically discuss the significance and the methods of conditioning of metal powders.

7. What is compaction? What changes do take place during compaction?

8. What are the various important techniques for compaction of metal powders? Explain the role of different factors on the degree of compaction of a metal powder. To what extent can the theoretical density be approached by compacting?

9. Briefly describe various powder metallurgy compaction processes enlisting their suitability for specific applications.

10. What is sintering? What are the changes occurring during sintering?

11. Explain the stages of sintering. Why do green compacts shrink during sintering? What are the factors that determine the shrinkage in a compact?

12. What is liquid phase sintering? What are its stages and advantages and applications in industry?

13. What is infiltration and how is it accomplished? Explain advantages, and disadvantages and the stages that occur in the process of infiltration. What are the essential requirements in choosing a suitable infiltrant?

14. What are the prerequisites of sintering furnace? Describe the essential parts of a sintering furnace.

15. Explain the technique of sintering a metal powder compact. What precautions are required to be taken?

16. What are the functions of sintering almosphere? What atmospheres are used for sintering of different kinds of powders?

12

METALS PROCESSING

The shaping of metals into useful final shapes by various means is called metals processing. This includes mainly four different groups:

1. Mechanical working in either hot or cold state.
2. Metal joining.
3. Machining and grinding, and
4. Casting of molten metals.

12.1. MECHANICAL WORKING

In mechanical working metals are plastically deformed by the forces of loads applied by special tools such as rolls, forging dies, flat hammer, etc., and metals are finally converted into the desired shapes. Mechanical working changes the shape and dimensions of the metal piece but the volume of metal remains substantially constant throughout the process.

External forces acting on the metal bring the essential changes in the structure and properties of the metal due to the alterations in the size and shape of the grains Working of metals in cold state results in strain or work hardening. Strain hardening is associated with an increase in the tensile strength and hardness of the metal with an appreciable decrease in plastic properties (elongation, impact strength, etc.). In work hardening, the grains are stretched in the direction of tensile deformation resulting into *anisotropy* (directional properties) of the metal. After heavy work hardening it may not be possible to further deform the metal in the cold state due to the development of discontinuities (cracks etc.).

If metal is heated to a certain definite temperature before subjecting it to mechanical working, there is less danger of nonuniform deformation of grains and the consequent development of stresses due to the recrystallisation process that takes place simultaneously with deformation.

Various factors affecting the plasticity of metals during mechanical working. Metals and alloys of different nature do not have the same ductility and, therefore, behave differently when subjected to hot and cold working. Various factors affecting the plasticity of metals are:

(a) *Chemical composition.* Pure metals have a higher plasticity than their alloys since in the latter case new structural constituents may be formed which change the plasticity of the base metal. For example, steel with low carbon has higher plasticity than steel with high carbon, pure copper is many times more plastic than its alloys with tin, zinc, etc.

(b) *Structure.* Metals having fine grained structure are more plastic than metals having cast coarse-grained denderites. Annealed metals having structural phases in an equilibrium state are more ductile than the same metal after hardening in which a nonequilibrium structure is obtained.

(c) *Temperature.* As a rule, the ductility of a metal increases with temperature, and its resistance to deformation is decreased.

(d) *Rate and degree of deformation.* Rate and degree of deformation affects the plasticity of the metal in various ways. An increase in the deformation rate within a definite limit will result decrease in plasticity. However, a further increase in this rate after a certain limit may improve the plasticity.

(e) *System of stressed state or deformation.* Usually there are two different stressed systems, (i) three dimensional compression, e.g. rolling, forging, extrusion, etc., and (ii) three dimensional stressed state (compressive stresses along two directions and tensile in one direction) as in drawing. Metal has higher ductility in the former system than the latter one.

Commonly, starting materials used for mechanical working of metals are ingots and billets of various cross-sections and weights. Mechanical working processes include rolling, drawing, extrusion, forging, press working and some special methods.

12.1.1. Rolling

The process of deforming metals and alloys plastically into the semi-finished or finished shapes by passing the ingot or billet between rolls is known as rolling. This technique is most widely used for processing of metals because it gives high production rate and close control of the final product. In deforming metal between rolls, the work is subjected to high compressive stresses from the squeezing action of the rolls and to surface shear stresses by the friction between the rolls and the metal. The frictional forces are also responsible for drawing the metal into the rolls.

The initial breakdown of ingots into blooms and billets is generally done by hot rolling. This is followed by further hot rolling into plate, sheet, rod, bar, pipe, rails, etc. Cold rolling produces sheets, strip and foil with good surface finish and increased mechanical strength. In cold rolling, close control of dimensions of the product is also obtained.

A rolling mill consists basically of rolls, bearings, a hosing for containing these parts, and a drive for applying power to the rolls and controlling their speed. The forces involved in rolling are quite high and therefore, very rigid construction is needed, and very large motors are required to provide the necessary power. Rolling mills can be conveniently classified with respect to the number and arrangement of the rolls.

(*i*) **Two-high non-reversing mill**. This type of mill is shown in Fig. 12.1. Rolls of equal size are rotated only in one direction. The stock is returned to the entrance or rear of the rolls for further reduction by hand or mechanical means. These mills are employed where the bar passes through the rolls only once and in open-train plate mills.

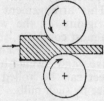

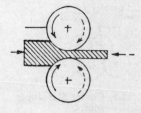

FIG. 12.1. Two-high non-reversing mill.

FIG. 12.2. Two-high reversing mill.

(*ii*) **Two-high reversing mill**. In this metal can be passed back and forth through the rolls by reversing their direction of rotation (Fig. 12.2). These are employed in blooming and slabbing mills and as roughing stands of plate, rails etc.

(*iii*) **Three-high mill**. It consists of an upper and lower driven rolls and a middle roll arrange in a single vertical plane. The middle roll rotates by friction. All the three-rolls have a constant direction of rotation (Fig. 12.3). It finds extensive application in open-train section mills.

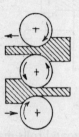

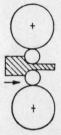

FIG. 12.3. Three-high mill.

FIG. 12.4. Four-high mill.

(*iv*) **Four-high mill**. This mill consists of four rolls, one above another in vertical plane. The two rolls are smaller in diameter which are working rolls and the larger two rolls are back-up rolls which give support to the working rolls and reduce their spring. By the use of small working rolls, power required for rolling is reduced considerably. This arrangement is shown in Fig. 12.4. This type of mills is used for hot rolling of armour and other plates as well as for the cold rolling of steel sheet in continuous manner.

(v) **Cluster or multiple rolls**. In this diameter of the working rolls is very small (10-30 mm) and each of the work rolls is supported

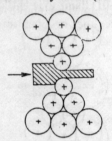

FIG. 12.5. Cluster of multiple rolls.

by two backing rolls. Due to very small diameter of work rolls, they can not be driven directly and they are supported by a row of driving rolls which in turn are supported by a row of back-up rolls. This arrangement ensures exceptional rigidity of the whole roll system and almost complete absence of deflection in working rolls. There may be six, twelve, and twenty high mills. Very thin sheet can be rolled to very close tolerance by such mills. This type of mill is shown in Fig. 12.5.

(vi) **Universal roll stands**. This type of mill is shown in Fig. 12.6. This mill consists of vertical rolls as well as horizontal rolls in a single stand. Here the metal is reduced by both horizontal and vertical rolls, the latter roll the edges of the bar even and smooth. Vertical rolls are mounted on one side (front or back) or on both

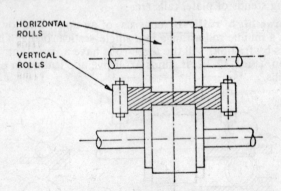

HORIZONTAL
ROLLS

VERTICAL
ROLLS

FIG. 12.6. Universal mill.

sides of the horizontal roll stand. The horizontal rolls may be of 2, 3 or 4 high arrangement. These mills are used for rolling wide strip, steels, plates, wide flanged beam (H) and slabs.

(vii) **Planetary mill**. This mill consists of a pair of heavy backing rolls surrounded by a large number of small planetary rolls (Fig. 12.7). The main feature of the planetary mill is that it hot reduces a slab directly to strip in one pass through the mill. Each planetary roll gives an almost constant reduction to the slab as it sweeps out a circular path between the backing rolls and slab. The overall reduction is the summation of a series of small reductions by each pair of working rolls. The action in the planetary mill is nearer to forging type than rolling. It is necessary to use feed rolls to introduce the slab into the mill, and a pair of planishing rolls may be needed on the exit side to improve the surface finish.

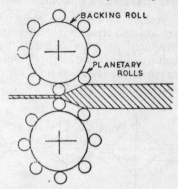

FIG. 12.7. Planetary rolling mill.

Hot rolling. The first hot-rolling operation for most steel products is done on the primary roughing mill (also called blooming, slabbing or cogging mill) These mills are generally two-high reversing mill with 60-130 cms diameter rolls. The objective of this operation is the breakdown of the cast ingot into blooms or slabs for subsequent finishing into bars, plate or sheet. The initial breakdown passes often involve only small reductions. There is appreciable spreading of ingot width in hot rolling. To maintain the desired width and preserve the edges, the ingot is turned to 90° on intermediate passes and passed through edging grooves in the rolls. A reversing primary mill has relatively low production rate and in order to increase the production rate, edging passes are eliminated by using a universal mill. Various products such as plate, strip, different sections (channels, I-beam etc.), rails, etc. are produced by hot-rolling.

Cold rolling. Cold rolling is used to produce sheet and strip with superior surface finish and closer dimensional tolerances compared to hot-rolled strip. In addition, the strain hardening resulting from the cold reduction may be used to give increased strength. A greater percentage of rolled non-ferrous metals is finished by cold rolling. The starting material for cold rolled steel sheet is pickled hot-rolled break down coil from the continuous hot strip mill. Cold rolled non-ferrous sheet may be produced from hot-rolled strip, or in the case of certain copper alloys, it is cold rolled directly from the cast state.

High speed four-high tandem mills with three to five stands are used for the cold rolling of steel sheet, aluminium and copper alloys. A continuous mill has high capacity and less labour is involved. The total reduction achieved by cold rolling generally varies from 50-90 per cent In each pass, reduction is uniformly distributed and in the last pass lowest reduction is given to permit better control of flatness, gauge and surface finish.

Rolling of bars and shapes. Bars of circular or hexagonal cross-section and structural shapes such as I-beams, channels and rails are produced in huge quantity by hot rolling with grooved rolls. The rolling of bars and shapes differs from the rolling of sheet and strip in that the cross-section of the metal is reduced in two directions. However, in any one pass, the metal is usually compressed in one direction only. On the next pass it is rotated by 90°. Since the metal spreads to a great extent in the hot-rolling of bars than in cold rolling of sheet, an important problem in designing passes for bars and shapes is to provide allowance for the spreading. A typical method of reducing a square billet to a bar is by alternate passes through oval and square shaped grooves. The design of roll passes for structural shapes is much more complicated and requires extensive experience. A rolling mill designed to roll bars

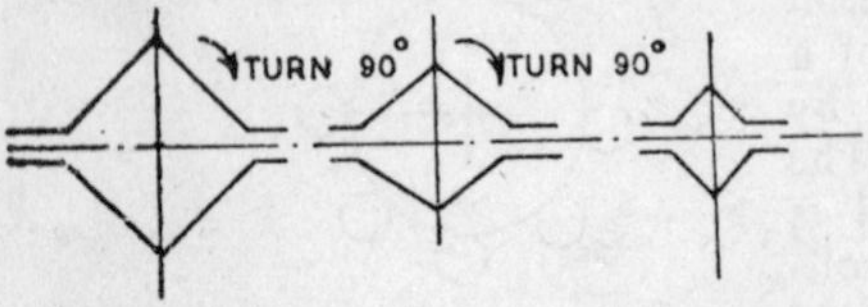

FIG. 12.8. Rolling sequence for squares.

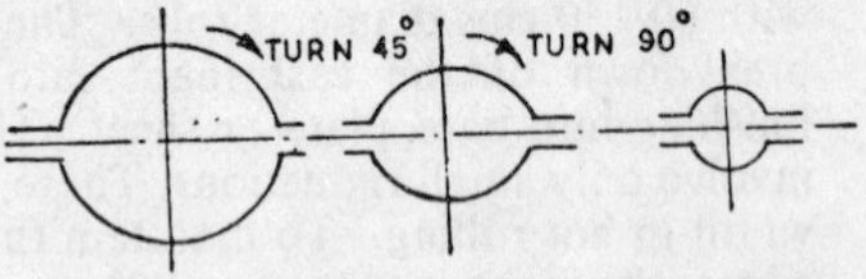

in known as bar mill, or merchant mill. Mill of this type are generally either two-or three-high. A common installation consists of roughing stand, and a finishing stand. It is common practice to arrange bar rolls in train, i.e.,

FIG. 12.9. Rolling sequence for rounds.

several mills are set close together side by side and the rolls of one stand are driven by connecting them to those of the adjacent. Pass sequences for rolling square and rounds are shown in Figs. 12.8 and 12.9, respectively.

For rolling rails and structural beams, the mills are usually arranged in two or more lines and comprise several roll stands. This mill generally uses two high-mills and three-high mills. Light weight structural beams are rolled in structural mills equipped with an interchangeable universal roll stand which may be installed in place of the two-high finishing mill stand. Various pass sequences may be employed in these mills depending upon the size and shape of the beam to be produced.

Powder rolling. This has been discussed in Chapter 11.

12.1.2. Extrusion

This is a process by which a block of metal is reduced in cross-section by forcing it through an opening of die under high pressure. In general, extrusion technique is used to produce cylindrical bars or hollow tubes, but shapes of irregular cross-section are also produced from the readily extrudable metals, like aluminium. Because of the large forces required in extrusion, most metals are extruded hot under conditions where the resistance of metal to deformation is low. However, cold extrusion is possible for many soft metals such as lead, tin, aluminium etc. The reaction of the extrusion billet with the container and die results in high compressive stresses which help in reducing the cracking of material during working. This is an important reason for the increased utilization of extrusion in the working of metals which are difficult to work such as stainless steel, nickel based alloys, and other high temperature materials.

There are three types of extrusion, i.e. (i) direct, (ii) indirect, and impact extrusion.

(i) **Direct extrusion**. Principle of direct extrusion is illustrated in Fig. 12.10. A metal billet heated to a required temperature is

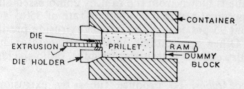

FIG. 12.10. Direct extrusion.

placed in a container of the press and forced through the die by the ram. A dummy block, or pressure plate is placed at the end of the ram in contact with the billet. In this way the metal is subjected to plastic deformation and flows through the opening of die.

(ii) **Indirect extrusion**. Principle of indirect extrusion is illustrated in Fig. 12.11. In this a hollow ram carries the die, while the other end of the container is closed with a plate. Extrusion can be performed either by moving ram or moving the container. During the travel of either, the die applies pressure on the billet and the deformed metal flows

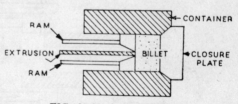

FIG. 12.11. Indirect extrusion.

through the die opening in the direction opposite to the ram. In indirect extrusion there is no relative motion between the wall of the container and the billet, and therefore, friction forces are lower and the power required for extrusion is less than required in direct extrusion (about 25-30 per cent less). Another advantage in indirect extrusion is less quantity of scrap (5-6 per cent) compared to 18-20 per cent in case of direct extrusion. However, there are practical limitations to indirect extrusion due to the limited load carrying capacity of hollow ram.

(*iii*) **Impact extrusion**. Low strength, ductile metals such as lead, tin and aluminium can be extruded by the impact extrusion process (Fig. 12.12), into short lengths of hollow shapes such as col-

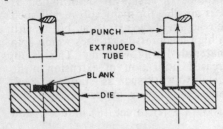

FIG. 12.12. Impact extrusion.

lapsible tooth paste tubes. It may be either indirect or direct extrusion and it is usually performed on a high speed mechanical press. In the process a flat slug of metal is placed on a solid bottom die, and a single blow causes the metal to flow between the die and punch. The outside diameter of the tube is the same as the diameter of die and the thickness is controlled by the clearance between the punch and die. On the upstroke, the tube is blown from the ram by compressed air. The entire operation is automatic with a production rate of 35 to 40 tubes per minute. About 95 per cent of the impact extrusion product is collapsible tubes. Other applications include refrigerator headers, condenser cans, dry cell cups, transformer cups, radio shields, flash light cans etc.

Extrusion of tubes. To produce tubes by extrusion, a mandrel is attached to the end of the extrusion ram. The clearance between the mandrel and the die wall determines the wall thickness of the tube. Generally a hollow billet is used so that the mandrel can extend to the die. Otherwise, a two-step extrusion operation is used in which a solid billet is first pierced to make hollow billet and then extruded

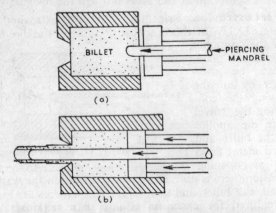

FIG. 12.13. Tube extrusion: (*a*) piercing, (*b*) extrusion.

(Fig. 12.13). In order to produce concentric tubes, the ram and mandrel must move in axial alignment with the container and the die. The axial hole in the billet must also be concentric, and should offer equal resistance to deformation over its cross-section.

Production of Seamless Pipe and Tubing

Extrusion is suitable method for producing seamless pipe and tubing, especially for metals which are difficult to work. However, due to economic reasons, the Mannesmann mill (Fig. 12.14) is used extensively for the rotary piercing of steel and copper billets. The process employs two barrel shaped dirven rolls which are set at an angle to each other. An axial thrust and rotation developed to the billet assist in opening up the centre of the billet as it flows round the piercing point to create the tube cavity. The

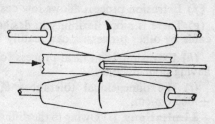

FIG. 12.14. Mannesmann mill.

Mannesmann mill does not provide sufficient large wall reduction and elongation to produce finished hot-worked tubes. ·Various types

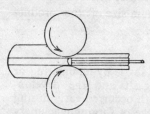

FIG. 12.15. Plug rolling mill.

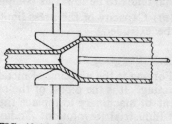

FIG. 12 16. Three-roll piercing mill.

of plug rolling mills which drive the tube over a long mandrel containing a plug (Fig. 12.15) are used. A three-roll piercing machines (Fig. 12.16) produce more concentric tubes with smoother surfaces inside as well as outside. Lastly a reeling mill (Fig. 12.17) burnishes the outside and inside surfaces and removes the slight oval shape if any.

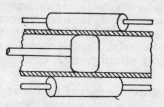

FIG. 12.17. Reeling mill.

Advantages of extrusion over rolling and forging. In extrusion high compressive stresses are developed due to the reaction of billet with container and die which helps in reducing the cracking of material during working. In addition, there are various advantages of extrusion such as:

(a) The extruded product has excellent transverse flow lines because of the high reduction ratio. This condition adds to the strength and makes the secondary process easier.

(b) Almost any cross-sectional shape can be extruded that are costly to produce by other means.

(*c*) By increasing the forming pressure very thin walls can be obtained.

(*d*) The cost of extrusion dies is relatively low.

(*e*) Extruded shapes can often replace weldments and members which are machined from bar stock.

(*f*) Extrusion process allows low-cost in process design.

(*g*) There is more flexibility in design, e.g. sharp corners not practicable by other processes, can readily be obtained by extrusion.

(*h*) Extrusion is an ideal process for obtaining rods from metals having poor ductility.

(*i*) The dimensional tolerances of extrusion are very good i.e. ±.003 cm/cm.

Limitations. (*i*) Owing to the difference in temperature at the beginning and the end of the cycle, there is a considerable variation in the properties and heterogeneity of the metal structure along the length.

(*ii*) For simpler shapes the rate of production and the yield of the metal tends to be lower as compared to the process like rolling.

(*iii*) Capacity of the press limits the maximum size of the product to be extruded.

12.1.3. Forging

Forging is the working of metal into useful shape by hammering or pressing. It is the oldest of the metal working arts and the development of machinery to replace the arm of smith occurred early during the Industrial Revolution. Today, a wide range of forging machinery is available for making parts ranging from a very small size such as bolt to a large size such as turibine rotor or an entire airplane wing.

Most forging operations are carried out hot, but certain metals may be cold forged. Two types of forging machines, i.e., forging hammer (drop hammer) and press are used. Forging hammer delivers rapid impact blows to the surface of the metal while the forging press delivers a slow-speed compressive force to a metal. Various operations in forging include edging, fullering, drawing, swaging, and upsetting which are shown in Fig. 12.18.

(*i*) **Edging**. This operation is used to shape the ends of the bar and together metal (Fig. 12.18*a* and 12.18*b*). The matal is confined by the die from flowing in the horizontal direction but it is free to flow laterally to fill the die.

(*ii*) **Fullering**. It is used to reduce the cross-sectional area of a portion of the stock. The metal flow is outward and away from the centre of the fullering die (Fig. 12.18*c*). An example is the forging of connecting rod for an internal combustion engine.

(*iii*) **Drawing down or drawing out**. In this operation cross-section of the work is reduced with concurrent increase in length (Fig. 12.18*d*).

(iv) **Swaging**. If the drawing down operation is carried out with concave dies (Fig. 12.18*e*) so as to produce a bar of smaller diameter, the operation is termed as swaging.

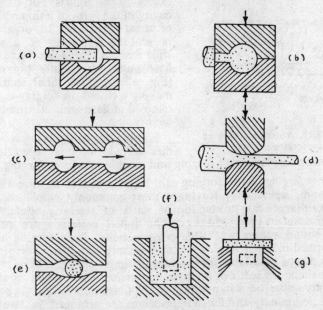

FIG. 12.18. Forging operations: (*a,b*) edging, (*c*) fullering, (*d*) drawing, (*e*) swaging, (*f*) piercing, and (*g*) punching.

(v) **Upsetting**. In upsetting, the cross-sectional area of bar is increased due to reduction in height. By repeated upsetting from different sides, the bar can be made to its original shape but metal of higher quality will be obtained (Fig. 12.18*f*).

Other operation which can be achieved by forging are bending, twisting, extrusion, piercing, punching, indenting, etc.

Forging processes can be grouped into two main categories, i e. closed-die forging and open-die forging.

(i) **Closed die forging**. In closed die forging the work piece is deformed between two die halves which carry the impressions of the desired final shape. The work piece is deformed under high pressure in a closed cavity and thus precision forgings with close dimensional tolerances can be made. In closed die forging the billet is usually first fullered and edged to place the metal in the correct place for subsequent forging. The preshaped billet is then placed in the cavity of the blocking die and rough forged close to the final shape. The greatest change in the shape of metal usually occurs in this step. It is then transferred to the finishing die, where it is forged to final shape and dimensions. It is important to use enough metal in the

forging blanks so that the die cavity is completely filled. As it is difficult to put just the sufficient quantity of metal, normally a little excess
of metal is used. In the finishing when the dies come together, the
excess metal squirts out of the cavity in the form of a thin ribbon of metal called flash. In order to prevent the formation of a very wide flash, a ridge known as a flash gutter, is usually provided (Fig. 12.19). The final step in making a closed die forging is the removal of flash with a trimming die.

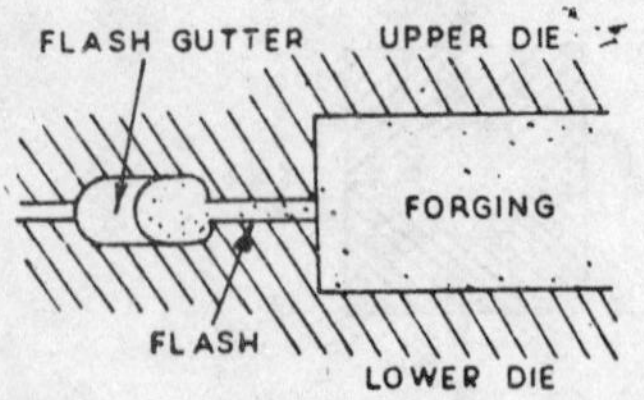

FIG. 12.19. A sectional view of closed die forging.

Forging hot metal in impression dies include various operations, such as drop forging, press forging and machine or upset forging.

(a) *Drop forging.* Drop forging can be obtained in a wide range of sizes and shapes. Drop forging is most commonly employed for the mass or large-scale production of parts of steel or nonferrous metals of a weight upto 350 kgs. The initial materials are rolled stock of round, square, and other cross-sections. Drop forging may be performed in either single or multiple impression dies. The single impression type is suitable for forgings of simple shape. Forgings of irregular shape are made in multiple impression dies which contain preliminary impressions in addition to the finish impression. In some cases the preliminary and finish impressions are arranged in two or more separate dies. Forging blanks heated to the forging temperature can be drop forged in power hammers and crank friction presses. Production of a simple piece by drop forging from a cylindrical slug is shown in Fig. 12.20.

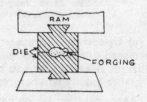

(b) *Press forging.* The character of metal deformation in press forging substantially differs from that of hammer forging One blow of the hammer works the metal only in the surface layers of the forging so that

FIG. 12.20. Production of simple forging with drop hammer.

deformation does not effectively penetrate into the volume of the metal. The squeeze pressure of press applied to the metal block gradually increases and penetrates deep into the metal, involving its whole volume.

(c) *Machine, or upset forging.* Forgings of the ring and rod types with all kinds of heads and shoulders such as bolts, nuts, washers and collars can be conveniently produced in horizontal forging machines. A forging sequence for a horizontal machine is illustrated in Fig. 12.21. The heated end of the bar stock is inserted into the stationary die upto stop. At this time, punch is in its left hand position (Fig. 12.21a). Next the movable die grips the bar stock and at the same time an impression is formed in the closed dies for shaping the projecting stock. The stop is automatically retracted to

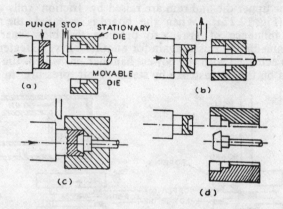

FIG. 12.21. Sequence of operations in a horizontal forging operation.

its idle position (Fig. 12.21b). Then the punch advances to upset the bar and perform the finished forging (Fig. 12.21c) and finally, the movable die and the punch are withdrawn to their initial positions (Fig. 12.21d). The rod and forging are shifted to the next pass where the forging is cut off.

(ii) **Open die forging.** Open die forging is mostly used for large objects and relatively simple shapes. Open die forging is also used to perform the work piece for closed die forging. This operation is performed between flat dies or simple shapes in a large hydraulic press or power hammer. Examples are ship propeller shafts, rings, gun tubes, and pressure vessels. Since the work piece is always larger than the tool, at any time deformation is confined to a small portion of the work piece. The chief mode of deformation is compression accompanied by considerable spreading in the lateral directions. Probably, the simplest operation of open die forging is reduction of cross-sectional area of a bar without changing the final shape of the cross-section.

Forging equipments. Forging equipments may be classified with respect to the principle of operation. In forging hammers the force is applied by falling weight or ram. These are energy restricted machines since the deformation results from dissipating the kinetic energy of the ram. Mechanical forging presses are stroke-restricted machines since the length of the press stroke represents their capability. Hydraulic presses are load-restricted machines since their capability for carrying out a forging operation is limited chiefly by the maximum load capacity. Important forging equipments are (i) forging hammer, (ii) forging presses, (iii) screw presses and (iv) forging machines.

(*i*) *Forging hammer.* The most commonly used forging equipment is the forging hammer. The two basic types of hammers are the *board hammer* and the *power hammer* (Fig. 12.22). In the board hammer the upper die and ram are raised by friction rolls gripping the board (Fig. 12.22*a*). When the board is released, the ram falls under the influence of gravity to produce the blow energy. The board is immediately raised again for another blow. Greater forging capacity is achieved with the power hammer in which the ram is accelerated on the downstroke by steam or air pressure in addition

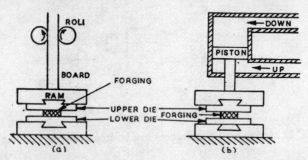

FIG. 12.22. Forging hammers: (*a*) board hammer, and (*b*) steam hammer.

to gravity (Fig. 12.22*b*). Steam or air is also used to raise the ram on the upstroke. An important feature of the power hammer is that the energy of the blow can be controlled, whereas in the board hammer the mass and height of fall are fixed. Power hammers are preferred over board hammers, for closed-die forging. However, hammers generally do not provide the accuracy which is obtainable in presses.

(*ii*) *Forging presses.* Forging presses are of either mechanical or hydraulic type. Presses are rated on the basis of the force developed at the end of the stroke. Next to hammers, mechanical presses are most widely used equipment for closed-die forging. Most

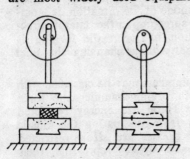

FIG. 12.23. Mechanical forging press: (*a*) top stroke, and (*b*) bottom stroke.

mechanical presses utilize an eccentric crank (Fig. 12.23) to translate rotary motion into reciprocating linear motion of the press slide. The ram stroke is shorter than in a hammer or hydraulic press, and therefore, mechanical presses are best suited for low profile forgings. The blow of a press is more like a squeeze than like the impact of a hammer. Because of this, dies can be less massive and die life is longer than with a hammer. However, the initial cost of a press is much higher than that of a hammer. Forging presses thus are used for larger production rates.

Hydraulic presses are load-restricted machines (Fig. 12.24) in which hydraulic pressure moves a piston in a cylinder. A chief feature is that the full press load is available at any point during the full stroke of the ram. This feature makes the hydraulic press most suited for extrusion type forging operation. The ram velocity can be controlled and even varied during the stroke. The hydraulic press is a relatively slow-speed machine.

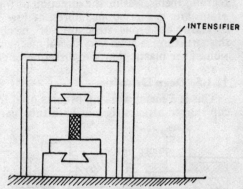

FIG. 12.24. Hydrolic forging press.

This results in longer contact time, which may lead to problems such as heat loss from the work piece and die deterioration. On the other hand, the slow sequeezing action of hydraulic press results in close tolerances. The initial cost of a hydraulic press is higher than that of mechanical press of equal capacity.

(*ii*) *Screw presses.* In screw presses the ram is connected by a rotary joint to a spindle, which is a large screw. The rotary motion of a flywheel is transformed into linear motion by the multiple thread on the spindle and its nut.

(*iv*) *Forging machines.* There are also known as upsetters or headers. There are horizontal mechanical presses which are used for the high production forging of symmetrical shapes from bar stock, such as bolts, rivets, and gear blanks.

12.1.4 Directional Properties of Mechanically Worked Components

All the mechanical processes are associated with a change in the macrostructure of the metal that leads to a rearrangement of the fibres and alters the grain size. Fig. 12.25 illustrates the fibre grain flow in crank-shaft produced by two different manufacturing processes. Fibre grain flow is much more favourable in the forged one since it promotes high strength in the crank shaft. Directional working of the metal, characteristic of most forging processes enables parts to be produced with accurate dimensions, a smooth surface and sufficiently high mechanical propertie

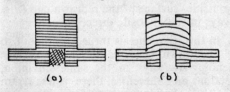

(a)   (b)

FIG. 12.25. Grain flow lines shown schematically in a crank shaft (a) machined from a solid, and (b) drop forged.

In mechanical processing of metals, the crystals/grains of the metal

get elongated along the direction of the plastic flow, i.e. along the direction of forging or rolling. The crystals tend to reform and regroup themselves in the direction of forging/rolling. The polyhedral grains are converted into fibres at low temperature. This structure is known as fibrous structure. If mechanical shaping is done on this structure, it gives very useful mechanical properties in the direction of the plastic flow, i.e. direction of elongation.

12.1.5. Deep Drawing

This is a metal working process used for shaping flat sheets into cup shaped articles such as bath tubs, cartridge cases, and automobile

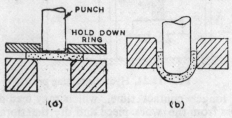

FIG. 12.26. Deep drawing of cylindrical cup: (a) before drawing, and (b) after drawing.

parts. This is accomplished by placing a blank of appropriate size over a shaped die and pressing the metal into the die with a punch (Fig. 12.26). Generally a clamping or hold-down pressure is required to press the blank against the die to prevent wrinkling. This is best done by means of a blank holder or hold-down ring in a double action press. The average maximum reduction in deep drawing is about 50 per cent, and therefore to make tall slender cups (such as cartridge cases and closed end tubes), it is necessary to used successive drawing operations. Reducing a cup or drawn part to a smaller diameter and increased height is known as redrawing. The two basic methods of

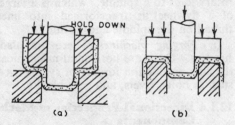

FIG. 12 27. Redrawing methods: (a) direct redrawing, and (b) reverse redrawing.

redrawing are (i) direct or regular redrawing (Fig. 12.27a) and (ii) reverse or indirect redrawing (Fig. 12.27b).

(i) **Direct redrawing.** In this original outside surface of the redrawn cup remains the outside surface of the redrawn cup (Fig. 12.27a). The bending is always in the opposite direction.

(ii) **Indirect redrawing.** In this, the cup is turned inside out so that the outside surface of the drawn becomes the inside surface of the redrawn cup. The bending is always in the same direction, rather than in opposite directions and therefore, there is less strain hardening of the walls of the shell. Better control of wrinkling can be obtained in indirect redrawing because of the snug control of the metal around the die radius and the fact that there is no geometrical limitation to the use of a hold-down-ring.

The metal to be deep drawn must possess a good ductility. If very severe deep drawing is required, the part is annealed between successive draws.

12.1.6. Drawing of Rods, Wires and Tubes

Drawing operations involve pulling the metal through a die by means of a tensile force applied to the exit side of the die. Most of the plastic flow is caused by compression force which arises from the reaction of the metal with the die. The reduction in diameter of a solid bar or rod by successive drawing is known as bar, rod or wire drawing depending on the diameter of the final product. When a hollow tube is drawn through a die without any mandrel to support the inside of the tube, it is known as tube sinking. When a mandrel or plug is used to support the inside diameter of the tube as it is drawn through a die, the process is called tube drawing. Bar, wire and tube drawing are usually carried out at room temperature. However, because of large deformations involved, there is considerable temperature rise during the drawing operations.

(i) **Rod drawing**. The rods which can not be coiled are produced on draw-benches (Fig. 12.28). The rod is pointed with swager, inserted through the die and clamped to the jaws of the draw-head. The draw-head is moved either by a chain drive or by a hydraulic mechanism. Draw-benches with

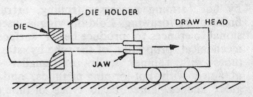

FIG. 12.28. Schematic diagram of rod drawing bench.

1,50,000 kgs. pull and 30 metres of run out are available. Draw speeds may vary from about 10 to 100 metres per minute.

(ii) **Wire drawing**. Wire drawing starts with hot-rolled wire rod. The rod is first cleaned by pickling to remove any scale which would lead to surface defects and excessive die wear. For the production of steel wire, the next step consists in coating the wire rod with lime or plating it with thin layer of copper or tin. The lime serves as an absorber and carrier of the lubricant during, dry drawing and it also serves to neutralise any acid remaining from pickling. In dry drawing the lubricant used is either grease or soap powder, while in wet drawing the entire die is immersed in a lubricating fluid.

Long lengths of wire are produced by drawing with a bull block (Fig. 12.29). For coarse wire, a single bull block is used, but for fine wire a large number of draw blocks are required, with the wire passing through a number of dies until it is reduced to its final size in one continuous operation. For fine wires reductions per pars of 15-25 per cent are commonly used, while for coarse wires the reduction per pass may be 20-25 per cent. Drawing speeds of modern wire drawing equipment may exceed 1500 metres per minute.

Nonferrous and low carbon steel wires are made in a number of tempers ranging from dead soft to full hard. Intermediate annealing

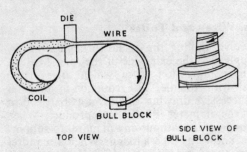

FIG. 12.29. Schematic representation of wire drawing.

may be required depending upto the metal and reductions involved. Steel wire with a carbon content more than 0.25 per cent is given a special patenting heat treatment. This consists in heating above the upper critical temperature and then cooling at a controlled rate or transforming in a lead bath at a temperature around 300°C to cause the formation of pearlite. This patenting process produces the best combination of strength and ductility for the successful drawing of high-carbon musical and spring wire.

(*iii*) **Tube drawing process**. Hollow cylinders or tubes made by hot forming processes (rolling, extrusion etc.) often are cold finished by drawing. Cold drawing is used to obtain closer dimensional tolerances to produce better surface finishes, to increase the mechanical properties of the tube by strain hardening, to produce tubes with thinner walls or smaller diameters than can be obtained with hot-forming methods, and to produce tubes of irregular shapes. Three basic types of tube drawing processes are (*a*) sinking, (*b*) plug drawing, and (*c*) mandrel drawing.

(*a*) *Sinking*. The process is shown in Fig. 12.30 *a*. In this case the inside of the tube is not supported and because of this reason, the wall thickness and surface become slightly uneven. The shearing at the entry and exit of the die is large, and as a result reduction strain is higher for sinking and the limiting deformation is lower than for other tube producing processes.

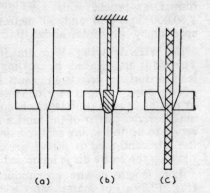

(*b*) *Plug drawing*. This process is shown in Fig. 12.30 *b*. Both the inner and outer diameters of the tube are controlled in drawing on a plug. The may be either cylindrical or conical.

FIG. 12.30. Methods of tube drawing: (*a*) sinking, (*b*) fixed plug, and (*c*) moving mandrel.

The plug controls the size and shape of the inside diameter and produces tubes of greater dimensional accuracy than in tube sinking. Because of the increased friction from the plug, the reduction in area rarely exceeds 30 per cent.

(c) *Mandrel drawing*. It is shown in Fig. 12.30 c. Problems with friction in tube drawing are minimised in drawing with long mandrel. The mandrel consists of a long hard rod or wire that extends over the entire length of the tube and is drawn through the die with the tube. In tube drawing with a moving mandrel, the draw force is transmitted to the metal partly by the pull on the exit sections and partly by the friction forces acting along the tube mandrel interface. After drawing, the mandrel is removed from the tube by rolling (reeling), which increases the tube diameter slightly and facilitates the removal of mandrel.

12.2. WELDING OR JOINING OF METALS

Welding is the process of joining together pieces of metal or metallic parts by bringing them into intimate proximity and heating the places

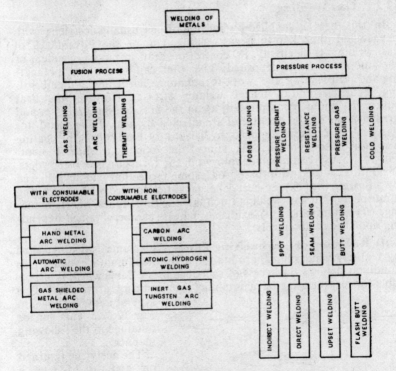

12.31. A chart showing the various welding processes.

of contact to a state of fusion or plasticity. It leads to the interpenetration of metal atoms in the weld zone and a strong inseparable joint is formed after cooling of metals. Welding is extensively used for the fabrication and erection of steel structure in industrial construction and civil engineering, vessels of welded-plate construction, etc. The wide use of welding at present is due to its economic advantages over other methods of joining metals such as rivetting, casting, etc. Welding processes may be classified according to the source of energy employed for heating the metals and the state of metal at the welding place. A chart showing the various welding processes is shown in Fig. 12.31.

12 2.1. Fusion Welding

In fusion welding, area is heated by a concentrated source of heat to a molten state and filler metal is added to the weld. Depending upon the method for feeding the filler metal to the weld, welding procedures are classified as manual, semiautomatic or automatic welding.

12 2.2. Gas Welding

In this heat is supplied by burning of gas usually acetylene with oxygen and thus known as gas welding. One of the advantages of gas welding is flexibility in control of heat in-put independent of the amount of metal deposited. The torch can be used for preheating and post heating the work to minimize hardening and embrittling tendencies and to relieve welding stresses. However, the heat source is not as concentrated as in the arc welding processes and greater areas of the base metal are affected by heat. Filler metal for gas-welded joints is supplied by coated or bare rods. The coating also shields or protects the joint from oxidation while it is hot. Fluxes are also commonly employed in the form of pastes or powders. If no flux is used with base rod, some protection can be achieved by adjusting the oxygen-acetylene gas ratio to provide a reducing atmosphere. In gas welding torch, all the three types, i.e. (*i*) reducing, (*ii*) neutral and (*iii*) oxidising flames can be obtained depending upon the requirements.

(*i*) **Reducing or carburising flame**. This flame is distinguished by feathery white plume around the inner blue luminous cone. This condition denotes the excess of acetylene in the flame which is responsible for recarburising or maintaining the reducing atmosphere This type of flame is shown in Fig. 12.32*a*. This can be obtained in the following manner:

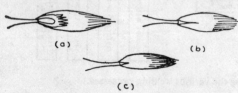

(a)　　(b)

(c)

FIG 12.32 Three types of gas flames for welding: (*a*) reducing, (*b*) neutral, and, (*c*) oxidising.

The acetylene is turned on and lit to give a yellow and smoky flame. The acetylene pressure is then increased until the smokiness just appears and the flame is quite bright. This condition gives approximately the correct amount of acetylene for the particular jet in use. The oxygen is then turned on as quickly as possible, and as its pressure is increased the flame ceases to be luminous and this will be reducing or carburising flame.

(*ii*) **Neutral flame.** If more oxygen is supplied to the carburising flame, the plume decreases in size until there is a clear-cut blue cone with no white fringe (Fig. 12.32*b*). This is the neutral flame which is used for most welding operations.

(*iii*) **Oxidising flame.** If the oxygen supply is further increased to the neutral flame, the inner blue cone becomes smaller and thinner and the outer envelope becomes streaky and the flame will be oxidising (Fig. 12.32*c*). Since the oxidising flame is more difficult to distinguish than the carburising flame, it is always best to start with excess acetylene and increase the oxygen supply until the neutral condition is reached instead of trying to obtain the neutral flame from the oxidising condition.

12.2.3. Arc Welding

Arc welding derives heat from an electric arc. The most common arc welding processes employ an arc between an electrode and the work piece. Some arc welding is performed with a twin-electrode torch held above the work, the arc being formed between the two electrodes. On the basis of the type of electrode used, arc welding can be classified into, (*i*) processes using consumable metal electrode and (*ii*) processes using a unconsumable electrode.

Processes using consumable electrode. It is most widely used process of welding employed in the engineering industries, building construction and for various types of repair. In this electrodes are made of various metals (steel, cast iron, stainless steel, copper, brass, bronze, aluminium etc.) depending upon their purpose and the chemical composition of the metals to be welded. Both bare and coated electrodes are widely employed. Various types of arc welding using consumable electrodes are:

(*a*) *Shielded metal arc welding.* This is commonly used for joining mild steel. Usually a coated consumable electrode is used which not only conducts the current for the arc but also supplies filler metal, fluxing and shielding material. Heat input to the weld is closely related to rate of metal-deposition, and hence the method is not as flexible as gas welding. However, since the heat source is more concentrated, efficiency is improved. Shielded metal arc welding is accomplished manually by using a hand electrode holder and start electrodes, or automatically by using long coiled electrode wire.

(*b*) *Submerged arc welding.* It is most widely used as an automatic process, employing uncoated coiled electrode wire. The flux and shielding compounds are fed into a funnel with the electrode projecting from the bottom. The arc formed between electrode and work is not visible because it is covered by the granulated flux. The electrode provides the filler metal needed for the purpose. Fig. 12.33 illustrates the principle of two types of welding.

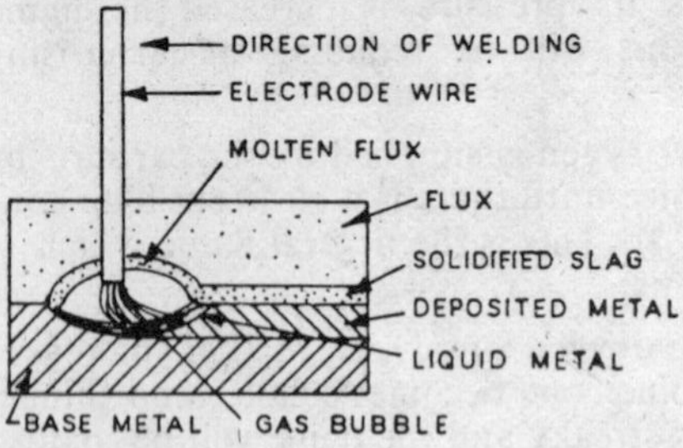

Processes using unconsumable electrodes. In this process electrodes may be of carbon, graphite, or tungsten. The carbon and graphite varieties are used only in d.c. arc welding. Tungsten electrodes are used for both a.c. and d.c. welding procedures in the atomic hydrogen and inert gas shielded

FIG. 12.33. Formation of the submerged-arc welding pool

arc processes. In these processes, function of electrodes is only to carry the current to the point of arcing.

(a) *Carbon arc welding*. This utilizes a single, slowly consumed inert gas shielded electrode or twin carbon electrodes held above the work. Both methods provide a means of controlling heat input independently of the rate of metal deposition.

(b) *Inert gas metal arc welding*. It uses a slowly consumed tungsten electrode. A water cooled electrode holder is used which also brings a supply of an inert gas, such as helium, down to the tip of the electrode, arc, and hot work piece. In this way oxidation and volatilization of the tungsten is retarded and the work is protected from reaction with the atmosphere making use of a flux unnecessary for most applications. Filler metal is supplied as a separate rod if

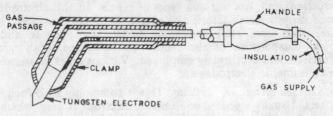

FIG. 12.34. Torch for argon welding.

required. In this process due to elimination of flux, troublesome problem of cleaning the joint after welding is also not required. A torch used for inert gas metal arc welding is shown in Fig. 12.34.

(c) *Atomic hydrogen welding*. In this alternating current arc is formed between two tungsten or carbon electrodes along which streams of hydrogen are fed to the welding zone. The molecules of hydrogen are dissociated by the high heat of the arc in the gap between the electrodes. The formation of atomic hydrogen proceeds with the absorption of heat. The stream of atomic hydrogen strikes the cooler surfaces of the metal and is again converted into molecular hydrogen. The metal is heated by the indirect arc and heat evolved due to conversion of atomic hydrogen into molecular form $(2H \rightleftharpoons H_2 + 1,00,600$ cals per mole). This produces a flame with a temperature of about 3700°C which shields the welding pool from oxidation and from saturation with nitrogen. Atomic hydrogen welding is applied in joining steels and light alloys of 2-10 mm thickness, welding critical designs operating under dynamic loads, high pressure or in a vacuum as well as other cases of air tightness.

12.2.4. Thermit Welding

This technique makes use of the heat supplied by the exothermic reaction involving the combustion of thermit (a mixture of powdered aluminium, 20-22 per cent and iron oxide in the form of mill scale 80 per cent). Thermit burns according to the following reaction:

$$Fe_2O_3 + 2Al \rightarrow Al_2O_3 + 2Fe + 1,85,000 \text{ cals.}$$

$$\text{per mole} \quad \ldots (12.1)$$

The reaction will proceed if the thermit is heated locally at one point to 1200-1300°C by means of ignition powder. A temperature of 3000°C may be attained in the reaction of thermit mixture, and a liquid reduced iron and slag are produced.

Thermit welding can be performed with or without pressure. In some cases coalescence may be achieved by applying the pressure after the parts are heated to a state of fusion. In all the thermit welding processes, a two piece refractory mould is fitted over the joint in which the abutting surfaces have been preliminarily cleaned. The chemical reaction occurs within a special crucible and the molten metal is poured into the mould. This metal either melts the abutting surfaces or brings them to a plastic state. Thermit welding is used in joining rails and pipes, and in repairing heavy parts.

12.2.5. Pressure Welding

This involves the heating of the metallic parts only to a plastic or slightly fused state and forcing them together with external pressure. Welding processes involving pressure include, (i) forge welding, (ii) pressure thermit welding, (iii) pressure gas welding, (iv) pressure resistance welding, and (v) cold welding. Out of these last three are of particular importance and are thus discussed as following:

Pressure gas welding. Abutting surfaces of the parts being welded are heated by oxyacetylene flame to a state of fusion or plasticity and then coalescence is produced by the application of mechanical force (Fig. 12.35). The parts to be welded are clamped in the special fixture and the abutting ends are rapidly heated over a restricted area by means of a multiple flame circular torch. Upsetting is done by the action of the pressure mechanism after the joint reaches the welding heat and the metal is brought to the plastic condition. Pressure gas welding finds wide application for joining pipe line mains, rails, tools etc. In this case atoms diffuse across the interfaces and recrystallisation takes place and the grains grow from one side to the other of the welded faces, since they are in close contact due to the applied pressure.

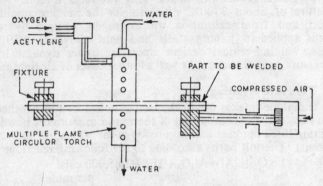

FIG. 12.35. Schematic diagram of pressure gas welding.

Cold pressure welding. This is a method of joining sections of metal together by application of pressure alone without heat or flux. Pressure is applied to the points to be welded at temperatures usually below the recrystallisation temperature of the metals. As a result the atoms on the welding interfaces become so close that they diffuse and thereby, a weld is obtained. The most important factor is cleanliness. Oxide and grease films are very troublesome, even when they are present in microscopic thickness. This type of welding can be applied satisfactorily in joining of dissimilar metals such as aluminium and copper.

Resistance welding. The resistance of the work to the flow of current is the source of heat in resistance welding. In this, the surfaces of the metals to be joined are heated first to plastic condition and then a high pressure is applied which facilitates the penetration of the atoms of each piece of metal into the other. A special feature of the resistance welding is the rapid heating of the surfaces being welded due to the application of currents of high amperage. Resistance welding is a high production process; it can be easily mechanised and automated. This finds extensive use in construction and engineering industries. The principal types of resistance welding are butt, spot and seam welding.

(*a*) *Resistance butt welding.* Resistance butt welding can be subdivided into upset, continuous flash butt, and intermittent flash butt welding.

Upset butt welding. In this the ends of the parts are brought into contact and heated by current to a plastic state, then the current is switched off and the metal is upset by the pressure applied between the abutting surfaces. This technique is illustrated in Fig. 12.36. This method is employed for joining parts of low carbon steel or non-ferrous metals having clean surfaces not over 1000 sq. mm. in area.

Continuous flash butt welding. In this, parts to be welded are un-prepared and are held in the jaws of the machine and brought into

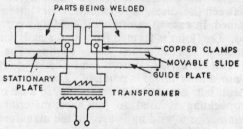

FIG. 12.36. Upset butt welding.

contact with the current switched on. After heating, the metal is upset with a pressure of 250-500 kg/cm². This squeezes out liquid metal and oxides formed on the joint surfaces and the abutted parts are welded together. This techique is used for joining thin walled tubes, rails, chain links, tools, and combinations of different metals such as steel-copper-brass, aluminium-copper, etc. The advantages of the process are high productivity and high quality of the welded joint. One disadvantage associated with the process is loss of metal in burning and flash.

Intermittent flash butt welding. This operation is performed by alternating tight and lighter contact of the parts to be joined by varying the pressure applied during the welding process. When the required stage of fusion is attained, the surfaces being welded are forced together sharply with a high pressure. This method is suitable in cases when the capacity of the equipment employed is insufficient for continuous flash welding.

(b) Resistance spot welding. In spot welding the parts are lapped and clamped between two bar-type metal electrodes which bring current to the work as well as apply the pressure. When the current is switched on, the lapped pieces of metal are heated in a restricted area. The generated heat melts the surface layer of metal in the central, highly heated area of contact with the electrodes and the adjacent layers are softened to a plastic state. Then the current is switched off and the electrodes are pressed. The spot weld pro-duced has a cast structure. For making elec-trodes, cold rolled electrolytic copper, tungsten base alloys and cadmium-bronze are suitable materials. Electrodes are of hollow design and are water colled. Spot welding is illustrated in Fig. 12.37.

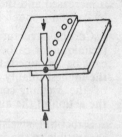

Spot welding is most widely used of the resistance welding processes. It finds extensive application in the air craft and automobile industries for manufacturing air frames and bodies, as well as railway, car building and the instrument industry, etc.

FIG. 12.37. Resistance spot welding.

(c) *Resistance seam welding*. In seam welding the electrodes are water cooled discs or rollers, carrying a pulsating current. As the work moves between the discs, a continuous or intermittant seam welding is obtained. In case of intermittent welding a current interrupter is employed. The joint is formed from the small portion of the work which melted and solidified upon cooling. The fusion zone has a typical cast structure. Fluxes and shielding gases are not usually used, nor a filler metal is required. The base metal, though affected by heat but not to the extent as in case of gas or arc welding. Seam welding is used to join sheet material with a total thickness of 4 mm. Seam welding is used in the manufacture of tanks, tubes and other articles of steel and nonferrous metals which must have airtight joints.

12.2.6. Weldability

Weldability may be defined as the capacity of being welded into reliable inseperable joints having specified properties (required strength and proper structure). The metals which are capable of forming a continuous series of solid solutions with each other exhibit the highest degree of weldability. Metals with limited solubility in the solid state have a lower weldability. Metals which are mutually insoluble in the solid state are entirely unweldable by fusion methods. Such metals are heated to plastic state and then a mechanical force is applied to bring the particles into close contact. In some cases, an intermediate metal is introduced when the metals to be welded are mutually insoluble. This third metal must be capable of diffusing or dissolving in both metals.

12.2.7. Weldability of Steels

The factors affecting the weldability of steels are their chemical composition, physical properties and the heat treatment given to steels. Carbon has a strong influence on the quality of weld. An increase in the carbon content affects the strength, hardness and toughness of steel. When the carbon content exceeds 0.3 per cent, the air hardening capacity of the transition zone in the base metal is increased and the steel becomes more brittle. The effect produced by carbon is much less in arc welding than in gas welding process.

Carbon structural steels have good weldability with any welding technique for carbon contents upto 0.27 per cent; satisfactory welds can be obtained for carbon contents upto 0.35 per cent. Welds of the highest quality can be made in these steels with proper selection of the welding conditions and if required protection is given against the action of the air on the molten metal.

Structural steels containing more than 0.36 per cent carbon are susceptible to the formation of hardening cracks, and thus require preheating before welding and subsequent heat treatment. The application of filler metal with a low carbon content prevents the hardening. Weld strength can be obtained by alloying the metal of the weld, with manganese, silicon and other elements. Sulphur and phosphorus are always deferimental to steels as brittleness and red shortness are caused by them, respectively.

12.2.8. Welding of Alloy Steels

Various difficulties arise in the welding of alloy steels. These include the burning out of the alloying elements, precipitation of carbides in heating, air hardening of the deposited metal and the transition zone, development of shrinkage stresses, and formation of cracks due to the low heat conductivity of certain grades of alloy steel. These difficulties can be overcome by not allowing the overheating of alloy steels by strictly observing the necessary welding conditions, using fluxes and coatings of special composition, preheating the work beforce welding and by heat treatment of the work piece after welding.

12.2.9. Welding of Cast Iron

The structural features of cast iron (presence of free graphite) and the high carbon content lead to considerable difficulties in welding. Furthermore, cracks may form in cast iron upon heating since ductility is low. Cast iron may be welded either hot or cold.

(i) **Hot welding.** Hot welding is performed by preheating the work to 600-650°C and maintaining at that temperature throughout the whole welding process. This retards the cooling of molten metal and thereby prevents chilling. Retarded coollng rate ensures more complete graphitization of the cast iron, prevents cracking, and enables a weld of high density. Cast iron welding rods containing upto 3.6 per cent silicon are used as filler metal. The flux is either calcined borax or a mixture of borax, sodium bicarbonate and silica. The welding ffame should be either carbonising or with a slight excess of acetylene. After making the weld, the part is covered with asbestos or coal dust to retard cooling.

(ii) **Cold welding.** The more common method is the cold welding of cast iron with an electric arc and no preheating is required in this method. The electrodes employed are cast iron or steel rods with a special coating, rods of copper and nickel alloys (monel metal) and others. Monel metal (70 Ni-30 Cu) is used to repair various defects in grey castings by welding. Since the temperature in welding cast iron should not exceed 30-34°C, the cold welding process should be done with a short weld. The finished weld is covered with asbestos sheet to retard cooling.

The welding of malleable iron is much simpler because it possesses a certain degree of ductility which avoids crack formation. Welding of high strength cast irons is much more difficult. First, it is difficult to obtain a weld with high mechanical properties and secondly these cast irons have an increased susceptibility to hardening and chilling.

Defects in grey cast iron castings may be repaired by means of gas welding, using rods of magnesium cast iron. Small defects can be welded over in such castings using arc welding with iron-nickel electrodes.

12 2.10. Welding of Aluminium and its Alloys

There are a number of unfavourable factors affecting the welding of aluminium and its alloy such as, (i) quick oxidation of aluminium to its oxide having melting point of 2050°C being higher than boiling point of aluminium, (ii) oxide film impedes fusion of edges, (iii) aluminium quickly passes from solid to liquid state which is often accompanied by buckling and sagging of whole areas of work or the formation of fractures, (iv) high conductivity and high latent heat of fusion requiring more heat for welding, (v) solubility of hydrogen in liquid aluminium, (vi) decreased solubility of hydrogen with fall in temperature, resulting in the formation of fine bubbles, which weaken the weld and the area near the weld zone, and (vii) large shrinkage of aluminium and its alloys upon solidification which results in cracks near the weld.

Taking into consideration the above facts, the edges of aluminium parts and filler rods are cleaned properly before welding, degreased with gasoline or a caustic soda solution and subjected to pickling in a solution (commercial caustic soda 45-55 gms, commercial NaF 40-50 gms and water 1 litre). The temperature of the pickling bath ranges from 50-70°C while the pickling time is 1 minute. After pickling, the parts are washed consecutively in cold and hot water.

Due to intensive oxidation in welding aluminium and its alloys, a flame with only small excess of acetylene is used. Powdered fluxes of special composition (50 KCl, 28 NaCl, 14 $LiCl_2$, 8 NaF) are used to dissolve the aluminium oxide film and to remove it from the welding pool. After welding, the slag and the remaining flux are removovd from the surface by scrubbing with warm water then a 5 per cent solution of nitric acid with 3 per cent potassium bichromate and again with water for 5 minutes. Finally the worked weld is dried. Welding of aluminium and its alloys can be performed by carbon-arc welding, atomic hydrogen welding and argon arc welding.

Tungesten inert gas (TIG) and metal inert gas (MIG) welding techniques are now a-days successfuly employed for welding of aluminium and its alloys. In the TIG process, a nonconsumable tungsten electrode is used and the molten metal is shielded by an inert gas, such as argon during and after the welding. Process to prevent oxidation of the metal. This process generally given a low rate of metal deposition and only thin sections can be joined. In the MIG process a consumable electrode in the form of a metal wire is fed continuously surrounded by an inert gas (argon) shield. The MIG process has largely overcome to limitations mentioned for the TIG process and the welds produced are sound and of high quality.

12.2.11. Welding of Magnesium Alloys

Magnesium actively combines with oxygen and form weaker oxide film which is poor in protection against corrosion of magnesium alloys. Problems arising in welding magnesium alloys are high inflamability, low melting point and the formation of the very refractory magnesium oxide (m.p. 2500°C) on the surface of the welding pool. Magnesium alloys not only oxidise on heating, but also actively combine with nitrogen, forming magnesium nitride which weakens the weld. Magnesium also dissolves hydrogen which leads to porosity of the weld. The techniques involved in welding magnesium alloys are similar to those used for aluminium alloys.

12.2.12. Welding of Copper and Its Alloys

Copper is welded either with a gas flame or a carbon arc. The filler rod used in gas welding is pure electrolytic copper or of copper containing upto 0.2 per cent phosphorus and 0.3 per cent silicon. These two elements act as intensive deoxidisers of the welding pool. Flux used is normally a mixture of borax (70 per cent), boric acid (10 per cent) and NaCl (20 per cent). Because of the high heat conductivity of copper, the torch used should be about 1.5-2 times larger than for welding steel. Both open and submerged-arc techniques are employed in the carbon arc welding of copper. In the open arc method the filler rods used are of phosphorus-copper and have a coating which includes borax, sodium acid phosphate, silicic acid, and charcoal. Special fluxes are employed in submerged arc welding.

12.2.13. Brazing and Soldering

These are the processes for joining solid metal parts by introducing a molten alloy (brazing filler metal or solder as the case may be, between them. The alloy used has lower melting point than that of base metal of the components joined. To obtain a strong joint, it is necessary that the brazing alloy or solder should properly wet the surfaces of the base metals and form solution with them. The greater the degree of interdiffusion between the molten alloy, or solder and the base metal, higher will be the mechanical strength of the joint. The joint strength also depends upon the cleanness of the joint parts in the area of the joint and therefore, a precleaning operation is required. Brazing and soldering can be employed to join parts of carbon and alloy steels of all grades, nonferrous metals and their alloys, as well as dissimilar metals and alloys. The distinction between brazing and soldering is in the temperature range in which the process is performed and thus depends upon the melting point of filler metal used.

(*i*) **Soldering**. Solders employed for this operation have a low melting point (upto 400°C) and the joint has a comparatively low strength. Soldering is employed when liquid tight joints are needed, with relatively low strength. Common solders are tin, lead, cadmium, bismuth, or zinc base alloys which are often known as soft solders to distinguish them from silver (hard) solder used for special uses. The soldering process comprises of preparing the surface for soldering and the actual soldering process. Surface preparation involves fitting the surfaces to each other, cleaning them of dirt, grease and oxide films and covering the cleaned surfaces with a flux ($ZnCl_2$, $ZnCl_2 + NH_4Cl$, or rosin). Soldering may be done by hand type soldering iron, a blow torch, by dipping in molten solder and other methods.

(*ii*) **Brazing**. Brazing alloys have a much higher melting point (upto 900°C) and produce a joint with high mechanical strength. Brazing filler metals are copper, silver, aluminium, magnesium and nickel base alloys. In brazing, the parts are first precleaned and a flux is applied to them. The parts are then heated together with the filler metal to the melting point of latter. Brazing may be done in a mechanised and automatic way which includes resistance brazing, induction brazing, arc brazing, dip brazing and others.

12.2.14. Arc and Oxygen Cutting of Metals and Alloys

Various metals and alloys can be cut by electric arc or a gas flame.

(*i*) **Arc cutting**. Both carbon and metal electrodes are employed in the arc cutting of metals. Removal of metals is affected by melting the metal with the heat of an electric arc at the cut. The application of compressed air to blow out the molten metal speeds up the cutting process. This type of cutting is used for demolition of steel structures and pipe line mains, for cutting up scrap, removing the gating system from castings, cutting nonferrous metals, steel and cost iron, etc. The use of metal electrodes improves the quality of the cut, reduces the width of the kerf and produces more evenly cut edges.

(*ii*) **Oxygen cutting (gas cutting)**. In various gas cutting processes the necessary temperature is maintained by means of flame obtained from the combustion of a fuel gas. Two most widely used processes are (*a*) straight oxygen cutting; and (*b*) metal powder and chemical flux cutting. The cutting is performed by ordinary gas welding equipment using a cutting torch.

(*a*) *Oxygen gas cutting*. It is based upon the ability of certain metals to burn in oxygen with the evolution of a large amount of heat which melts the metal and forms oxides. Carbon steels with a carbon content upto 0.7 per cent and low alloy steels are cut by this technique. High alloy steels are preheated to 650-700°C before cutting. However, cast iron, high alloy chromium and chrome nickel steels and nonferrous alloys cannot be cut effectively.

(*b*) *Metal powder cutting*. It consists of introducing a finely divided metal power into the cutting zone with a stream of oxygen along with the oxy-acetylene cutting torch. The powder burns in the oxygen stream and generates additional heat which facilitates the melting of the refractory oxides and their removal from the cutting zone by the stream of oxygen. This process is suitable for cutting stainless and heat resistant steels, cast iron and certain nonferrous metals and alloys. The metal powder is generallv iron powder of 0.2 mm size or finer.

(c) *Oxygen-arc cutting*. It involves the preheating of the metal to be cut by an electric arc. The electrode is a steel tube through which the cutting oxygen is delivered.

12.2.15. Metallurgical Processes Occurring in Welding

The metal filling and adjoining the weld (near weld zone) area undergo phase transformations in fusion welding due to the rapid heating to the melting point and subsequent cooling. The melting and cooling conditions in the weld itself and the asso-ciated structural changes in the metal of the near-weld zone determine the properties of the welded joint as a whole The structure of a single 'V' weld after solidification and the temperature distribution curve in steel at the moment of welding are shown schema-tically in Fig. 12.38. The depo-sited layer in zone-2 is obtain-ed by the melting of the filler

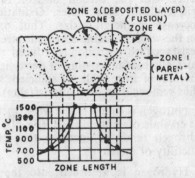

FIG. 12.38. Weld structure and tempe-rature distribution in welding steel.

metal and by its mixing with the parent metal in the narrow fusion zone-3. In the fusion zone, the parent metal is brought to the molten state so that it is rapidly penetrated by the deposited metal and a sound weld is formed

After solidification various impurities and dirt which get into the deposited metal (oxide, slag, inclusions etc.) are located on the grain boundaries which decrease the strength and ductility of the deposited metal. The pure the deposited metal, higher will be the mechanical properties of the welded joint. As a rule, the deposited metal is of columnar (dendritic) structure, which is a characteristic of cast steel. If the deposited metal or the adjacent zone of the parent metal is overheated to a high degree, then during cooling, the grains of the parent metal will acquire an acicular (needle like) shape, forming the so-called widmänstaten structure. The overheated metal has a lower strength and the weld is more brittle.

A zone of heat-affected metal-4 is formed in parent metal of welds. In this zone only the structure of the metal is changed by the rapid heating and cooling during the welding process; its chemical compo-sition remains unchanged. The size of the heat affected zone depends upon the welding method employed and the nature of metals. The structure changes of the parent metal in the heat affected zone of the weld have a negligible effect on mechanical properties of low-carbon steel regardless of the welding method employed. In welding of certain grades of structural steel, however, hardened structures may be formed in the heat affected zone of the weld which sharply reduce the ductility of the welded joint and frequently lead to crack formation.

12.2.16. Absorption of Gases in Welding and Their Effect

The weld may absorb oxygen, nitrogen, and hydrogen during welding. Oxygen may be absorbed into the weld forming iron oxide (Fe_3O_4) and other oxides such as SiO_2. This iron oxide formed may react with the carbon of iron forming carbon monoxide and thus will result in blow holes. Oxidation of the weld produces great increase in the grain size. Thus, oxygen absorption has a bad effect on the weld, reducing its tensile strength and ductility, whereas its resistance to corrosion is reduced. Therefore, arc welding electrodes normally contain coating of deoxidising material to prevent the formation of iron oxide, or sufficient silica to react with iron oxide and thus remove it as iron silicate (slag).

Nitrogen is found in the weld metal as trapped in blow holes and as crystals of iron nitride (Fe_4N), known as nitride needles. The nitrogen tends to increase the tensile strength but decreases the ductility of metal.

Hydrogen is absorbed into the ferrite of mild-steel weld metal during arc welding with covered electrodes. The hydrogen is present in the composition of the flux coating and in its moisture content. It begins to diffuse out of the ferrite of the weld metal immediately after the welding process, and continues over a long period. The presence of this hydrogen reduces the tensile strength of the weld.

12.2.17. Weld Decay

The austenitic stainless steels have one great drawback that on heating between 500 to 900°C, carbon is absorbed by the chromium and its carbide is precipitated along the grain boundaries. This results in reduction of chromium content from adjacent metal near grain boundaries to such an extent that corrosion resistance of stainless steel is highly reduced. This temperature range (500-900°C) is encountered during welding, and a zone at this temperature exists near the weld and runs parallel to the weld. This zone is now non-resistant to corrosive attack and when corrosion occurs in service, it is termed as *weld decay*, although no decay occurs in the weld itself but it happens in a zone near the weld. This trouble can be eliminated by a heat treatment in which the welded parts are heated to 950-1100°C and water quenched. However, this heat treatment presents a difficulty in case of larger parts. This difficulty, however, has been overcome by addition of titanium or niobium metal to stainless steel as an alloying element because titanium has a greater affinity for carbon than chromium. Thus the formation of chromium carbide is prevented and there is no deficency of chromium in these regions and no weld decay occurs.

12 3. MACHINING OF METALS

Machining operations produce the required shape by removal of selected areas of the work piece. Most machining is accomplished by straining a local region of the work piece by the relative motion of the tool and work piece. Machining usually is employed to produce shapes with high dimensional tolerance, good surface finish, and often with complex geometry. Machining in general is secondary processing operation, since it is normally carried out on a work piece produced by other processes such as hot rolling, forging or casting. In the machining, working motion is imparted to the work and cutting tool by the mechanisms of the machine tool so that the work and tool travel relative to each other. A combination of two types of motion i.e. primary cutting motion (given to work) and feed motion (given to tool) are required in machining. Most widely used metal cutting machining methods are turning, drilling, boring, milling, planing and grinding.

12 3.1. Turning

This operation is performed on lathe type machine tools where the primary cutting motion (rotary) is imparted to the work and feed motion (along the axis of the work) is imported to the tool. This is illustrated in Fig. 12.39.

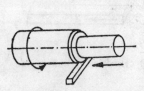

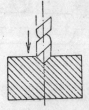

FIG. 12.39. Illustration of turning.   FIG. 12.40. Illustration of drilling.

12.3.2 Drilling

This operation is used to produce round holes. Drilling machines use a rotating tool, such as twist drill, which is fed into the work as the drill turns (Fig. 12.40) The simplest drilling machine is a drill press with a single spindle. Very complex multiple spindle machines have been developed which drill upto 100 holes simultaneously. These are used for drilling cylinder blocks for internal combustion engines.

12.3.3. Boring

This generally consists of finishing holes which have been drilled or cast. Usually the boring is accomplished by rotating a single point offset tool while the work is held stationary. On some boring machines, particularly on the larger sizes, the tool is held in fixed position while the work rotates. Some boring machines are also used for drilling and milling.

12.3.4. Milling

In this a rotating tool is used with multiple cutting edges. Thin

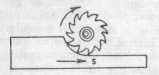

milling cutters are silmiar to circular saws. As in other machines using multipoint cutters, metal is removed very rapidly by miller (Fig. 12.41). Milling is used to produce flat surfaces, helical grooves, contours, splines, and similar work. The similar

FIG. 12.41. Milling operation.

operations such as planing and shaping are performed on planers and shapers.

12.3.5. Grinding

This operation is essential in all metal cutting operations because by grinding the cutting tools are shaped. In all cases, the primary cutting motion is rotary and is imparted to the grinding wheel. The feed motion is imparted to the work in external cylindrical grinding

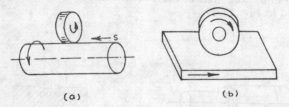

(a)   (b)

FIG. 12.42. Grinding operation: (a) cylindrical grinding, and (b) surface grinding.

(Fig. 12.42). In surface grinding a longitudinal reciprocating feed motion is imparted to the work and cross-feed motion to the grinding wheel. The cutting characteristics of the wheels are controlled by selection of abrasive materials. The grinding wheels themselves are shaped by dressing their surfaces with diamond-tipped tools. The action of the abrasive particles in a grinding wheel is similar to that of the cutting teeth of a milling cutter. An accuracy with in 0.000125 mm can be achieved by grinding.

12.3.6. Machinability

The ability of a material to be removed combined with the ability to maintain dimensions and develop a satisfactory finish is termed as machinability. The ease of removing metal depends upon tool wear and power consumption. A material has good machinability if the tool wear is low, the tool life is long, the cutting forces are low, the chips are well behaved and break into small ringlets instead of long snarls, and the surface finish is acceptable. Ideal mechanical properties for good machinability are low strength and hardness combined with poor ductility. According to this, magnesium-alloys are among the most machinable of the common structural alloys. Following factors affect the machinability of a metal:

(*i*) **Proper use of the cutting fluids.** A large number of materials are used for cutting fluids, each suited to particular cutting requirements. The cutting fluid acts as a lubricant, thereby contributing to tool life and reducing power consumption. The cutting fluid also functions as a coolant to prevent localised heating of the cutting tool and stabilizes the over-all temperature of the work piece. This avoids the phase change due to which residual stresses and cracks are formed. It also prevents thermal expansion and contraction due to which better dimensional control is possible. Cutting fluids also retards the corrosion of the work piece and machine tools in some instances.

(*ii*) **Temperature of the work-piece.** An increase in temperature decreases the hardness of the work, sometimes resulting in longer tool life and lower power consumption. This is accomplished by gas torches and induction heating. Lowering the temperature eliminates the built of edge and improves surface finish of some alloys. This may be associated with decrease in ductility or welding tendencies, or both. Lowering the temperature is not practised industrially.

(*iii*) **Residual stresses.** Residual stresses present in the work piece as a result of prior history may cause distortion after metal removal. For example, a cast slab with residual stresses in the surface will warp to produce an upward cavity on milling or planing the upper layers. Micro-residual stresses are introduced in the surface layers of metal by machining operation. Though these stresses usually do not cause warping, they may seriously affect service behaviour under fatigue loads or in a corrosive environment.

(*iv*) **Machinability ratings.** As a general rule, the nonferrous structural metals are more easily machined as compared to ferrous metals. In the decreasing order of machinability, some common metals and alloys are: magnesium, aluminium, brass, bronze, free machining steel, grey cast iron, carbon steel, alloy steel, stainless steel, etc. Machinability ratings vary depending upon the technique by which they are determined. One technique is based on the amount of metal removed for a given amount of tool wear; another depends upon measurement of power consumption. Ratings are not only dependent upon the method of determination but they also depend upon the particular metal cutting operation used in their measurement.

12.4. CASTING PROCESSES

Many metallic articles may be produced in the foundary in the form of castings. This method involves melting the metal and then pouring or forcing it into a properly formed mould where it solidifies as a casting with a size and shape as a reproduction of the mould cavity. After removing the gates, risers etc. the casting becomes acceptable for further processing step or direct use. Castings are made of almost all ferrous as well as non-ferrous metals and their alloys. Casting processes enable the production of intricate shape, e.g. cylinder blocks of automobile and airflame engines, pistons and piston rings, machine tool beds and frames, mill rolls, wheels and housings of steam and hydraulic turbines, water supply, etc. This feature has found widest application in engineering, metallurgical, building, chemical and other industries.

The principal casting processes are classified according to the kind of moulding devices used. These are: Sand moulds, resin bonded shell moulds, permanent and semipermanent metal moulds, die casting metal moulds, plaster moulds, and investment moulds. A mould is a kind of container in which molten metal flows and fills the cavity and then solidifies to give the required shape.

12.4.1. Sand Casting

The first step in the production of sand casting is to make a metal or wooden pattern. The pattern is a replica of the part being made but has slightly larger dimensions to allow for shrinkage during solidification and cooling of the casting. However, the pattern is not an exact copy of the part to be cast since it incorporates projections (core prints) which form recesses in the sand to hold cores in the mould. The pattern is often made in two or more parts so that it can be removed easily from the mould. To make the mould, a suitable sand mixture (consisting of pure sand, clay and moisture) is rammed or packed around the pattern, the sand being held in place by a box-like container consisting of cope and drag known as a flask. After the flask is filled with sand and the necessary gates, risers etc. are added, the pattern is withdrawn leaving a mould cavity similar to the finished casting. If some hollow spaces are required in the casting, such as axle hole in a wheel, sand moulded in the shape of the hollow space (cores) must be placed in the mould cavity. The sand in mould and clay are held together by clay and other bonding agents. If the moulds are baked, they are known as dry sand moulds. If used in the moist condition, they are known as green sand moulds. Dry sand moulds are stronger and show greater resistance to corrosion and crushing. To allow opening of the mould to remove the pattern after ramming, the flask is made in two parts. the cope and drag, which are held in alignment with guide pins. The cope and drag sand bodies separate at the parting line or flask joint.

Foundry sands are sufficienty refractory to resist the high temperatures encountered, and their porosity allows free escape of gases formed inside the mould. Surface quality of sand casting is improved by covering the pattern with fine sand known as facing sand.

Although dry sand moulds are more expensive than green, but the advantages such as avoiding defects caused by the presence of mois-

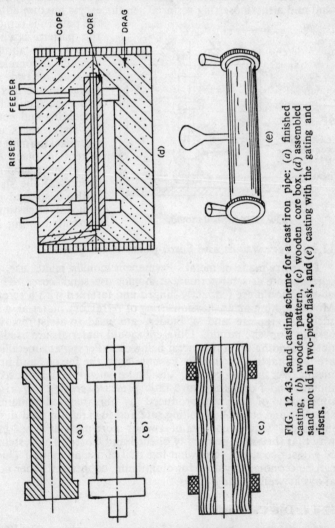

FIG. 12.43. Sand casting scheme for a cast iron pipe: (a) finished casting, (b) wooden pattern, (c) wooden core box, (d) assembled sand mould in two-piece flask, and (e) casting with the gating and risers.

ture leads to production of smoother castings and no chill areas formed. Another variation of sand mould is a skin dried mould in which only the surface of the mould cavity is dried. A simple arrangement for casting a pipe in sand mould is shown in Fig. 12.43.

12.4.2. Plastic Bonded Shell Moulding

This is a modification of sand casting. It involves heating of a metal pattern to about 175-250°C and then spraying with a silicon emulsion to prevent adhesion of the moulding material. After this, the pattern is brought into contact with a batch of a dry mixture of sand and a thermosetting resin. Then the excess mixture adhering to

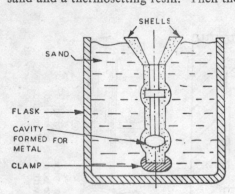

FIG. 12.44. Shell mould.

the pattern is removed and the pattern is cured for a period of about 25-30 seconds. A complete mould consists of two matching shells held firmly together either mechanically or by cementing and surrounded by metal shots or some other backing material wnich is kept in place by flask. As in other sand moulding processes, the shell mould is also destroyed after the removal of casting. This is illustrated in Fig 12.44.

12.4.3. Permanent and Semi-permanent Mould

There are made of metal. Permanent moulds make use of metal cores, where as semi-permanent moulds use sand cores. The halves of the mould are fequently hinged and fastened with a screw device. Mould coating or washes consisting of refractory material, a lubricant such as graphite and a binder, are used to assist removal of the casting from the mould. Different mould materials are used in practice depending upon the metal being cast. Permanent metallic moulds are adaptable for use in casting both the ferrous and nonferrous metals. As in sand casting, the liquid metal is introduced to the moulds under only the hydrostatic pressure, created by risers The superiority of castings produced by this method is mainly due to selective and controlled colling rate and to careful mould design. An individual mould consists of two or more parts attached in such a way that they may be readily opened and closed. The system consists of gates, risers, etc. somewhat like that of a sand mould. This method can be economically used for aluminium, copper and other nonferrous alloys as well as alloy steels.

12.4.4. Die Casting

It is an improved variation of permanent mould casting. The essential features of die casting are shown in Fig. 12 45. In die casting the metal is forced into the mould or die under pressure, whereas in case of permanent mould casting only hydrostatic pressure created by gravity is employed. Half of the die is rigidely attached and the other half is movable. Design of the casting is such that the casting tends to adhere to the movable protion of the die. As the mould

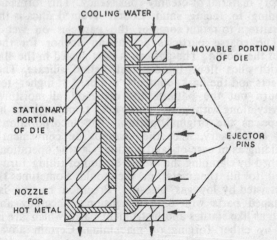

FIG. 12.45. Schematic diagram for die casting.

opens, the casting is carried with the movable portion of the die until knocked clear by the ejection pins shown in Fig. 12.45. Dies are oil or water cooled to permit more-rapid operation. When hot metal enters the mould, it forces the air from the die cavity through shallow grooves ground in the die faces.

Die casting process possesses numerous advantages. The method permits repetition and lends itself efficiently to mass production programmes. Complicated shapes and close dimensional tolerances are easily obtained in the die casting parts. Inserts made from different types of metals may be integrated with the die casting with little difficulty. Numerous alloys having wide range of properties may be adopted to die casting to meet the diversified demands of modern industry. A high percentage of all die castings utilized today are of the zinc-base alloys. Other than the zinc alloys, aluminium and its alloys, magnesium and its alloys and brass are commonly used for die casting. The automobile industry uses high percentage of all die castings made which include speedometer parts, grill work, wind shield motor parts, ash trays, horns, parts of telescopes, house-hold machines, bathroom hardwares, cameras, clocks, locks, pulleys etc.

12.4.5. Investment Moulds

These are used for making precision castings. This technique is also known as lost wax process. The process is unique in that both a new pattern and a new mould are required for each casting. Thermoplastic or themosetting resins, low melting alloys, and waxes are used to make pattern. The pattern in real sense is a die casting or injection moulded part reproducing the datails of the finished objects. The pattern is dipped into a mixture of water and fine grained refractory material of creamy consistency. This forms a thin layer corresponding to facing sand. Coarse grained silica is then shifted over the pattern to retain some of the particles on wet refractory coating. The coarse particles act as an anchor for the backing material of the mould. The pattern is next placed in the flask which is filled with silica flour bonded with ethyl silicate. The backing material sets and the flask contents are fired at higher temperature to melt/burn out the pattern and drive off all moisture. A clean mould cavity along with gates, risers ect. remains there having the same shape as the original pattern. The incorporation of gates, risers, etc. is necessary, since they cannot be conveniently formed after moulding as in case of sand casting. Casting operation is usually accomplished by clamping the mould on top of tilting furnace which is inverted to fill the metal in the mould. Sometimes the flow of metal is assisted by low gas pressure. Precision casting is done to obtain shaped parts with high dimensional accuracy and surface finish such as like statues and instrument parts which are impractical to make by either forging or machining. Certain advantages of precision investment casting are:

(i) Casting of high pouring temperature alloys can be obtained to accurate dimensions. The metallic mould processes are not suitable for steel and other alloys which must be poured at high temperature.

(ii) Casting of exterior and interior intricacy can be cast.

(iii) Thin sections may be cast even in the high pouring temperature alloys because of the heated moulds.

12.4.6. Plaster Moulds

These are similar to sand moulds excepting that a mixture of plaster (gypsum and some ingredients such as talc, asbestos fibre, silica flour, etc.) and water is poured in a flask which holds a pattern. When the plaster has commenced to set, the pattern is withdrawn. If cores are required, they too are made of plaster. Moulds and cores are baked at about 200°C for 10-20 hours (depending upon metal to be cast) to eliminate water and produce a porous mould through which entrapped air and gases can escape. For making plaster moulds, generally metal patterns are necessary because the water in the plaster raises the grain on wood pattern and makes them almost impossible to draw. The plaster can be partially dehydrated at higher drying temperatures but the mould strength will be lost with dehydration. The time required for curing plaster moulds is a disadvantage of the process. However, because of dimentional accuracy and surface finish, many castings such as rubber tier moulds, foam rubber moulds, cast match plates, etc. are produced by this process.

12.4.7. Centrifugal Casting

This is a special form of permanent mould casting, using a rotating mould which throws the metal outward against the mould walls. In this method the centrifugal force created by the rotation of mould about either horizontal or vertical axis causes the molten metal to flow into the mould cavity to produce a casting of higher density than is possible from the hydrostatic head of risers. Where thin and intricate sections, surface lettering, numerals, or other details are involved and high densities are required, centrifugal casting is used with great satisfaction. The centrifugal casting of hollow parts is possible at a lower production cost. Cost iron pipe is made in a centrifugal mould having a horizontal axis.

Centrifugal casting of some parts may be effectively accomplished with the axis of rotation in a vertical position. Wheels, pulleys and similar parts are sometimes made with advantage in a stack mould

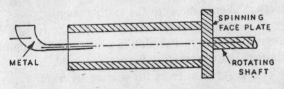

FIG. 12.46. Centrifugal casting of a pipe (rotating on horizontal axis).

by means of semi-centrifugal casting with the axis of rotation being vertical. A schematic diagram of centrifugal casting technique is shown in Fig. 12.46.

12.4.8. Continuous Casting

The process consists of pouring molten metal into the upper opening of a vertical mould from which the heat is being dissipated rapidly. The solidified material is removed in a continuous and uninterrupted manner from below. The mould is surrounded by high velocity water to carry the heat away rapidly. To initiate the process, a starting bar that fits up into the mould is brought into position near the upper end of the mould space to support the first metal poured (Fig. 12.47). After solidification starts, the withdrawing rolls lower the starting bar, and the piece is thus cast at a rate that corresponds to the pouring rate. After the starting bar has cleared the withdrawing rolls, it is removed, subsequently, the

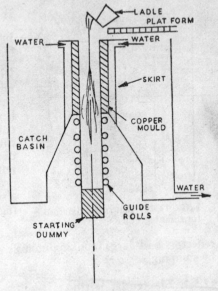

FIG. 12.47. Schematic illustration of cotinuous costing.

casting is cut to convenient length by means of an oxygen cutting torch located below the withdrawing rolls. The advantages of the process include:

(*i*) High yield of casting from a given liquid metal.

(*ii*) Good casting surfaces that require little or no conditioning.

(*iii*) Extremely low capital costs per tonne year of producing capacity.

(*iv*) Continuous casting is successfully applied to copper, aluminium and their alloys, steel etc. for making various solid sections and tubes.

In short, continuous casting involves the following sequence of operations:

(*i*) Delivery of liquid metal to the casting stand.

(*ii*) Flow of metal through a distributor into the casting mould.

(*iii*) Formation of the cast section in a water cooled mould.

(*iv*) Withdrawal of the casting from the mould.

(*v*) Further heat removal from the casting by water spray beneath the mould.

(*vi*) Cutting and removal of the cast pieces.

12.5. SPECIAL METHODS OF METAL PROCESSING

12.5.1. Spinning

It is used to shape blanks held in a spinning lathe under the action

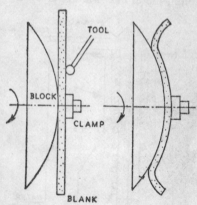

FIG. 12.48. Schematic diagram for spinning.

of pressure brought to bear by a spinning tool. The metal blank is clamped against a block of the form required which is rotated at high speed. The blank is progressively formed against the block either with a mannual tool or by means of small diameter work rolls (Fig. 12.48). Spinning is restricted to shapes which are concentric about the axis of rotation. It is used in place of deep drawing if production does not justify the high cost of deep drawing punches and dies. It is also used for necking down, flanging, bulging, and curling the ends of a tubing and cylinder. Tank heads, television cones, light reflectors and large cooking utensils are examples of products made by spinning.

12.5.2. Electrodeposition

Electroplating and electroforming are two processes based on electrodeposition. Eelctroplating usually involves application of a fairly thin (0.0008 to 0.025 mm) coating of metal on metallic or nonmetallic objects. The purpose of such coatings is to improve resistance to corrosion, corrosion fatigue, fatigue and wear. Plating is also used to improve appearance and to build up undersized parts. Electroforming in contrast to electroplating, involves deposition of fairly thick (upto about 15 mm) layers of metal over a mandrel or matrix. The mandril, which is made of low-melting alloy, wax, rubber, or similar material, is later removed from the electroformed shape. The process is advantageously used in the production of complicated parts, particularly those having complex internal shapes and required to produce to close dimensions. Examples of the etectro-formed objects are wave guides for radar and television equipment, moulds used in forming plastics, and moulds for rubber tires. Control of quality is accomplished in electrodeposition by careful regulation of current density and temperature of the plastic bath.

12.5.3. Explosive Forming

This technique is well suited for producing large parts of sheet metal with a relatively low number of objects. The sheet metal blank is placed over a die cavity and an explosive charge is detonated in water stored in a pit at an appropriate stand off distance from the blank. The shock wave propagating from the explosion serves as a "frictionless punch" to deform the blank. The pit must withstand repeated inpact of explosive shocks and be large enough to contain the effects of the maximum weight of charge used. Most of the pits are provided with some means of moderating the shock wave before it strikes the pit wall.

The capital cost of an explosive-forming facility is less than that of conventional equipment of equal capability by a factor ranging from 10:1 to 50:1. On the other hand, labour costs per part can be appreciably higher for explosive forming since production rates are lower and automation is difficult. The explosives used are of two types:

(i) high explosives such as dynamite, PETN, TNT, and RDX developing a pulse of very high pressure for a relatively short duration, and

(ii) low explosives such as gun powder or cordite developing much lower pressures sustained over longer periods. The explosives may be used in a closed or open system of tooling.

In the closed system (Fig. 12.49 a), the die encloses the explosive completely and the work piece is interposed between the forming surface of the die and explosive. The process is generally used with low explosives, and because the pressure is sustained by the confinement of the gases, it is particularly useful for the forming of thin materials to close tolerances. The system is limited by the size of part which it can produce because the thickness of the die wall must be increased proportionately with the size of object. For the forming of tubular shapes having diameter more than 50 mm, the die cost becomes uneconomical whereas for nontubular shapes it is uneconomical for less than 50 mm. The die cavity detriorates progressively because of gas erosion, whilst explosion debris may mark the surface of the object. The premature failure of a closed die system may present a safety hazard.

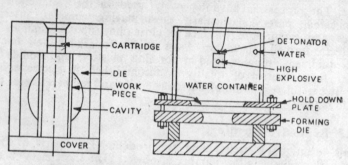

FIG. 12.49. Schematic diagram of explosive forming:
(a) forming tubular products in a closed system, and
(b) forming dished products in an open system.

In the open system (Fig. 12.49 b), an explosive charge is detonated at a predetermined distance from the work piece. The complete assembly may be immersed, in water tank, or a plastic bag filled with water may be placed over the work piece. The explosive force acts equally in all directions, and in consequence only a small part of the total energy released is used in the forming operation. The magnitude of the pressure pulse depends on:

(i) the type and amount of explosive charge,

(ii) the stand-off distance,

(iii) the intervening medium (water, air, plasticine, rubber etc.) and

(iv) the manner in which the explosive charge is confined.

The shapes produced by explosive forming have range from stainless-steel dentures, steel helmets, and hemispherical dishes, etc. to communication reflectors and contoured panels in sizes from millimetres to metres.

QUESTIONS

1. What are the metallurgical advantages of hot working over cold working?
2 What effect will preheating have on the microstructure of the weld area in high carbon steel?
3. What effect does welding have on the grain size of the metal?
4. Explain briefly with a neat sketch, the process of extrusion.

5. What are the advantages of extrusion over rolling and forging?

6. Write short notes on, (a) drop forging, (b) fusion welding, electroforming, deep drawing, spinning, explosive forming.

7. How are neutral, reducing and oxidising flames obtained in a welding torch? Sketch the flames and state their specific uses.

8. How does thermit welding process differ from ordinary arc welding? State their applications in metallurgy.

9. Explain briefly with a neat sketch, the process of wire drawing.

10. Compare hot rolled and cold drawn steel bar with reference to the tensile strength, yield strength and machinability.

11. Explain with a neat sketch the process of forging. How and why are the directional properties obtained in a forged component?

12. What is the method of production for making either beams or rails? Briefly state the principle of operation.

13. Describe with sketches the two methods of hot working steel, viz. forging and rolling.

14. What are the various metal processing methods?

15. What are the various types of casting processes? Discuss them briefly.

16. Describe the process of continuous casting with its merits and limitations.

17. What are the various types of rolling mills? Illustrate with simple sketches.

18. Write short notes on the following:

    (a) Brazing,

    (b) Soldering,

    (c) Welding of aluminium and its alloys,

    (d) Gas welding,

    (e) Resistance spot welding,

    (f) Welding cast iron.

19. Define weldability. Discuss it in case of alloy steels, cast iron and aluminium alloys.

20. What are the various processes of machining? Discuss briefly with the neat sketches.

21. Define machinability. Describe briefly the various factors affecting machinability.

22. Describe briefly the various steps involved in forging.

23. What are the various equipments used in forging? Give their neat sketches.

24. Describe briefly with neat sketches the processes of tube, rod and wire drawing.

13

CORROSION

Corrosion is an unintentional gradual destruction of a metal by chemical or electrochemical attack. This includes the destruction of materials in all types of environments atmospheres and liquids, and at any temperature. As a result of corrosion the metal gets converted to its compounds such as oxide, chloride, nitrate, sulphate etc. depending upon the environment. Due to corrosion, the metal loses its strength, ductility and finally it may fail suddenly under service conditions.

13.1. TYPICAL CHEMICAL REACTIONS INVOLVED IN CORROSION

Common types of corrosion may be expressed by one or more of the following general reactions:

(a) Combination of metals with nonmetals in the absence of water

$$M + X \rightarrow MX \qquad \qquad \ldots (13.1)$$

where M is a metallic element, and X is a nonmetallic substance. For example, oxidation of iron or steel at high temperature in dry air

$$2Fe + O_2 \rightarrow 2FeO \qquad \qquad \ldots (13.2)$$

and finally Fe_2O_3 may be formed as a corrosion product.

(b) Combination of metals with oxygen in the presence of water

$$M + 1/2\ O_2 + H_2O \rightarrow M(OH)_2 \qquad \qquad \ldots (13.3)$$

An important example of this type of reaction is the rusting of iron under atmospheric conditions:

$$Fe + 1/2\ O_2 + H_2O \rightarrow Fe(OH)_2 \qquad \qquad \ldots (13.4)$$

In dry air at room temperature iron and steel do not rust. In moist air the iron hydroxide which is formed [$(Fe(OH)_2$ or $Fe(OH)_3$] frequently decomposes to the appropriate oxide (FeO or Fe_2O_3) with loss of moisture;

$$Fe(OH)_2 \rightarrow FeO + H_2O \qquad \qquad \ldots (13.5)$$

The net reaction may be represented as

$$\overset{H_2O}{Fe + 1/2\ O_2\ \rightarrow\ FeO} \qquad\qquad \ldots (13.6)$$

(c) Displacement of hydrogen from acids or acid solutions:

$$M + H_2Y \rightarrow MY + H_2 \qquad\qquad \ldots (13.7)$$

where Y may be sulphate/chloride/sulphide etc. Examples of this reaction are, the attack of iron by sulphuric acid or hydrochloric acid and tarnishing of silver by H_2S in the presence of moisture

$$\overset{H_2O}{2Ag + H_2S\ \rightarrow\ Ag_2S + H_2} \qquad\qquad \ldots (13.8)$$

(d) Displacement of hydrogen from water which usually contain small amounts of dissolved inorganic substances;

$$M + 2H_2O \rightarrow M(OH)_2 + H_2 \qquad\qquad \ldots (13.9)$$

The rusting of iron in water is a form of corrosion involving this reaction.

(e) Displacement of one metal by another metal from a salt solution,

$$M' + MSO_4 \rightarrow M'SO_4 + M \qquad\qquad \ldots (13.10)$$

If iron is immersed in a solution of copper sulphate, copper will get precipitated and the iron will go into solution.

13.2. MECHANISM OF CORROSION

There are three basic mechanisms of corrosion, of which *direct chemical attack* and *electrochemical attack* are important. A third ore involving *physical mechanism* is less common.

13.2.1. Physical Mechanism

Corrosion by molten metals involves the dissolution or cracking of solid metals in acontact with liquid metals. The attack is caused owing to physical dissolution with alloy formation and sometimes due to penetration of liquid metal into the grain boundaries. Examples are (i) attack of mercury on brass leading to cracking in presence of mechanical stress, and (ii) attack of mercury on aluminium which is rapidly oxidised after amalgamation, since a protecting oxide film can no longer form.

13.2.2. Direct Chemical Attack

It includes all kinds of mechanisms in which there is no appreciable flow of current through the metal for reasonable distances and on macroscopic scale. Direct chemical attack usually results in fairly uniform attack over the surface of the metal. The examples are (i) rusting of iron and steel according to reactions (13.4) and (13.9); (ii) high temperature scaling of iron according to reaction (13.2); (iii) corrosion of copper by combustion products containing oxygen, moisture and oxides of sulphur. In this case adherent basic copper sulphate is formed which mostly provides protection against further corrosion; (iv) tarnishing of silver were in which direct chemical attack occurs according to reaction (13.8), (v) corrosion of aluminium in chlorinated hydrocarbons, such as CCl_4 and $CHCl_3$ and in alcohols; and (vi) corrosion of magnesium and titanium in methanol.

These reaction mechanisms are similar whether the corroding medium is liquid or gaseous and is largely nonelectrochemical in nature.

13.2.3. Electrochemical Corrosion

This important mechanism of corrosion characterised by the establishment of anode and cathode areas separated by finite distance in the metal causing flow of current between these two areas. Depending upon the conditions, either galvanic or concentration cells are set-up. Sometimes both kinds of cells may exist simultaneously.

Galvanic corrosion. When two dissimilar metals immersed in an electrolyte solution are electrically connected, a galvanic cell is formed as shown in Fig. 13.1. The metal higher in e.m.f. series tends

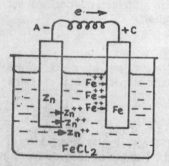

FIG. 13.1. Schematic illustration of galvanic cell.

to be attacked and becomes the anode. As the anode dissolves, an electrochemically equivalent amount of hydrogen or metallic element is deposited at the cathode. In this way, the anode gets dissolved and the cathode is protected. When the metal at the anode goes into solution, it forms ions and electrons are liberated which flow through any electric circuit provided to arrive at the cathode. The electrons neutralise the positive charges on the ions at the cathode as the ions come out of the solution. Galvanic corrosion occurs on the unprotected steel of ship's hulls. The steel is anodic to brass of the screws and therefore the hull is selectively attacked.

The rate of galvanic corrosion depends upon the relative areas of cathodic and anodic surfaces and the rate of attack varies directly with the ratio of cathode to anode. A relatively small anode area will be attacked faster as compared to a larger one. In the case of ship's hulls, as the anode area is quite large the attack does occur but it is comparatively slower. Area effects also explain the very rapid rate of attack encountered when steel rivets are used for copper members. In this case the steel undergoes rapid attack, where as attack of steel members would be negligible if copper rivets were used.

Concentration Cells. When two pieces of the same metal are immersed in an electrolyte or solution having different concentrations of oxygen, a concentration cell is formed and the corrosion occurs at the electrode which is immersed in the solution of lower ion or oxygen concentration, and the cathode is protected. Concentration cells are of two types: (*i*) metal ion cells; (*ii*) oxygen cells.

Metal ion concentration cells. These cells may be formed by differences in metal ion concentration. If a copper rod is in contact with one dilute and one concentrated copper salt solution, the part in contact with the dilute solution will be corroded. This type of cell is shown in Fig. 13.2 in which the copper in 5 pct. solution of cupric chloride will be anodic to the copper in 10 pct. solution.

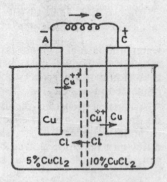

FIG. 13.2. Schematic diagram of metal-ion concentration cell.

Such metal ion concentration cells are, important in the corrosion of copper and its alloys in flowing media. Parts of a surface exposed to a fast moving liquid will be negative and thus anodic due to more rapid transport of copper ions away from the metal. A case of metal-ion concentration cell is shown in Fig. 13.3, which represents a section through a submerged rivetted lap joint. The space between the lapped plates in Fig. 13.3 become progressively smaller as the rivet is approached. The ion concentration between the plates increases as the distance from the rivet decreases. The area at A near the extremities of the joint becomes anodic with respect to C owing to lower ion concentration and corrosion occurs as shown.

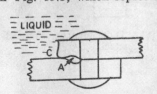

FIG. 13.3. Mechanism of metal-ion concentration cell corrosion. ('A' is anodic of low metal ion concentration in moving solution proventing build-up of the ions and 'C' is cathodic of high ion concentration in a stagnant solution).

Oxygen concentration cells. These are also known as differential aeration cells and are formed by solution with different concentrations of dissolved oxygen. Parts of the metal surrounded by a high oxygen concentration form positive poles, whereas parts in contact with a solution of low oxygen concentration form negative poles in corrosion cells. An example of an oxygen concentration cell is shown in Fig. 13.4. Here oxygen is depleted down inside the crevice and there is little opportunity to replace it. At the extremities of the joint, a flow of fresh solution of higher oxgyen concentration continually replaces any oxygen which tends to be consumed here. Thus, the anodic area A in this case is deep within the crevice, and the cathodic area C is at some distance from the rivet. Compared to the metal-ion concentration cell, the location of anode and cathode area is now reversed.

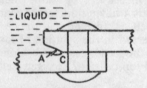

FIG. 13.4. Mechanism of oxygen concentration cell corrosion ('A' is anodic of low oxygen concentration and 'C' is cathodic of high oxygen concentration).

Another typical case of a differential aeration cell is water-line attack which is illustrated in Fig. 13.5. The corrosive attack takes place just below the liquid level on metals immersed in water.

A surface tension meniscus on the metal forms an effective cathode surfaces with short diffusion path for dissolved oxygen. In a similar way, a steel pole driven into the soil is attacked particularly just below the ground water level. A steel pole driven into the bottom of the sea is attacked maximum just below the bottom level since the part in contact with oxygenated sea water serves as a cathode and is attacked less strongly.

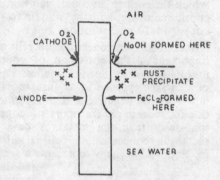

FIG. 13.5. Differential aeration cell-water line attack.

13.3. TYPES OF CORROSION

13.3.1. Dry Corrosion

The corrosion phenomenon that involves chemical reactions with a gas or a liquid which is not an electrolyte, is known as dry corrosion. For example, corrosion of steel with SO_2, CO_2, O_2 etc. at ordinary temperature is a case of dry corrosion.

13.3.2. Wet Corrosion

When the corrosion phenomena involves the presence of an electrolyte such as the solution of salt, acid or alkali in contact with the metal, the resulting corrosion is called wet corrosion, e.g. corrosion of steel in sea water, acids and alkalies.

13.3.3. Uniform Corrosion

Uniform corrosion is characterised by electrochemical or chemical reactions that proceed uniformly over the entire surface of the materials exposed to the corrosive media. The common example is unprotected and exposed steel structure which is rusting away more or less uniformly. This form of corrosion can be easily eliminated by proper selection of materials and use of protective coatings.

13.3.4. Pitting Corrosion

Pitting is an extremely severe form of localised corrosion in which both galvanic and concentration cells may cause the attack. It results in the formation of small holes which may penetrate deeply through the metal. If the pits are small, they may get covered over by corrosion products and thus it may be difficult to discover this type of corrosion till a sudden service failure of the part occurs.

Pitting may require comparatively long initiation period, but once started, it becomes autocatalytic and its rate accelerates rapidly. A pit is normally initiated by the adsorption of activating anions, particularly chloride ions, on certain defect sites in the oxide film, such as slag inclusions or precipitates of secondary phase. Pitting is very common in stainless steels, aluminium alloys, copper alloys and some high nickel alloys in solution containing chlorides. Fig. 13.6 illustrates the mechanism of pitting on iron surface.

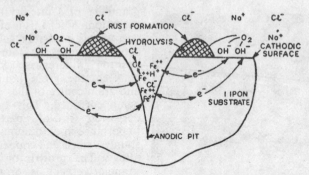

FIG. 13 6. Schematic illustration of pitting on iron surface.

13.3.5. Crevice Corrosion

This is a destructive form of localised electrochemical corrosion and is generally associated with small volumes of stagnant liquid which might form in shallow holes, under gasket surfaces, and the crevices under bolt and rivet heads. Two characteristically different types of crevice corrosion may be observed (i) gasket corrosion, and (ii) filiform corrosion.

(i) **Gasket corrosion.** This type of corrosion requires the presence of a crevice that is wide enough to admit liquid but narrow enough to allow this liquid to remain stagnant. Fibrous gaskets, which act as wicks to absorb an electrolyte solution and to maintain its contact with the metal surface, provide nearly perfect location for this type of corrosion. Both metal ion and oxygen concentration cell formation contribute to gasket corrosion.

(*ii*) **Filiform corrosion**. It is a form of crevice corrosion which has a different appearance from that of gasket corrosion. It may normally be observed on the surfaces of the enameled or lacquered containers for food and beverages. After developing pin hole breaks near the edges, if the surfaces are exposed to atmosphere, the corrosion appears as a network of tiny trails or filaments resembling the trails of tiny bugs or worms. This form of crevice corrosion occurs primarily at higher humidities and at relative humidities of higher than 90 per cent the attack becomes so pronounced that it takes the form of large blisters. Although this type of corrosion is generally not harmful to the structures, it is undesirable from the stand point of the marketability of food and beverage containers. The remedy is to store the containers in low humidity environment using coatings with low water permeability.

13.3.6. Intergranular or Intercrystalline Corrosion

The grain boundary regions in metals can be greatly activated under certain conditions making these areas susceptible to corrode severely whereas the bulk grains are protected cathodically. This

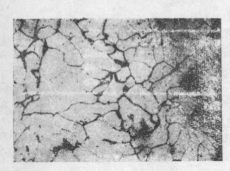

FIG. 13.7. Microphotograph showing the intercrystalline (intergranular corrosion along the grain boundaries.

phenomenon is called intergranular or intercrystalline corrosion. Mechanism of such corrosion is probably galvanic action which results from composition differences existing between the grain boundary and grain centre of the metal being corroded. This type of corrosion is of particular importance in chromium-nickel stainless steels and copper-base alloys. The growth of intergranular cracks is promoted by establishment of oxygen concentration cells and the relatively small anode area. Acid solutions and neutral chloride solutions such as sea water favour the intercrystalline corrosion. In austenitic steels with more carbon such an attack may occur around welds, where chromium carbide ($Cr_{23}C_6$) precipitation occurs at the grain boundaries. This is illustrated in Fig. 13.7. In case of brass, grain boundaries tend to be rich in zinc thereby increasing the susceptibility to intergranular corrosion.

13.3.7. Stress Corrosion Cracking

This may be regarded as the combined action of stress and corrosion resulting into the cracking or embrittlement of the metal. The stresses may be residual stresses from the previous fabrication operations or use of the metal under applied loads. However, in both the cases the stresses must be at the surface and tensile in nature. Most probably the failure starts by corrosion at anodic areas on the surface of the metal, and surface tensile stresses are intensified at the bottom of minute corrosion notches. These stresses cause continual breakdown of the formed passive film and corrosion proceeds at the root of the fissure. As the crack extends deeper, stresses from applied loads are intensified thereby accelerating the rate of corrosion. The oxygen concentration cells may also be present and aggravate the problem. Under applied loads, final fracture may occur with sudden violence. The problem of stress corrosion cracking can be illustrated by two specific examples (i) season cracking of brass in which the residual tensile stresses in the metal caused during manufacture along with the effects of corrosive atmosphere, such as moisture, salt, air, nitrogen compounds etc. result in the development of cracks (ii) Caustic embrittlement of steel which occurs in rivetted boilers at locations where escaping steam from the boiler causes a concentration of dissolved solids (such as Na_2SO_4, NaCl and NaOH). These solids form corrosive concentrated solutions and when combined with residual stresses produced during rivetting cause a form of stress corrosion resulting in failure.

13.3.8. Erosion Corrosion

When mechanical erosion is combined with corrosion attack, erosion-corrosion results. The metals which resist corrosion due to the formation of passive layers, lose their stability when the passive film is mechanically eroded away due to the movement of the corrosive fluid relative to the metal surface. In most cases where this type of corrosion is appreciable, the effects of mechanical wear and abrasion are considerable. Erosion corrosion is characterised by the appearance of grooves, valleys, waves, and rounded holes on the metal surface which usually occur in a directional pattern that reflects the flow direction of the corrosive liquid. Erosion is caused by turbulent flow of fluids due to changes in pipe diameter, elbows and fittings. Normally three types of erosion-corrosion are observed in practice:

(i) **The erosion of metal surfaces by impingement or the rapid flow of corrosive liquid streams**. Due to physical removal of protective films by the rapidly moving streams of corrosive liquid fresh metal surfaces are exposed to the galvanic action of the solution, thus perpetuating the corrosion. The presence of entrained air bubbles or suspended solids in the corrosive liquid stream (as in slurries) greatly accelerates the erosion process.

(ii) **Cavitation damage or cavitation corrosion**. In this cavities are formed in metals by rapidly moving liquid over the metal surface. It is believed that the cavities are produced by the formation and sudden collapse of vapour bubbles at the surface. Because of the low pressure in the bubbles, collapse occurs and pounding action is exterted tending to wear away metal or protective films. This type of corrosion is common in pump impellers, hydraulic turbines, ship propellers etc. where very high velocities and low pressures are encountered at the same time.

(*iii*) **Fretting corrosion**. When materials under load are subjected to vibration and relative slipping of contacting parts, corrosion pits or grooves are developed in the area between the mating parts. The corrosion pits or grooves are surrounded by corrosion products and this type of corrosion is termed as fretting and is ofter accompanied by considerable abrasive action which increases its severity. Examples are areas of contact between bearings and shafts, sleeves etc.

13.3.9. Corrosion Fatigue

When the action of a corrosive medium is combined with variable stresses, corrosion factigue is caused. In this type of failure a corrosive medium attacks the surface of the metal, producing stress raisers which nucleate a fatigue failure. Normally the portions of the fracture which are caused by corrosion are intergranular but the final fracture is transcrystalline. In the heat-exchanger tubes of chemical equipment corrosion fatigue is a common feature. Failure of sucker rods used in oil wells is the another example of corrosion fatigue.

13.3.10. High Temperature Corrosion or Oxidation Corrosion

It involves the oxidation or reaction with the products of fuel combusion. Corrosion under these conditions often proceeds as direct chemical attack. In iron and steels, presence of chromium as an alloying element provides resistance to oxidation. For more severe conditions, a higher percentage of chromium is needed. However, after 30 per cent chromium content, the resistance does not improve appreciably. The protection afforded by chromium is attributed to the formation of the passive film of chromium oxide. The common combustion products such as CO_2, SO_2, water vapour etc. enhance the corroding tendency of steels at high temperatures. Further, high temperature corrosion is accelerated by alternate heating and cooling cycles as the passive scale formed expand and contract at different rates than the metal resulting in spalling or flaking of film and exposure of fresh metal surface to further attack.

13.3.11. Dezincification

This type of corrosion is peculiar to copper-zinc alloys (brasses). As the name implies, dezincification results in loss of zinc from brass leaving behind a spongy mass of copper. This is normally caused by microdifference in composition and a small variation in solution potential. Two types of dezincification are commonly observed in practice: (*i*) plug type and (*ii*) uniform attack, the former being probably caused by local removal of passive films from the metal surface and corrosion starting over a small area and proceeding into the metal.

13.3.12. Hydrogen Damage

This is caused by the presence of hydrogen in the metal or in environment giving rise to various types of defects. Three types of hydrogen damage are common in practice i.e. *hydrogen blistering, hydrogen embrittlement* and *decarburisation.*

(*i*) **Hydrogen blistering.** This is the result of atomic hydrogen diffusion into steel, most of the atomic hydrogen diffusing through and escaping from other side of the metal as molecular hydrogen gas. However, some of the atomic hydrogen may find its way into internal cavities or microcracks existing in the steel wall, where it can combine to form molecular hydrogen developing high pressure and causing blister formation. Rupture of steel occurs in such a case since the equilibrium pressure of molecular hydrogen in small bubbles or holes may be several thousand atmospheres.

(*ii*) **Hydrogen embrittlement.** This is a phenomenon where atomic hydrogen reacts with steel to form a more brittle material, i.e., hydride which then fails by brittle cracking. If a metal embrittled by hydrogen is subjected to tensile stresses above a certain critical values, hydrogen cracking takes place, the critical stress being lower for higher hydrogen content. Sometimes the necessary tensile stress is caused by the hydrogen itself and crackings takes place independently of any overload, e.g., longitudinal cracks in stressed wire are observed when subjeced to hydrogen embrittlement.

(*iii*) **Decarburisation.** In this case, the carbon in steel reacts with hydrogen to form methane gas (CH_4) thereby reducing the carbon in steel and affecting its tensile strength. The reverse of this process, i.e. carburisation is the breakdown of hydrogen-hydrocarbon gas streams, with the subsequent absorption of carbon by steel. Although not as harmful to the properties of steel as decarburisation, carburisation can also produce some degree of embrittlement through the formation of excess carbides in the iron structure.

13.3.13. Liquid Metal Embrittlement

In the nuclear industry liquid metals are employed as high temperature heat transfer media. This type of metal can seriously attack its container if an incorrect choice is made. Such a corrosive attack is more physical than chemical in nature. Four types of such case are observed in practice, i.e., (*i*) solution of the structural metal, (*ii*) diffusion of liquid metal into solid metal, (*iii*) intermetallic compound formation, and (*iv*) mass transfer resulting from either composition or thermal gradients. Since liquid metals are generally used in heat exchangers, the last two types of attack are the most troublesome. In liquid metal heat exchangers, the greatest resistance to heat flow lies in the walls of the tubes through which the liquid metal flows.

TABLE 13.1. *Various Important Forms of Corrosion with Examples.*

S.No.	Corrosion type	Definition	Examples
1.	Dry Corrosion	Involving chemical reaction with non electrolytic gas or liquid.	Corrosion of steel with SO_2, CO_2, O_2 etc.
2.	Wet Corrosion	Corrosion in contact with electrolyte such as aqueous solution of salt, alkali and acid.	Corrosion of steel in sea water, acids and alkalies.
3.	Uniform Corrosion	Uniform attack of electrochemical or chemical reaction over the entire surface.	Steel immersed in dilute sulphuric acid.
4.	Pitting Corrosion	Localised attack in the form of pit.	Stainless steel, aluminium alloys, copper alloys, and nickel alloys immersed in chloride solution.
5.	Crevice Corrosion	Intense localised corrosion in shallow holes.	The crevices under bolt and rivet heads.
6.	Galvanic Corrosion	Dissimilar metals immersed in a corrosive media and connected electrically.	Zinc and iron in salt solution.
7.	Intergranular Corrosion	Corrosion occurring in the vicinity of grain boundaries.	Weldment of stainless steel.
8.	Stress Corrosion cracking	Cracking caused by simultaneous presence of tensile stress and particular corrosion medium.	Season cracking of brass and caustic embrittlement of steel.
9.	High Temperature Oxidation	Oxidation or reaction with the products of fuel combustion.	Corrosion of steel with combustion products such as CO_2, SO_2, O_2 etc.
10.	Erosion-corrosion	Acceleration of corrosion because of relative movement between corrosive fluid and the metal.	Corrosion in pumping equipment, corrosion in the areas between bearings and shafts.
11.	Corrosion Fatigue	Combined action of corrosive medium and variable stresses.	Heat exchanger tubes of chemical equipments.

Consequently, large thermal gradients and stresses exist in this region, and the formation of brittle intermetallic compounds, either on the surface or in the substrate, can result in the brittle cracking of the tube walls, e.g. stainless steels are attacked by liquid magnesium.

Table 13.1 given on p. 390 gives the various important forms of corrosion with examples.

13.4. ACTIVE-PASSIVE CELLS

A common reason of local corrosion cells is defects in passivating oxide films which may be due to inhomogenities in the composition of the metal. Secondary phases in aluminium alloys and sulphide inclusions in steel determine the location of pitting corrosion, and precipitates in grain boundaries. The precipitates at grain boundaries give rise to intercystalline corrosion and stress corrosion cracking. Active-passive cells may also be considered as corrosion cells formed between the metal and scale, when the latter is damaged. It should be noted that while an initiating potential difference results in an active-passive cell, this may not be enough to maintain the corrosion process, as dissolved oxygen is necessary to maintain the cathode process. In this way, an active-passive cell is developed into a differential aerantion cell.

13.5. PASSIVITY

Passivity may be defined as a markedly reduced corroding tendency of metals due to a protecting layer or corrosion product. In general, the rate of corrosion for most active metals increases with the increased concentration of a dissolved oxidising agent. Contrary to this behaviour, certain active metals such as chromium, aluminium, nickel, titanium and many of their alloys become passive or more noble in behaviour when exposed to suitable oxidising agents at high enough concentrations. The active-passive transition shown by these metals and alloys is usually the result of formation of a surface film of hydrated oxide that interferes with the anode reaction and drastically lowers the corrosion rate.

13.5.1. Types of Passivity

There are two types of passivity i.e. (i) chemical and (ii) mechanical.

(i) **Chemical passivity.** This type of passivity is ascribed to an invisible thin but dense and semiconducting oxide film on the metal surface, displacing the electrode potential of the metal strongly in the positive direction. Examples are iron, platinum group metals, chromium, molybdenum, tungsten, titanium, zirconium and aluminium.

(ii) **Mechanical passivity.** This may occur on all metals and alloys in environments which are favourable to the precipitation of solid salts on the metal surface. In this case the corrosion rate is greatly reduced due to a thick but porous salt layer which is usually non·conducting. The electrode potential may not be displaced in the positive direction, rather it may be displaced in negative direction from the standard potential, if the solubility of salt is low. Examples are lead in H_2SO_4, magnesium in water or fluoride solution, silver in chloride solution, phosphatizing layers on metals and calcium carbonate scale on steel in water.

However, distinction between the two types of passivity is dfficult. The natural invisible thin oxide films on certains metals such as aluminium, magnesium and tungsten can be extended by anodic treatment (anodizing) to from thick and still better protective oxide films. Chromatizing film on zinc or light metals also constitute a border line case.

13.5.2. Passivation

Passivation can be obtained in two different ways i.e. (*i*) electrically by an external current of adequate strength and, (*ii*) chemically by means of oxidizing agents of sufficient oxidising power.

(*i*) **Passivation by an external current**. Passivation can be effected electrically through anodic polarisation. When the electrode potential reaches a critical value (V_A), the current abruptly decreases due to the formation of a passive film, which is disrupted only at a much higher voltage (V_B) as shown in Fig. 13.8. Examples are iron, chromium and stainless steel.

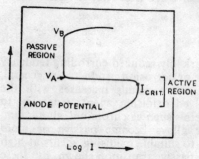

FIG. 13.8. Illustrative diagram for passivation by external current.

(*a*) *Passivity of iron*. Fig. 13.9 shows the anodic polarisation curve of iron in 1-M sulphuric acid solution. Without outer current, a steady state corrosion potential develops. If the potential of the specimen is raised, an anodic net current flows from the electrode into the solution and the corrosion velocity of the specimen is increased correspondingly and removal of corrosion product (iron sulphate) takes place. The anode film in contact with the electrode consists of a saturated nonconducting but porous layer of iron sulphate ($FeSO_4$). On a further increase of potential a higher oxide of iron is formed as a thin, nonporous and passivating oxide film.

(*b*) *Passivity of chromium*. Chromium behaves electrochemically similar to iron with certain important differences. The passivation potential of chromium is considerably lower than that of iron; the passivating current for chromium is only a few milli amp. per dm^2

whereas iron needs about 15-20 amps./dm^2. Therefore, chromium is passivated much more easily than iron and the corrosion rate of chromium in the passive state is much lower than that of iron, despite of the fact that the passivating oxide film is much thinner. At a potential of about 1.25 volts, Cr^{3+} passive film is oxidised to soluble Cr^{6+} state and the passive film dissolves completely and the transpassive corrosion of chromium is so rapid that, as a rule no oxygen evolves.

(c) *Passivity of stainless steel.* The fact that chromium and nickel are readily passivated accounts for the use of these metals as alloying elements in stainless steels. At chromium content of 12-18 per cent the passivity properties approach those of chromium because the value of the passivation potential shifts from that of iron to almost that of chromium. In the passive state, the corrosion current is about 100 times lower than for pure iron, which gives an imporvement of passivity and corrosion resistance. An addition of nickel and also of molybdenum, silicon and copper reduces the passivating current as well as activity range. Thus stainless steels containing these alloying elements have still better corrosion resistance in non-oxidising media and are also more easily transferred to the passive state.

(*ii*) **Passivation by chemical means**. Passivation can be obtained by means of oxidizing agents fulfilling two conditions; (*a*) thermodynamic its redox potential should be above the passivation potential, and (*b*) kinetic-cathodic reduction occurs so easily that it creates a cathodic limiting current stronger than the passivating current below the passivation potential. Passivity is therefore favoured by conditions which increase the rate of the cathode process or decreases the rate of the anodic metal dissolution process below the passivation potential. Non-oxidising anodic inhibitors, such as orthophosphates favour passivity by reducing the rate of the anode process. Oxidising anodic inhibitors or passivators, such as chromic acid and nitric acid act in both the ways, i.e. both by stimulation of the cathode process and by retardation of the anode process. Examples are:

(*a*) An ordinary iron electrode when immersed in a solution of potassium dichromate ($K_2Cr_2O_7$), develops a noble potential like that of stainless steel. The $Cr_2O_7^{2-}$ ions are reduced at the iron surface and iron is oxidised with the formation of protective film consisting of hydrated Cr_2O_3 or Fe_2O_3.

(*b*) Stainless steel becomes passive in tap-water because dissolved oxygen is a suitable oxidising agent to form a protective film on stainless steel, which is comparable to that developed on iron by $Cr_2O_7^{2-}$ ions.

(*c*) Some metals and alloys such as titanium and stainless steel acquire a natural oxide layer when exposed to air but a more protective one after prolonged exposure in oxygenated aqueous solution.

13.6. FACTORS AFFECTING THE CORROSION

When two galvanically different metals are electrically coupled in the presence of an electrolyte, a corrosion current flows and one of the metals is preferentially detriorated or corroded. The origin of this action is generally influenced by two types of factors: (1) environmental factors, and (2) metallurgical factors.

13.6.1. Environmental Factors

(i) **Concentration difference at two points on the metal surface.** Difference in concentration at two points on the metal surface will result in differences in electrode potential at those points. As soon as a potential difference developes, the region having more negative potential becomes anodic relative to the more positive area, and thus, a cell is established causing the corrosion.

(ii) **Concentration of dissolved oxygen.** If the concentration of dissolved oxygen is decreased near one area the reaction rate of oxygen with water as well as its ability to combine with electrons to form hydroxyl ions in that area will be decreased. In this way cathodic reaction gets polarised and makes the area more anodic. Consequently, an area when this oxygen concentration is decreased relative to its surrounding becomes a relatively anodic region, and a cell is established again. Such a cell is called an oxygen concentration cell (discussed in section 13.2.3), which is a very important source of corrosion cell formation in single metal corrosion. Deposition of dirt or scale on the surface of metal restricts the area under the deposit from access to dissolved oxygen. This creates an anode which in turn, results in the anodic deterioration of the surface under the deposit. In this manner, the areas underneath rivets, bolt heads, washers etc. become anodes for oxygen concentration cells. Breaks in paint or other protective coatings also create these cells.

(iii) **Presence of dissolved oxygen in non-oxidising acid solution.** When dissolved oxygen is present in non-oxidising acid solution such as hydrochloric acid, corrosion cells are formed. For example, under ordinary conditions copper is passive in hydrochloric acid solution due to its positive electrode potential and therefore it is cathodic relative to hydrogen evolution and thus the copper will be attacked by the acid solution having dissolved oxygen.

(iv) **Stress.** Stress is another environmental factor which helps in producing galvanic couples on the surface of a single metal. Whenever a metal is cold worked, the region undergoing the greatest amount of plastic deformation stores the maximum amount of strain energy, and therefore, it is in a higher energy state. Thus the areas of a metal surface which are locally work hardened will behave as anode relative to the annealed or less work hardened areas. Rusting of an ordinary iron wire nail is an example of this type in which head and point of this nail are work hardened to a greater extent and thus are anodic relative to its shank.

13.6.2. Metallurgical Factors

If two phases having different electrode potentials are present in the alloy or metal, they create a myriad of tiny microcells in the material itself that are intimately connected electrically and the presence of an electrolyte establishes a galvanic cell. In ordinary steel, ferrite and cementite have different electrode potentials and thus an ordinary steel rusts rapidly in moist atmosphere. In zinc metal, myriads of tiny galvanic couples exist in the surface by virtue of its structure. Grain boundaries and other crystalline imperfections represent strained areas possessing higher energy than their neighbouring atoms due to the strain energy of their imperfections. These areas, therefore, are slightly anodic relative to the bulk grains.

Locally strained regions which surround impurity inclusions, surface cracks, and any other source of crystalline irregularity also introduce tiny anodes into the surface of the metal. In fact, all metal surfaces (with the possible exception of carefully grown, perfect single crystals) are covered with a net work of tiny anodes and cathodes which can be activated on contact with a suitable electrodes.

13.7. CORROSION CONTROL AND PROTECTION

By making use of the basic principles of electrochemistry and oxidation kinetics, corrosion can be controlled resulting in considerable economy. A number of successful methods for preventing or inhibiting corrosion are discussed below:

13.7.1. Selection of Material

The easiest way of controlling corrosion is to use a material that minimizes the undesirable effects of the corrosive environment. In general, some metals give better performance under certain environmental conditions. Examples are: (i) copper-nickel alloys are resistant to reducing or non-oxidising acids (hydrochloric acid), (ii) lead is very resistant to dilute sulphuric acid under static condition, (iii) aluminium is resistant to atmospheric oxidation, (iv) tin is mostly chosen as the container or piping material for very pure distilled water since it is completely inert to water, (v) titanium and its alloys are used for severe oxidising conditions due to the absence of transpassive region, (vi) ordinary structural steels can be used for containing concentrated sulphuric acid, but tegs attacked by dilute or aerated acid, (vii) chromiun-containing alloys are useful under oxidising conditions, and (viii) tantalum is the most suitable corrosion resistant metal which resists most acids at all concentrations and temperatures.

13.7.2. Alteration of Environment

Environment is an important factor in determining the seve

of galvanic corrosion. Corrosion rates are considerably influenced by the presence of cations and oxygen and change in the concentration would decrease the corrosion current and would be beneficials in controlling the corrosion rate. Some examples of this practice are given in Table 13.2.

TABLE 13.2. *Some Examples of Environment Alteration in Control of Corrosion.*

S. No.	Method	Conditions under which recommended
1.	Deaeration of water.	When the chances of air dissolution exists.
2.	Reduction in concentration of corrosive agent in solution.	Removal of chloride ions when such ions accelerate corrosion.
3.	Decreasing temperature.	When corrosion rate is temperature dependent.
4.	Decreasing the velocity of corrosive medium.	When chances of cavitation corrosion exist.

Addition of inhibitors to the electrolyte is another method of restricting corrosion by the manipulation of the environment. These are essentially retarding catalysts or reaction poisons. These are chemical which when added to the corrosive media, render it inert, or which when applied to the surface of the metal react to produce passivity. The use of rust inhibitors (soluble oils in water) for automobile cooling system is a well known case of this practice. There are different types of inhibitors; (*i*) in one case inhibitors are adsorped on the surface and from a protective film which seals the surface and restricts the contact of metal with the electrolyte, (*ii*) other types of inhibitor act to retard the evolution of hydrogen at the cathodic area. These inhibitors are very effective in acid media, and (*iii*) known as scavengers, react with the corrosive agents (particularly in the case of oxygen) and removes it from the solution. Examples are addition of sodium phosphate and sodium nitrate to boiler water.

13.7.3. Coatings

By application of different types of coatings on the metal surfaces, corrosion can be controlled. In general there are three types of coating i.e. (*i*) metallic, (*ii*) ceramic and non-metallic inonganic, and (*iii*) organic.

(*i*) **Metallic coatings.** Metallic coatings are used to protect the parts against structural damage and to preserve their appearance. In general, metal coatings are applied in thin layers by electro plating, dipping or spraying with atomized molten metal. The selection of coating material depends upon the requirements. The effectiveness of metal coatings in governed to a great extent by the nature of a coating method used. By the application of metallic coatings corrosion is inhibited in following three ways:

(*a*) *Metal coating is resistant to corrosion where as the base metal is not.* For example, a sprayed coating of aluminium on stainless steel gives protection from atmospheric oxidation at temperatures upto 750°C. High-strength aluminium alloys are often coated with pure aluminium-skin, which provide a corrosion barrier protecting the underlying alloy from stress corrosion.

(*b*) *Coating acts as cathode with respect to base metal.* In this case coating is resistant to corrosion only if the coating is continuous. For example, tin cases are used in the food packing industry because it is not toxic. If a scratch or a pin hole is developed on the tin plate, the underlying steel plate will start corroding more rapidly. For this two reasons can be assigned;

(*i*) tin is cathodic to iron due to which undesirable galvanic couples are induced; and

(*ii*) the exposed iron anode is very small compared to the tin cathode and thus a very unfavourable electrode area ratio is created. The overall effect will be accelerated corrosion of the steel beneath the tin.

(*c*) *Coating acts as an anode with respect to base metal.* In this case coating behaves as an anodic to base metal and then the coating prevents corrosion by sacrificing itself until appreciable portions of the metal coating are removed. This is called cathodic protection, e.g. zinc coated or galvanised steel sheet and fence wire. The steel is protected because the zinc coating is anodic relative to iron and gets sacrificed. If the surface coating gets scratched, the anode/cathode area ratio is the reverse to tin plate situation as the small scratch is cathodic while the large unbroken surface of zinc is anodic. Thus, very small corrosion current will result, leading to corrosion at a slow and uniform rate.

(*ii*) **Ceramic and non-metallic inorganic coatings.** These coatings are applied to achieve smoothness, durability, corrosion resistance and good appearance. Porcelain coatings of house-hold appliances, bath tubs, sinks and wash basins are common examples. An inorganic non-metallic coating is also used for obtaining hard and thick surfaces which can withstand the action of various corrosive agents, e.g., the steel vessels lined with glass are used for handling various chemicals in the industry due to the inertness of glass to a large number of chemicals.

(*iii*) **Organic coatings.** These coatings include organic films such as paints, regins, varnish, tar, grease, asphalt compound, adhesive plastic tapes, polymers and rubbers. Although some of them may contain inorganic substances, the effective constituents are organic materials. By the use of inorganic fillers, the quality of covering may be improved and the cost is lowered. Protection is achieved due to exclusion of moisture, air and other corrosive media. However, th organic coatings can be used only below the boiling point of water as in higher temperature, the coatings deteriorate. For example, the lining of steel pipe with chemically resistant polymers such as poly vinyl chloride, poly-tetra fluoro ethylene, polyethylene, polypropylene etc. is a common practice in chemical industries. Tar and asphalt are also used to coat buried pipe lines to protect them from both bacterial corrosion and corrosion with soil water.

13.7.4. Proper Design

Choosing proper design of equipment may be as important in reducing corrosion as proper material selection. Many corrosion problems can be overcome or greatly reduced by considering the following general design aspects:

(i) An additional thickness of metal over the required one will reduce the problem of corrosion in case of pipes and tanks.

(ii) Welding of tanks and containers in place of rivetting generally reduces possibility of crevice corrosion.

(iii) In case rivetting is necessary, rivet material should be cathodic relative to the plates being joined. Further, insulating washers and gaskets may be used to prevent electrical contacts.

(iv) Use of galvanically similar material for the entire structure reduces the corrosion problem.

(v) In the empty tanks situation for stagnant pools of corrosive liquid should be avoided.

(vi) Selection of the replaceable components which are liable to failure due to corrosion solves the corrosion problem to some extent.

(vii) Sharp bends and corners in the piping system should be minimised as these cause entrapment of corrosive liquids.

(viii) While designing heating systems, situations for localised hot spot should be avoided.

(ix) Entrainment of air in the liquid system should be avoided. This is particularly important in making the designs for inlets to pumps, tanks and agitators.

13.7.5. Mechanical Treatments

Object of mechanical treatment is to prevent stress corrosion. Nitriding or cold-working operations such as shot peening or cold rolling help in reducing stress-corrosion because these operations produce residual compressive stresses on the surface which must be overcome by applied tensile stresses before stress-corrosion can occur.

13.7.6. Cathodic and Anodic Protection

Since most of the corrosion problems are galvanic in nature, by making use of the electro-chemical properties of the reacting system, desirable parts may be converted into non-deteriorating cathodes through the application of external current, i.e. (*i*) cathodic or (*ii*) anodic.

(*i*) **Cathodic protection**. In cathodic protection a metal structure liable to be attacked is made cathodic by impressing a reversed flow of current. This may be achieved by the use of an external power source or by suitable galvanic coupling with a more anodic metal. Figs. 13.9 and 13.10 illustrate the cathodic protection of an underground pipe by the first and second methods, respectively. Zinc, aluminium or magnesium are commonly used as sacrificial anodes. Cathodic protection is used for the protection of inside surfaces of storage tanks and condensers (by immersing

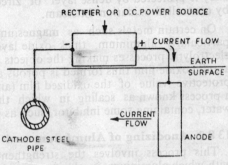

FIG. 13.9. Cathodic protection by an external power source.

magnesium, or zinc rods), prevention of ship's hulls, propeller struts and shafting pipe line etc. Ordinarily, steel portions of the ship are anodic to the brass screws but after the attachment of zinc or magnesium blocks, the steel becomes cathodic while the zinc and magnesium become anodic and thus steel is prevented from corrosion. In case of impressed current

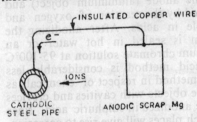

FIG. 13.10. Cathodic protection by suitable galvanic coupling

method, the anode materials used are steel, graphite and silicon iron.

(*ii*) **Anodic protection**. It is a relatively new form of corrosion protection. It is based on the formation of a protective and passive film on metal surfaces by externally impressed anodic currents. Many metals such as nickel, iron, chromium, titanium and their alloys which display active-passive transitions, can be passivated by the application of a suitable and controlled anodic currents which reduce their corrosion rate.

13.8. SOME SPECIAL METHODS OF CORROSION PROTECTION

13.8.1. Oxide Film Protection

A metal may sometimes be protected by forming a mechanically passivating oxide film on metal surfaces. For example, black oxidation of steel in caustic containing an oxidation agent. In this, a black-brown oxide layer, consisting of magnetite (Fe_3O_4), is obtained. Another example is the use of zirconium alloy (zircaloy) containing 1.5 per cent tin and 0.1 per cent iron, chromium and nickel for protection of uranium fuel rods in atomic reactor. In this case zirconium alloy is protected by dense layer of zirconium oxide (ZrO_2) formed by controlled oxidation in steam.

On certain metals such as magnesium, zirconium, titanium and particularly aluminium, thick oxide layer may also be deposited by electrolytic processes making the objects as anodes (anodizing). The anodic oxide film thus formed is porous and can easily be dyed. The protective value of the oxidized film (anodized) can be increased by a process known as scaling in which the object is treated in hot water, containing some inhibitor, such as potassium chromate.

13 8.2. Anodizing of Aluminium and its Alloys

This process involves the strengthening of the natural oxide film with which aluminium is always coated in contact with air. The aluminium object is taken as an anode in a suitable electrolyte (usully as aqueous solution of sulphuric acid or chromic acid) with a lead cathode. The electrodes are connected to a direct current source results in evolution of oxygen at the anode (aluminium object) and a layer of aluminium oxide is formed by the reaction of oxygen and aluminium. This layer is insoluble in acids. After anodizing the object in sulphuric acid, the film is sealed in hot water or an aqueous solution such as potassium chromate solution at 95-100°C for about $\frac{1}{2}$ hour. The sulphuric acid method is considerably less expensive than the chromic acid method in respect of chemicals as well as electric power. However, the objects with cavities and crevices such as rivetted joints cannot be anodized in sulphuric acid, since remaining residual electrolyte in such places will give rise to corrosion. In chromic acid process, there is no such chance due to the corrosion inhibiting properties of chromic acid.

TABLE 13.3. *Working Conditions for Anodizing in Sulphuric Acid and Chromic Acid Baths.*

Bath	Electrolyte concentration (per cent)	Temperature (°C)	Cell Voltage (Volts)	Current density (A/dm^2)	Anodizing time (min).	Film thickness (μm)
1. Chromic Acid	3-10	40	10-50 increased successively.	0.1-0.3	20-60	1-8
2. Sulphuric Acid	20	220	12-24	1 2-20	10-60	5-30

Anodized films from chromic acid bath are usually not sealed but they have better corrosion resistance than unsealed films from a sulphuric acid bath. However, the sealing gives still better resistance to corrosion. Films from the sulphuric acid bath are normally lighter and more decorative and also more suitable for subsequent dyeing. Working conditons for chromic acid and sulphuric acid baths are listed in Table 13.3 given on p. 400.

13.8.3. Vitreous Enamelling

Vitreous enamel is a glassy substance formed by glass former (SiO_2 + borax), flux (potassium and sodium oxides), stabilizer (CeO and Al_2O_3), opaque agents (TiO_2 and ZrO_2) and colour pigments (coloured metal oxides). All these chemicals are smelted together at 1200-1300°C and the molten mass is granulated and cooled in water. Afterwards, this product is finely milled in ball mills alongwith water, clay and sodium silicate to a viscous but not sedimenting dispersion. This is applied by dipping or spraying on cleaned objects. The coating is first dried at a temperature of about 125°C and then burnt at 500-800°C for 4-10 minutes, depending upon the kind and thickness of the base metal. The enamel, which is partly molten in this process, is strongly bonded to the base metal and forms a shining surface.

Vitreous enamel has good corrosion resistance towards alkali (not very strong), acids (except hydrofluoric acid), boiling water, water vapour and various organic solvents. Its other important properties are good colour, permanence, electrical insulation and a good resistance towards wear. However, its brittleness is the biggest weakness against its use.

13.8.4. Spray Coating

Molten metal and paints can be sprayed with or without compressed air on metal surface resulting into a smooth and uniform coating. In spray coating of zinc the metal is fed in the form of wire or a powder into an acetylene-oxygen flame where the zinc melts and fine droplets are thrown towards the steel surface by means of compressed air. While using zinc in the wire form, the melting can also be carried out by electric heating. Similarly spray coating of aluminium can be achieved on steel.

Spraying of paint is usually carried out by means of compressed air which gives very even coatings. If the paint is warmed, spraying may be done without adding thinners but such hot spraying of paint gives a film about 50 per cent thicker than spraying at an ordinary temperature with thinner. A new form of spray painting is airless spraying in which the paint is thrown out of a spray pistol towards the object with a very high pressure but without the presence of compressed air. The airless spraying is good substitute for brush painting due to good penetration into irregularities in the matal surface. In conventional spraying with compressed air, there is a considerable recoil of paint droplets from the object which is almost eliminated in airless spraying.

A special method of spray painting is electrostatic spraying, in which the spray aggregate is at a very high negative electric tension relative to the object which is earthed. The paint is finely dispersed in the spraying aggregate by mechanical means. The small paint droplets which are negatively charged migrate in the electric field and deposit on the object. The method is also used for spraying of powder such as polyvinyl chloride and epoxide which is then sintered to a continuous coating.

13.8.5. Plastic Coatings

Plastics are applid to metal surfaces in the form of claddings, which are made by glucing foils or plates of the material. Plastics used are thermoplastics and thermosets. The plastic materials are in general quite resistant towards aqueous solution of non-oxidising acids, salts and alkalies. The thermosets have good resistance also towards organic solvents, in which the thermoplastics tend to swell.

13.8.6. Phosphating (Phosphatising) Film

Phosphating of steel is usually carried out in phosphoric acid solutions containing acid phosphates of zinc or manganese. The solution may be applied by dipping or spraying method. As a result of chemical reaction, iron phosphates are formed which are strongly bonded to the metal surface. These phosphates also act as nuclei for crystallisation of sparingly soluble manganese or zinc phosphates. The phosphating process can be accelerated by the addition of oxidation agents such as nitrates and chlorates to the phosphating bath. Nitrate is preferable since it gets reduced to nitrite which later on gives an inhibitive action.

Phosphate films have a good adherence but are somewhat porous. Therefore, the phosphate film forms an excellent base for paints, lacquers, and rust preventing oils and greases. The protective value of a phosphate film alone is insufficient. Phosphatizing is also used to reduce friction in cold drawing operation. All phosphating films should be given a final rinse in a dilute solution of chromic acid and then be carefully dried in order to obtain better protection against corrosion Phosphating can also be done in the similar way on non-ferrous metals such as zinc, cadmium, aluminium and magnesium. However, it gives good results on zinc and cadmium only.

13.8 7. Chromating (Chromatizing)

Chromating is a process similar to phosphating and it is frequently used as a passivating treatment after phosphating. Chromating is not used alone on steel but can be used on light metals, zinc and cadmium. Chromating process is rapid, cheap and can be carried out easily. This involves an oxidising treatment of the metal surface in a chromic acid or chromate bath alongwith accelerating anions. The layers formed contain chromates and chromium oxide. The layers are usually very thin (0.5μm) but dense. The adherence of the films formed is very good and the films so formed work as an excellent base for painting. They have little resistance towards abrasion but however, if the layers are damaged at some point, self-healing takes place because the diffusion from the surrounding areas leads to passivation of the exposed surface.

Chromatising of aluminium is carried out in acid baths containing chromic acid and sulphuric acid. Sometimes fluoride ions also act as accelerators. Zinc and cadmium are chromated in solution containing chromic acid, nitric acid and sulphuric acid. Electrodeposited zinc coating on steel are also chromated. These chromate films extend their use in variety of applications particularly as a base for painting. They are also used as a substitute for anodizing, in which cases, anodizing is to be avoided due to high cost or special difficulties.

13.8.8. Zinc Coatings on Steel

Zinc coatings on steel can be applied in several different ways. Simple and small parts are zinc coated by electroplating or by dipping in molten metal. Larger objects may be zinc coated by spraying with molten zinc or by painting with zinc-rich paint. The protective power of electrolytic zinc-coatings is often improved by a subsequent process, such as chromatizing, painting or phosphatizing.

In the zinc-coating of steel by hot dipping known as galvanizing, the steel objects are first cleaned thoroughly and then dipped into a bath of molten zinc. A fluxing agent is used to dissolve the oxides formed on the steel surface between cleaning and galvanizing processes. Thus the flux added facilitates the reaction between iron and zinc. Other important methods of zinc coating are: (i) Sendzimir, (ii) Sherardising, and (iii) Spray coating.

(i) **Sendzimir method.** In this process the steel band is first carried through an annealing furnace with oxidizing atmosphere to burn away carbonaceous impurities. After this, it is passed through an annealing furnace with an atmosphere of cracked ammonia which reduces the surface oxides and performs the same work as oxide-dissolving flux in other methods. The band is then carried further through a zinc bath and then finally cooled, straightened and cut. This method gives a thin layer on the steel band.

(ii) **Sherardising.** It is a tumbling procedure for coating small articles with zinc. The articles and zinc powder are charged together in an annealing furance. The furnace is rotated and heated to a temperature just below the melting point of zinc. The process is continued for about an hour. By this process a well adhering thin layer of zinc is obtained.

(iii) **Zinc coating by spraying.** In this process, zinc is fed into an oxygen-acetylene flame in the form of wire or powder. The molten zinc, so formed is thrown as fine droplets towards the steel surface by means of compressed air. Melting can also be carried out by electric heating while using zinc in the form of wire.

13.8.9. Tinning

The major application of the process is to provide a hygienic protective coating as well as pleasing appearance to the articles made of steel, copper, brass etc. coatings of tin are widely used in food packing, food and beverage handling equipments in industry and houses and notably in dairry plant. In general there are three methods for tin coating: (*i*) hot dip coating, (*ii*) wiping and (*iii*) electroplating.

(*i*) **Hot dip coating process.** It involves the passage of pickled sheets successively through layers of flux, tin and palm oil. In tin plating, the sheets are not prefluxed but they are introduced in a wet condition and the film of water effectively speeds the fluxing reaction by keeping the flux layer in an embulliant and active condition. The fluxes used are mixtures of $ZnCl_2$, NaCl, NH_4Cl, KCl etc. e.g. a mixture containing 73 per cent $ZnCl_2$, 18 per cent NaCl, and 9 per cent NH_4Cl is a good flux for tin coating. Passing through the tin, the compound layer is compacted by the lower feed-rollers which serve also to carry the sheet onwards where it leaves the tin and enters a deep layer of palm oil called the grease pot. In the grease pot there are a number of spring-loaded pairs of tinned steel rollers which serve to reduce the coating from the thickness entrained to the finished required thickness.

(*ii*) **Wiping method.** Here the tin coating in fact is applied by a wiping process. In this case tin is applied in molten, stick or powder form, to the prepared and heated surface. The procedure is often employed where articles are large in size, for example, cast-iron or forged steel marine bearing shells. Such procedure is also useful for tinning the selected portions of the articles. In this process a thin layer of tin is applied to the heated surface of the article. The article is heated gently and evenly by any convenient means. As soon as melting is complete over the whole surface, excess metal and flux are gently wiped off. Since the first wiper will pick up some quantity of flux, a second light wipe is usually given with a clean wiper kept for this purpose. After the second wipe, a gentle flame may be passed over the surface just to remelt the tin and flatten out wiping marks.

(*iii*) **Electrolytic coating process.** Electrolytic method is capable for coating continuous strip or wire at a very high speed and thus harmenises with the technology of the continuous cold-reduction process. It also enables the deposition of very light coatings which are suitable and economical in their appropriate fields of use. An electrolytic tin plating line comprises of a series of processing units all connected in tandem. The line accepts a coil of temper rolled material and passes the strip successively through the operations of decoiling, welding, cleaning, pickling, plating, flow-brightening, chemical treatment, oiling, shearing, inspection and piling. Current densities employed are 20-25 amp./dm^2 and tin coating thickness range from 0.004 to 0.0015 mm with deposition time of seconds only. Several different plating electrolytes are used in electro-plating practice, but broadly they are of three types, (*i*) based on stannous sulphat, (ii) alkaline stannate solution, and (iii) halogen electrolyte based on stannous chloride.

13.8.10. Aluminizing

A combination of aluminium on the surface of steel produces a material high in strength as well as resistant to corrosion and oxidation. Aluminium coated steel is called *aluminized steel* and the process of aluminium coating is called *aluminizing*. In the recent time, aluminizing is taking place of galvanizing due to some specific properties of aluminium over zinc. The coating may be applied by several methods, which are, (i) hot dipping, (ii) pack calorizing, (iii) spraying, (iv) electroplating, (v) vacuum deposition, (vi) roll cladding and (vii) powder method. However, out of these, first three are of commercial importance.

(i) **Hot dip process**. This is the most versatile process for aluminium coating on steel. It consists in degreasing the steel base with either alkaline or solvents, pickling in sulphuric or hydrochloric acid, washing, drying, suitable fluxing and immersion in a bath of molten aluminium. This technique produces a continuous layer of aluminium on the surface ranging from 0.025 mm to 0.1 mm thick. There are two general methods of hot dip aluminizing, i.e. (a) continuous aluminizing for processing wire, strip and sheet, and (b) batch process for coating aluminium which will not be subjected to further forming operations.

(ii) **Pack calorizing method**. It is essentially a pack diffusion process in which steel is packed with a powdered mixture of aluminium and flux, and heated to a temperature of 850-1000°C for a couple of hours. This results in an exterior layer of 0.6 to 1.0 mm thick containing approximately 25 per cent aluminium.

(iii) **Spray method**. In this process aluminium is sprayed on to the surface of steel using a oxy acetylene flame, plasma-arc flame or gas atomization technique. Such a coating is generally 0.15 to 0.25 mm thick and is used to improve corrosion resistance and resistance to oxidation at higher temperatures.

(iv) **Electroplating**. Aluminium is electroplated on a clean steel surface using either molten salt or organic electrolytes. Such coatings have good appearance, a high degree of ductility and less thickness.

(v) **Vacuum deposition**. The aluminium is vaporised at temperature of about 1320°C in an evacuated chamber, and condenses on the cold surface of steel placed in the chamber. In this case also the coatings deposited are very thin and ductile.

(vi) **Cladding**. Aluminium is rolled, drawn or extruded on to the clean steel surface. These operations are conducted at elevated temperatures limited by the melting point of aluminium. Such a clad coating is produced in a wide range of thickness and is generally quite ductile because of a very thin iron-aluminium alloy layer.

(vii) **Powder method**. British steel corporation, U.K. were first to use a powder method on a commercial scale. In this method aluminium powder is deposited on a steel substrate, compacted by passing the strip through rolls, and heat treated to achieve the bonding. This technique results in a good quality aluminium coated steel and a controlled thickness of the alloy layer.

13.9. SOME TYPICAL EXAMPLES OF PRACTICAL IMPORTANCE

13.9.1. Corrosion of Iron Tanks Having Wetted Surfaces

Oxygen concentration cells are formed in the wet area where a drop of water is available in the iron tank having wetted surfaces. The oxygen in the drop combines with the iron and causes the corrosion. As the oxygen in the drop is used, more oxygen from atmospheric air enters the drop. A cathode is established near the boundary of the water drop and an anode is built up near the centre of the drop. If the cell operates for a longer time, a pit is formed at the centre of the drop. Therefore, the corrosion of wet tanks proceeds at much faster rate when exposed to air compared to the tanks kept full.

13.9.2. Corrosion of Underground Pipe Lines

Underground pipe lines are largely affected by the corrosive action of soil which depends on the composition and quality of the soil. In dry soil corrosion does not take place to a great extent, whereas in a marshy land, where the acid concentration is usually high, severe corrosion of pipe lines may be observed.

When a pipe line runs through different soils having varied composition and quality, concentration cell action as well as galvanic action may take place. If power lines are also running parallel to pipe lines, an accelerated form of galvanic type corrosion will result due to considerable current induction.

13.9.3. Corrosion of Brass Condenser Tubes Handling Salt Water

The corrosion of brass condenser tubes is the result of a process known as dezincification. Zinc is removed from the alloy due to the galvanic action in the presence of highly conductive salt water and thus corrosion takes place at localised spots.

13.9.4. Zinc Coating is Preferred over Tin for Structural Parts

Discussed in section 13.7.3.

QUESTIONS

1. Define corrosion. Give the typical reactions involved in corrosion.

2. What are various types of corrosion? Discuss the mechanism of electro-chemical corrosion.

3. Explain 'corrosion by oxidation' and 'galvanic corrosion'.

4. Discuss various mechanisms of galvanic corrosion.

5. Discuss the common types of corrosion alongwith the suitable examples.

6. Name and distinguish between two basic mechanisms of corrosive attack.

7. List some metals in order of decreasing solution potential.

8. Sketch a typical galvanic cell. Indicate the direction of electron flow.

9. Summarize the nature of concentration and galvanic cells.

10. What is passivation? Distinguish between two types of passivity.

11. How can passivation be obtained? Discuss with suitable examples.

12. Discuss various factors affecting the rate of corrosion.

13. How could corrosion fatigue be distinguished from intergranular attack?

14. What are the various methods of corrosion control? Discuss their advantages and limitations.

15. What are the various coatings employed for protection of metals from corrosion? Discuss their advantages and limitations.

16. How can the corrosion be controlled by choosing a suitable design?

17. Discuss 'anodic' and 'cathodic' protection methods with suitable examples.

18. Discuss three special methods of corrosion protection.

19. Describe an 'anodizing' process. Give its advantages and limitations.

20. Describe the process of tinning of steel with its specific application.

21. What is aluminizing? Give various methods by which aluminium coating can be applied.

22. Write short notes on the following:

   (a) Anodic and cathodic protection.

   (b) Mechanism of corrosion.

   (c) Chromatizing.

   (d) Phosphotising.

   (e) Electrolytic coatings.

   (f) Zinc coating on steel.

   (g) Vitreous enameling.

REFERENCES

Raghavan, V., *Materials Science and Engineering*, Prentice Hall of India Pvt Ltd, New Delhi, 1979.

Azaroff, L.V. and Brophy J.J., *Electronic Processes in Materials*, McGraw Hill Book Co. Inc.

Starfield, M.J. and Shrager A.M., *Introductary Materials Science*, McGraw Hill Book Co. 1972.

Hayden, W., Moffatt, W.G. and Wulf, J., *The Structure and Properties of Materials*, Vol. I, III and IV., Wiley Eastern Ltd, 1980.

Van Vlack, L.H., *Materials Science for Engineers*, Addison—Wesley Publishing Company, 1970.

Narang, G.B.S. and Manchanda V.K., *Materials and Metallurgy*, Khanna Publisher, Delhi-6, 1976.

Irving Granet, *Modern Materials*, Reston Publishing Co. Inc. A., Prentice Hall Co. Reston, Virginia, 1980.

Jastrzebski, Z.D., *The Nature and Properties of Engineering Materials*, Wiley International, Edition 1976.

Davies, D.E., *Practical Experimental Metallurgy*, Elsevier Publishing Co. Ltd, 1966.

Hanks, R.W., *Materials Engineering Science*, Harcourt, Brace and World, Inc. New York 1970.

Higgerson, C.A. Ed., *Experiments in Materials Technology*, Affiliated East-West Press Pvt Ltd, New Delhi, 1973.

Freeman, W.H. and Co., Ed., *Materials*, 1967.

Sehgal, S.D. and Lindberg, R.A., *Materials—Their Nature, Properties and Fabrication*, S. Chand and Company, New Delhi.

Cottrell, A.H., *The Mechanical Properties of Matter*, John Wiley and Sons Inc., New York, 1964.

Frados, J. Ed., *Plastics Engineering Handbook*, Van Nostrand Reinhold Company, 1976.

Smith, C.O., *The Science of Engineering Materials*, Prentice Hall of India Pvt Ltd, 1974, New Delhi.

Dieter, G.E., *Mechanical Metallurgy*, McGraw Hill Book Company Inc.

Hume-Rothery, W., *Electrons, Atoms, Metals and Alloys*.

Petty, E.R., *Physical Metallurgy of Engineering Materials*, George Allen and Unwin Ltd, 1968.

Sharp, H.J., *Engineering Materials*.

Lips, E.M.H., *Engineering Metallurgy*, Philips Technical Library, 1961.

Avner, S.H., *Introduction to Physical Metallurgy*, McGraw Hill Kagakusha Ltd, 1974.

Reed-Hill, E., *Physical Metallurgy Principles*, D. Van Nostr and Company Inc., New York, 1966.

Lakhtin, Y., *Engineering Physical Metallurgy*, Mir Publisher, Moscow, 1978.

Novikov, I., *Theory of Heat Treatment of Metals*, Mir Publisher, Moscow, 1978.

Zakharov, B., *Heat Treatment*, Peace Publisher, Moscow.

ASM Engineering Book Shelf, *Source Book on Heat Treating*, Vol. I, ASM Metals Park (Ohio), 1975.

Tikekar, C.V., *Materials Selection in Automobile Industry*, Trans. IIM, 29 (4), (1976) 231.

Frier, W.T., *Elementary Metallurgy*. McGraw Hill Co. Inc.

Brick, R.M., Gardon, R.B. and Philips A., *Structure and Properties of Alloys*, McGraw Hill Book Co. 1965.

Goldman, J.E., Ed., *The Science of Engineering Materials*, John Wiley and Sons, Inc., London.

Anderson, J.C. and Leaver K.D., *Materials Science*, ELBS and Nelson 1972.

Rollason, E.C., *Metallurgy for Engineers*, The ELBS and Edward Arnold (Publishers) Ltd, 1975.

Theling, K.E, *Steel and its Heat Treatment*, Bofors Hand Book.